from Better World
                  Books
-Vic ahe books
while in Bordeaux

Design of
TRANSISTORIZED CIRCUITS
for
DIGITAL COMPUTERS

Design of
TRANSISTORIZED CIRCUITS
for
DIGITAL COMPUTERS

ABRAHAM I. PRESSMAN, B.S., M.S.

Consulting Engineer

JOHN F. RIDER PUBLISHER, INC., NEW YORK

To Lotte

P R E F A C E

This book is concerned with the design of transistorized digital computer, and digital type circuits. Written from the viewpoint of the circuits designer, it is intended both for those who have no prior knowledge of either transistor or computer type circuits, and those with a knowledge of computer type circuitry but who have not yet converted to transistors.

Present day digital computer designers rarely think of circuitizing their block diagrams with vacuum tubes. The choice now lies between transistors and magnetics. If transistors are chosen, a major decision as to how to mechanize the basic logical elements — the AND and OR gates — must be made, because how these elements are circuitized in a large measure fixes power dissipation, d-c voltage levels, power supply requirements, cost, and reliability and operating speed of the entire computer.

This book discusses detailed design calculations of nearly all the main methods of circuitizing these computer logical elements and other building blocks, with transistors. Emphasis has been on worst-case design techniques so that the basic circuits may operate with resistors, voltages, transistor parameters, diode forward drops, and reverse leakages, all simultaneously at those extremes of their tolerance limits that would most tend to make the circuits inoperative.

Methods of calculating transistor switching speeds, and signal rise and fall times, have been shown, with numerous examples. Factors that influence important decisions such as range of operating currents and d-c voltage levels, have been discussed.

Calculation and analysis of the various circuits has been done without requiring use of the four-terminal network equivalent circuits primarily helpful in dealing with small-signal linear amplifiers. Circuits of the nature discussed herein are mainly large-signal, on-off current switches, and it is shown how they may be designed from the static volt-ampere curves of the transistors, and some knowledge of their transient response characteristics. The behavior of the circuits can be predicted from relatively simple arithmetic calculations.

The first two chapters of the book deal with computer logic, logical building blocks, and Boolean algebra, in sufficient detail that those without previous experience in computers may gain an appreciation of how the circuits designed in the latter part of the volume fit into the overall picture of a computer. Chapter 3 presents a brief discussion of transistor physics and transistor fundamentals.

It is hoped that such a book, emphasizing worst-case design techniques, switching circuits, and switching time calculations, will be found useful in this increasingly important field.

For the technical review of the manuscript, and their many helpful suggestions, my appreciation is particularly due to Dr. W. T. Chow, Mr. J. Tellerman and Mr. E. Keonjian of the Arma Corporation, New York.

ABRAHAM I. PRESSMAN, M. S.

Philadelphia, Pa.,
March 1959.

CONTENTS

Chapter 1

BASIC BUILDING BLOCKS IN DIGITAL COMPUTERS

Digital computer circuits are built by the interconnection of a relatively small number of basic building blocks. However complex a digital computer or control system may be, except for some small specialized portions, it can always be designed as a unique assembly of these fundamental blocks.

The actual fabrication of a digital system usually occurs in one of the following ways. A basic building block or multiples of these blocks in various combinations may be packaged on a single plug-in chassis. All the input and output points of the block are brought out to standard pins on the plug-in chassis. By varying the interconnections between input and output points any digital circuit may be realized. This has many advantages. Only standard packages are built, which simplifies the production problem. It also simplifies the trouble-shooting problem as suspected failures can be verified by merely replacing one standard package with another. Also, the same set of packages can easily be used to mechanize any number of completely different digital circuits.

Still another scheme uses a building block concept but does not package the block or combinations thereof in standard packages. It generally employs a standard plug-in chassis, but does not use a standard array of circuits. With the building block designed and its drive requirements and capabilities known, a nonstandard array of blocks is assembled to fill each plug-in chassis. Thus no two chassis are alike. This arrangement has advantages in that there are fewer redundant components, and circuits electrically related are usually close to one another, a desirable condition that eases the ever present computer problem of driving-wiring capacity between building blocks. Such a scheme is usually more effective in smaller machines.

Whatever the plan used, however, the circuit designer's problem is the same: to design building blocks that perform the required logical operations with the necessary speed, and calculate their input drive requirements and output load driving capability. In this chapter, the properties of such building blocks and their symbolic representation are discussed. They are treated here only as "black-boxes" that have certain operations to perform, without any consideration as to their internal construction. Later chapters go into the matter of detailed design and perform worst-case calculations to enable them to perform their operations when all components and voltages are at the extremes of their tolerance limits.

1.1 **Digital Signals and Their Significance.** Digital computer or control circuits are basically information processing devices. The information they pro-

O	O	O
O	O	I
O	I	O
O	I	I
I	O	O
I	O	I
I	I	O
I	I	I

Fig. 1-1. Eight possible combinations of a 3-bit code.

cess is in the form of a time or space sequence of signals. These signals may have either of two values having the significance of a "one" or a "zero." In writing a one or zero, two different marks of any sort, such as 1 or 0 may be used. These one or zero signals may be represented physically in various ways. Thus a one may be a positive voltage level, and a zero a negative voltage level. The levels need not be positive or negative with respect to a common ground point, only with respect to one another. A one may be represented by the presence of a voltage pulse, zero by the absence of a pulse at a specific time. A vacuum tube or thyratron may be in the "on" or "off" state, a relay may be energized or de-energized to represent the two valued signal. The presence or absence of a hole punched in card or paper tape may represent one or zero. A magnetic toroid may be magnetized in a clockwise or counterclockwise direction; the surface of a drum or tape coated with magnetic material may be magnetized in one or the other direction for ones or zeros, or ones may be represented by magnetic marks and zeros by the absence of magnetic marks.

Whatever the physical process involved, each such one or zero signal is commonly referred to as a "bit." A coded time or space sequence of such bits can be used to represent alphabetic or numerical characters. Because each bit can have the value of either one or zero, a code with n bits can represent 2^n different characters. A code where each character is represented by the position of bits in a three-column array is shown in Fig. 1-1. There are only eight possible combinations in such a 3-bit code.

To represent the 10 unique decimal digits, 1 through 9 and 0, would require a 4-bit code. To represent the decimal digits, alphabetic characters and various punctuation marks available on a standard typewriter keyboard — 56 characters — would require a 6-bit code. The number system in everyday use is based on the number 10. In this system there are 10 discrete possible marks, 1 through 9 and 0. Any number is represented by the sum of powers of 10, each power of 10 being preceded by one of these marks signifying the number of times that power of 10 is to be taken into the sum. Thus the number 1234 has the meaning $(1 \times 10^{+3}) + (2 \times 10^{+2}) + (3 \times 10^{+1}) + (4 \times 10^{0})$.

To design machines performing high-speed numerical computation directly in the decimal system would be extremely difficult in that this would require a device capable of changing rapidly to any of 10 different discrete states representing the 10 basic numbers. There are however, as already mentioned, any number of ways in which a device can change rapidly to either of two possible physical states. Consequently a number system based on powers of two rather than 10 is used in high-speed numerical machine computation.

In such a binary system there are only two permissible marks, 1 or 0. Numbers are represented by the sum of powers of two, each power of two being preceded by a 1 or a 0 coefficient signifying the number of times that power is to be taken into the sum. Numbers are written in the binary system merely as these coefficients set side by side, with the extreme right-hand coefficient usually representing the lowest power of 2, 2^{0} or 1. Thus the number 13 would be written in the binary system as 1101 signifying $(1 \times 2^{3}) + (1 \times 2^{2}) + (0 \times 2^{1}) + (1 \times 2^{0})$.

The operations of addition, multiplication, subtraction and division may be performed directly in the binary system. Some of these operations will be considered later.

In addition to representing an alphabetic or numerical character, a binary signal may represent a control condition or command. Thus a voltage level being in either its one or zero state may have the significance of "add" or "do not add", "read" or "do not read", "commence an operation" or "do not commence an operation", a "given condition is true" or a "given condition is not true". Any one of an infinite variety of conditions that can be sensed for or signalled by an electrical or mechanical device may be represented by such a one or zero signal.

The manipulation, routing and general processing of such binary data representing alphabetic or numerical characters under the control of binary signal commands or conditions, is performed essentially by six basic logical elements. These are the flip-flop, binary counter, AND gate, OR gate, time delay unit, and signal inverter. In addition, there are units — such as power amplifiers and transducers of various kinds to convert mechanical into electrical signals — that are essential, but which do not perform logical operations. There are also memory devices that have the capacity to store large numbers of binary bits, but they will not be discussed in this book.

1.2. Flip-Flops. The flip-flop performs the logical operation of remembering. It has two possible states, the one and zero state. It can be flipped or flopped from one state to the other by short duration impulses, and remembers indefinitely the last state into which it has been thrown. The usual symbol for the flip-flop is shown in Fig. 1-2.

Input signals are usually short duration impulses shown in the symbol by arrows directed *into* the side of the flip-flop. Output signals are indicated in the symbol by arrows coming *out of* the top of the rectangle from the same side as the corresponding input signal. Inherent in the logic symbol is the logical sense

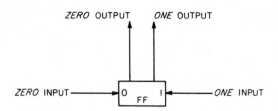

Fig. 1-2. Logical symbols for a flip-flop.

of "enable" or "inhibit", "true" or "false." That is, a signal last delivered to the zero input side will set the flip-flop so that the zero side generates an enable or true signal, and the one side generates an inhibit or false signal. This state is maintained indefinitely and is referred to as the zero state of the flip-flop.

A second impulse of the same nature delivered to the zero side of the flip-flop does not change its state, but an impulse delivered to the one input side reverses

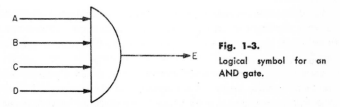

Fig. 1-3.

Logical symbol for an AND gate.

the state of the flip-flop so that its one output terminal generates an enable or true signal, and its zero side an inhibit or false signal. The flip-flop is now in the one state and remains there until an impulse is next delivered to the zero input terminal. Enable and inhibit signals have meaning only with respect to the AND and OR gates driven by the flip-flop. These signals are usually voltages of either of two levels. The gates driven from the flip-flop can be designed so that either the upper or lower voltage level constitutes a true signal.

The usual flip-flop — that dealt with here — contains two output signals at either of two d-c voltage levels. But in the logical sense a flip-flop is any device that can, upon receipt of a triggering pulse, assume either of two stable states, and will remain in that state until triggered to the opposite state. A flip-flop can be a thyratron with only one output terminal, its two states being "fired" and "not fired." Or it may be a square hysteresis-loop magnetic core magnetized to the state of either positive or negative remanence. In such a case the state in

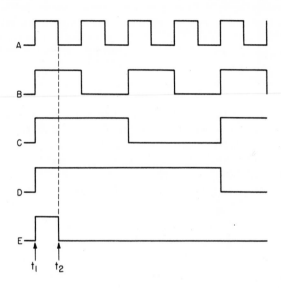

Fig. 1-4. A possible sequence of signals at AND gate inputs (A to D), and the resultant output at E.

which it resides is only known by attempting to set it back to a standard state.

The flip-flop discussed in this book contains two transistors of which one is turned off, generating one voltage level, and the other is switched on, generating the other voltage level.

1.3. AND Gates.   A logical AND gate is a device with a multiplicity of input terminals and a single output terminal. The signals on its input terminals are the true or false, enable or inhibit, one or zero binary signals discussed above. The AND gate performs the logical operation of emitting a true output signal only when all its input signals are simultaneously true. A false or inhibit signal on one or more of its input terminals produces a false or inhibit signal at its output. The logical symbol for the AND gate is shown in Fig. 1-3. Inputs are shown as arrows directed into the semicircle, and the output as the arrow directed out of it.

Figure 1-4 illustrates a typical sequence of signals at an AND gate for true upper-level and false lower-level signals. Only from t_1 to t_2 are all four inputs at the enabling level giving a true out for that duration at E.

Sometimes a logical AND operation must be inhibited under a given condition. For example, an AND gate output may be desired if conditions A and B are true, but if C is simultaneously true, a true output should be inhibited. This is

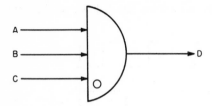

Fig. 1-5. Logical symbol for an AND gate with an inhibiting input at C.

shown symbolically by Fig. 1-5. Here the circle inside the AND gate indicates that a true signal at C is to inhibit or prevent an output at D, whatever the conditions at A and B. A typical set of waveforms in such a gate would be as in Fig. 1-6 for true upper-level, and false lower-level waveforms.

The lack of an inhibiting signal from t_1 to t_2 permits the gating of A and B to give ouputs for every enabling input at A because B is continuously at the

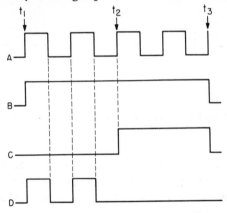

Fig. 1-6. Possible input and resulting output signals for the AND gate of Fig. 1-5.

enable level for this interval. From t_2 to t_3 the presence of a signal at C inhibits the gate and prevents any true output signal, even though A and B are at times both true in this interval.

1.4. OR Gates. The OR gate is a device with a multiplicity of inputs and one output. The inputs can each assume either of two possible values, one designated true, the other false. The gate performs the logical operations of producing a true output for the time duration that one or more of its inputs is true, and a false output for the time durations in which none of its inputs are true.

Chapter 2

LOGICAL CHAINS IN DIGITAL COMPUTERS

Chapter 1 described the basic logical building blocks used in digital circuits. This chapter discusses the way in which these blocks are assembled in chains to perform some of the more frequently occurring logical operations.

Interconnections of basic blocks can be described by the symbols already given, with connecting lines between input and output terminals. This description is facilitated however, by an algebraic symbolism with simple rules for its manipulation. This symbolism, Boolean algebra,* is not only useful as a shorthand notation for describing logical interconnections, but by manipulation of these symbols, a number of alternative arrangements that give rise to the same logical result can be arrived at. From these can be chosen the one it is preferable to circuitize on the basis of economy of total components and active components such as transistors or tubes, or for reasons primarily related to "hardware" rather than logic.

The elements of Boolean algebra and sample basic logical operations — including some of the fundamentals of binary arithmetic — are described below.

2.1. Fundamentals of Boolean Algebra. There are available some excellent discussions of Boolean algebra and computer logical arrays.[1] The subject is dealt with here only in sufficient detail to give the reader a picture of how the circuits to be designed in subsequent chapters are used in digital computer operations, and to familiarize him with Boolean symbols and their applications.

In Boolean algebra, variables have either of two values — 1 or 0. There are two fundamentals in this algebra — the AND operation and the OR operation.

---

* An extremely facile algebra of great value in the design of switching networks; named after George Boole who first introduced it in 1847 in a paper on mathematical analysis of logic.

[1] *Arithmetic Operations in Digital Computers,* Richards, R. K., New York: D. Van Nostrand Company, Inc., 1955.

If an AND operation is performed on a number of variables the result is 1 only when all inputs simultaneously have the value of 1. If one or more variables have the value of 0, the result is 0. The AND operation is written algebraically by simply placing the variables adjacent to one another with no interconnecting symbol, thus $D = ABC$. This definition of the algebraic AND

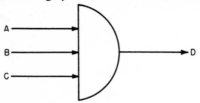

Fig. 2-1. Symbolic representation of an AND operation.

operation coincides with the AND gate of Chapter 1. An AND operation may then be described by its symbol, as in Fig. 2-1, or by its algebraic equivalent $ABC = D$. The eight possible combinations of three input variables and the resultant output are shown in Fig. 2-2.

It is sometimes necessary to describe an AND operation on two variables that are themselves the result of an AND operation. If $AB = C$ and $DE = F$, the

A	B	C	D
0	0	0	0
0	0	1	0
0	1	0	0
0	1	1	0
1	0	0	0
1	0	1	0
1	1	0	0
1	1	1	1

Fig. 2-2. Eight possible combinations of three variables A, B, C, and the result, D, of an AND operation for each combination.

AND operation on C and F, identified as G, is written $(AB)(DE) = CF = G$. Symbolically this would have been described as in Fig. 2-3.

A fundamental rule in Boolean algebra is that the AND operation is associative, i.e., the result is independent of how the various groups are associated in the AND operation. For instance

$$(AB)(DE) = A(BDE) = ABDE$$

as shown symbolically in Fig. 2-4.

The fact is significant because the three individual structures in Fig. 2-4 represent different circuit connections, some of which are easier to realize physically than others. For example, it is fairly simple to mechanize two input AND gates with tubes or transistors in ways that do not normally lend themselves easily to more than two-input gating. In general these schemes require input

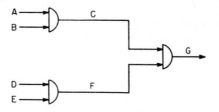

Fig. 2-3. Symbolic representation of an AND operation applied to the result of two other AND operations.

signals of a given polarity and produce a phase reversal in addition to the gating operation. Thus in Fig. 2-4 A, the outputs of the first two gates may have to be phase reversed before they could drive the final gate, and since gates and phase inverters generally introduce time delays, the structure of Fig. 2-4 A is likely to be slower than that of Fig. 2-4 C. The structure of Fig. 2-4 C will in

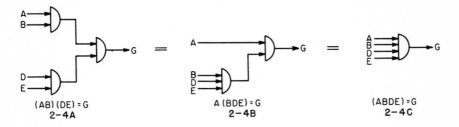

Fig. 2-4. Logically equivalent ways of performing an AND operation.

general be easier to mechanize using a combination of diodes and transistors. The different types of structures may require different values of absolute voltage levels, or transistors of markedly different price range to achieve the same operating speed. It is circuit considerations such as these that determine the exact logical interconnection used, although they all produce the same logical result.

The second fundamental operation, the OR operation, is as follows: The result of an OR operation is 1 when one or more of the input variables has a value of 1. Only if none of the input variables has a value of 1 is the result 0. The OR operation so described coincides with the properties of the OR gate in Chapter 1.

Algebraically the OR operation is written as the input terms connected with plus signs, thus, $A + B + C = D$. Symbolically this would be shown as in Fig. 2-5. Of the eight possible states of the input variables shown in Fig. 2-2 the result is zero only for the first state $(A = B = C = 0)$, and is one for the remaining seven states.

The OR operation too, is associative. Thus

$$(A + B) + C = A + (B + C) = A + B + C.$$

This is shown symbolically in Fig. 2-6.

Here also, each of the configurations represents a different connection of circuit elements, one of which would in general be preferable from a purely

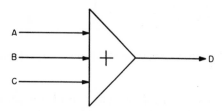

Fig. 2-5. Symbolic representation of an OR operation.

hardware point of view, although logically they each produce the same result.

From these definitions of the AND and OR operation a number of useful results follow. These are:

$$A + 0 = A$$
$$A\ 0\ \ \ = 0$$
$$A + 1 = 1$$
$$A\ 1\ \ \ = A$$
$$A + A = A$$
$$A\ A\ \ \ = A$$

They may be verified by allowing A to take on either of its two possible values.

Complex terms within parentheses indicating an AND operation may be simplified as in ordinary algebra, thus

$$(A + B)\ (C + D) = A(C + D) + B(C + D) =$$
$$AC + AD + BC + BD \tag{2-1}$$

The logical structures performing these equivalent operations are shown in Fig. 2-7.

An important function in Boolean algebra is the complement of a function, or the "not" function. It is symbolized by a line over the function and indicates the opposite sense of the function itself. Thus if a function is A, its complement is written $\bar{A}$ and is read as "not A." It has the significance that if A is 1, $\bar{A}$ is 0, or if A is 0, $\bar{A}$ is 1. The inverter building block of Chapter 1 operating on a function provides the not function. In a flip-flop the two output points correspond to a function and its complement. That side of a flip-flop which emits an enabling or 1 signal to a gate when the flip-flop is set to the one state is usually designated by the function symbol itself, the opposite side by the not function symbol. Thus in Fig. 2-8, if the flip-flop is in the one state, the output

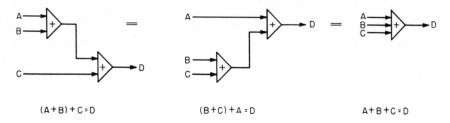

$$(A+B)+C=D \qquad\qquad (B+C)+A=D \qquad\qquad A+B+C=D$$

Fig. 2-6. Logically equivalent ways of performing an OR operation.

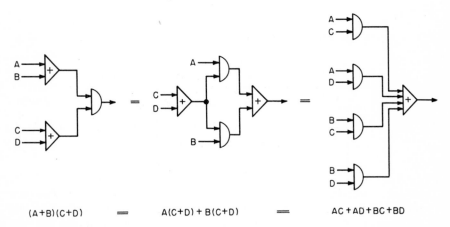

$$(A+B)(C+D) \qquad = \qquad A(C+D)+B(C+D) \qquad = \qquad AC+AD+BC+BD$$

Fig. 2-7. Equivalent logical interconnections for performing the operation $(A + B)$ $(C + D)$.

line A reads 1, and the output line $\overline{A}$ reads 0. When it is in the zero state, the output line $\overline{A}$ reads 1, and terminal A reads 0.

By definition of the AND and OR operation, and substituting the two possible values a function may have, the following useful relations may be verified:

$$A\overline{A} \quad = 0 \qquad\qquad (2\text{-}2)$$

$$A + \overline{A} = 1 \qquad\qquad (2\text{-}3)$$

$$\overline{\overline{A}} \quad = A \qquad\qquad (2\text{-}4)$$

The not operation applied to an AND operation signifies the complement of the result of the AND operation, and is identically equal to the OR operation applied to the complements of the input variables. Algebraically this is written as

$$(\overline{ABC}) = \overline{A} + \overline{B} + \overline{C} \tag{2-5}$$

It is true for any number of input variables, and can be verified for two variables from Fig. 2-9 which considers every combination of two variables.

This identity is shown symbolically in Fig. 2-10. It is useful, as often one of these logically identical expressions is easier to mechanize circuitwise than

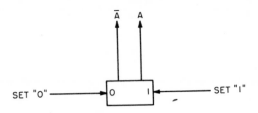

Fig. 2-8. A flip-flop showing its normal and complemented output.

A	B	$\overline{A}$	$\overline{B}$	(AB)	$(\overline{AB})$	$\overline{A}+\overline{B}$
0	0	1	1	0	1	1
0	1	1	0	0	1	1
1	0	0	1	0	1	1
1	1	0	0	1	0	0

Fig. 2-9.

Verifying that $\overline{AB} = \overline{A} + \overline{B}$.

the other. In many cases, where the functions are flip-flop outputs, the functions and their complements are available from opposite sides of the flip-flop, and the inputs to the OR structure in Fig. 2-10 do not need the additional inverters.

Applied to an OR operation, the not function signifies the complement of the result of the OR operation and is identically equal to AND operation applied to the complements of the input variables. This is written algebraically as

$$\overline{A + B + C} = \overline{A}\overline{B}\overline{C} \tag{2-6}$$

This is true also for any number of input variables and is verified for all possible combinations of two inputs in Fig. 2-11.

Here too, one of these logically identical expressions is often easier to mechanize from a circuits point of view than the other.

A good example of the usefulness of these Boolean relations and one that comes up frequently in binary arithmetic, is the determination of the complementary state of two flip-flops. This is mechanized in Fig. 2-12 by what is probably the method first to come to mind. Of the four states of the two flip-flops, 00, 01, 10, 11, the logical array of Fig. 2-12 determines when A or B and not $(A$ and $B)$, is true. Algebraically this is expressed as

$$(A + B) \; (\overline{AB})$$

This may be written alternatively from the relation in Eq. 2-5 as

$$(A + B) \; (\overline{AB}) = (A + B) \; (\overline{A} + \overline{B})$$

The right-hand side can be simplified by the relation in Eq. 2-1 giving

$$(A + B) \; (\overline{AB}) = A(\overline{A} + \overline{B}) + B(\overline{A} + \overline{B}) =$$

$$A\overline{A} + A\overline{B} + B\overline{A} + B\overline{B}$$

But from Eq. 2-2, $A\overline{A} = B\overline{B} = 0$, giving

$$(A + B) \; (\overline{AB}) = A\overline{B} + B\overline{A}$$

The three ways of mechanizing the required condition are shown in Fig. 2-13.
Later, when designing circuits to mechanize these logical arrays it will be seen that repetitive AND-OR-AND-OR chains are easiest to design, and are most

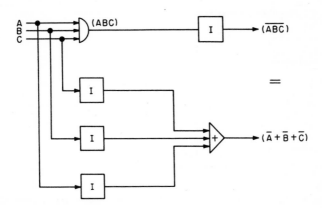

Fig. 2-10. Logical interconnections for performing the equivalent operations $\overline{ABC} = \overline{A} + \overline{B} + \overline{C}$.

economical in components. Consequently, it is in general preferable to mechanize the expression in the form $A\overline{B} + \overline{A}B$.

2.2. Binary Counting.   The binary number system as explained in Chapter 1 is best suited for high-speed machine computations. This section discusses some of the fundamentals of binary arithmetic and the way in which operations may be performed with basic logical building blocks.

The first operation to consider is binary counting. A binary number, as shown previously, is given by the sum

$$A_0 2^0 + A_1 2^1 + A_2 2^2 + \cdots A_n 2^n$$

where the A's have the value 0 or 1. The number is written by the coefficients arranged side by side usually with A_0 at the right, thus,

$$A_n \cdots A_3 A_2 A_1 A_0$$

The lowest number in any binary column is 0, the highest is 1.

The rule for counting (successive additions of 1 to the previous number), is to start at the lowest order column and proceed to higher order columns. At the

A	B	$\bar{A}$	$\bar{B}$	A + B	$\overline{(A+B)}$	$(\bar{A}\,\bar{B})$
0	0	I	I	0	I	I
0	I	I	0	I	0	0
I	0	0	I	I	0	0
I	I	0	0	I	0	0

Fig. 2-11.   Verifying that $\overline{(A + B)} = \bar{A}\bar{B}$.

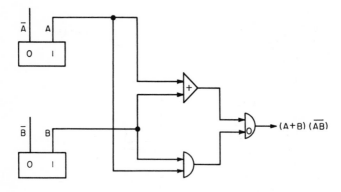

Fig. 2-12.   Logical building blocks seeking for the complementary state of two flip-flops.

first column where a 0 is found, replace it by a 1 and change all lower order columns to 0. In accordance with this rule, Fig. 2-14 shows the first 16 counts in the binary system.

Another way of looking at the counting process is as the result of the addition of 1 to the lowest order binary column. This addition results in a sum for the column plus a "carry" into the 2^1 binary column. The carry into the 2^1 column is added to the old count in that column resulting in a sum for that column and a carry into the next higher order column. This sequential column by column process continues until an addition is reached that produces no carry. The rules for the sum and carry values for any one column in this addition process are given in Fig. 2-15.

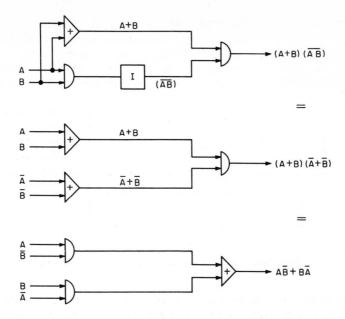

Fig. 2-13. Three different logical methods for determining when a pair of flip-flops are in opposite states.

BINARY REPRESENTATION				DECIMAL NUMBER
2^3	2^2	2^1	2^0	
O	O	O	O	O
O	O	O	I	I
O	O	I	O	2
O	O	I	I	3
O	I	O	O	4
O	I	O	I	5
O	I	I	O	6
O	I	I	I	7
I	O	O	O	8
I	O	O	I	9
I	O	I	O	10
I	O	I	I	11
I	I	O	O	12
I	I	O	I	13
I	I	I	O	14
I	I	I	I	15

Fig. 2-14.

Binary arithmetic equivalents of decimal numbers.

Any array of logical elements that performs the operations described in Fig. 2-15 serves as a counter. Such a counter may be mechanized with binary counter building blocks and 1 to 0 sensing devices, as shown in Fig. 2-16.

The 1 to 0 sensor is any device that senses the transition of a given binary column from the 1 to 0 state and thereupon transmits a count impulse to the

AUGEND (OLD COUNT IN A GIVEN COLUMN)	ADDEND (CARRY FROM NEXT LOWER ORDER COLUMN)	SUM	CARRY TO NEXT HIGHER ORDER COLUMN
0	0	0	0
0	1	1	0
1	0	1	0
1	1	0	1

Fig. 2-15.   Rules for adding two numbers in binary arithmetic.

binary count input terminal of the next higher order binary column. Usually it can be simply mechanized by an arrangement of diodes that distinguish between positive and negative going voltage changes.

The circuit of Fig. 2-16 will count in accordance with the rules of Fig. 2-15, but it may be slow. A binary counter requires a finite time to change state and

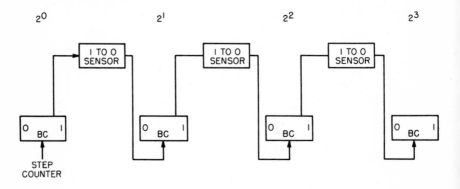

Fig. 2-16.   A binary arithmetic pulse counter.

consequently there is a time delay between a step input signal and the resultant carry output signal. For a many-stage counter this may add up to an appreciable delay.

Another method of binary counting that performs the logic of Fig. 2-15 and avoids the carry propagation delay is shown in Fig. 2-17. Here the AND gates at each stage sense whether a carry is to be propagated into the next stage. They sense for the combination of all ones from a given stage down to the lowest-order stage, as this and a step pulse at the first stage is the condition for a carry out of any stage. The sensing is done simultaneously at each stage by the count pulse that steps the first stage. Consequently there is no waiting for

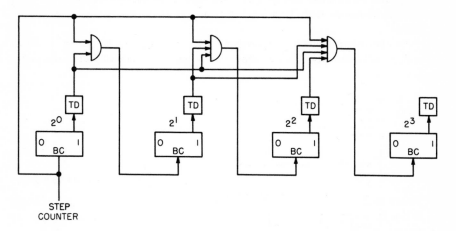

Fig. 2-17. A binary arithmetic pulse counter that avoids carry propagation delay.

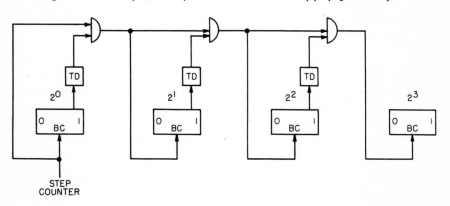

Fig. 2-18. A binary arithmetic pulse counter showing an alternative method for decreasing carry propagation delay.

transitions to occur before a carry can be generated. The elements marked TD are short time delays equal to the duration of the pulse that steps the first binary counter stage. They are logically necessary as each AND gate is required to sense the condition of the old count of a stage for at least the duration of the input pulse, and not the new count into which it will be thrown by a given count pulse.

Often these delay elements do not require additional components. The inherent transition time delay of a single stage normally suffices.

Although the scheme is fast, it is often difficult to realize from a circuits point of view because now, in addition to the external loads it has to drive, each stage must feed a number of these carry sensing gates, and the first stage being that which must change state most rapidly — and consequently the most difficult to design with large load driving capability — is the most heavily loaded.

An alternative method of speeding up the propagation of carries is shown in Fig. 2-18. Here also, the step input to any stage need not wait until the previ-

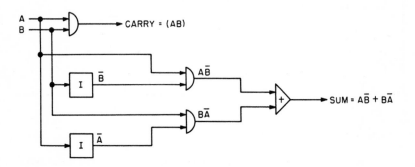

Fig. 2-19.   Performing a half adder operation in the form: Sum $= A\,\bar{B} + \bar{A}\,B$, Carry $= AB$.

ous stage completes a transition. But the step impulses to successive binary stages do suffer a delay in passing through the AND gates. As a result this scheme is only workable if the AND gate delay can be made less than a binary stage delay. There is a further drawback in that an AND gate output must drive both an AND gate input and a binary count input. These often require voltage impulses of opposite polarity. Also, as AND gates here are driving AND gates in sequence, the first one must have a large power output capability to be able to drive the last one without an amplifier interposed. Single-stage amplifiers in general would be unsatisfactory in that they also give either a phase inversion or a d-c level shift, both of which are undesirable.

Two-stage amplifiers would avoid the phase reversal but would be expensive and in themselves introduce appreciable delay.

If at all usable with transistor circuits, this last arrangement would probably require each gate output to drive a high-frequency transistor amplifier and pulse-transformer combination. Two secondary windings would be necessary on the pulse transformer to provide separate signals of the correct polarity and d-c voltage level for the AND gate and binary count input terminal.

2.3. Binary Addition. Two binary numbers, each having a number of binary digits or columns are added column for column. In general, for each column, three binary bits must be added. These are the two original bits in each column and the carry bit from the next lower order column. The addition of the two original bits produces a sum and carry term in accordance with the rules of Fig. 2-15. These partial sum and carry terms are combined with the carry bit

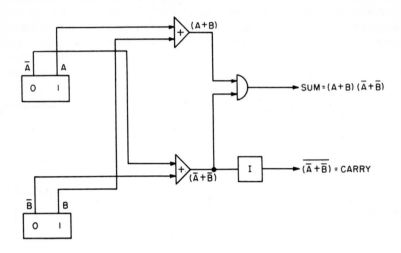

Fig. 2-20.   Performing a half adder operation in the form: Sum $= (A + B) \, (\overline{A} + \overline{B})$, Carry $= (\overline{\overline{A} + \overline{B}})$.

from the next lower order column to produce the final sum and carry term for each column.

The array of elements that adds two binary bits according to the rules of the table in Fig. 2-15 is called a "half adder," and an examination of the rules shows that they may be described algebraically as

$$\text{Sum} \;=\; A\overline{B} + \overline{A}B$$

$$\text{Carry} \;=\; AB$$

where A and B are binary bits to be added. The mechanization of the half adder of this algebraic form is shown symbolically in Fig. 2-19.

Inverters to produce the not functions will in general not be necessary as the terms come from flip-flops that have the not functions already available.

As explained earlier in this chapter, logical expressions identical to $A\overline{B} + B\overline{A}$ are $(A + B) \, (\overline{A} + \overline{B})$ and $(A + B) \, (\overline{AB})$. Thus the sum term of the table in Fig. 2-15 can be mechanized by either of the methods of Fig. 2-13. The carry term AB may be mechanized as an AND gate with two inputs A and B as above. Or if for some reason — such as the fact that the A and B sides of the flip-flops are already heavily loaded — it *may* be mechanized from the not side of the flip-flops as $(\overline{\overline{A} + \overline{B}})$. From the relations in Eqs. 2-4 and 2-6 this is seen to be identically equal to (AB). Mechanizing the carry term in this fashion and the sum term as $(A + B) \, (\overline{A} + \overline{B})$ is shown symbolically in Fig. 2-20.

To produce a final sum and carry the result of half adding the two bits of a given column must be combined with the carry from the next lower column. This is done by adding the sum term of the first addition with the carry term from the next lower order column, using a half adder similar to that which did the first addition. It yields a final sum term and a possible carry. The final

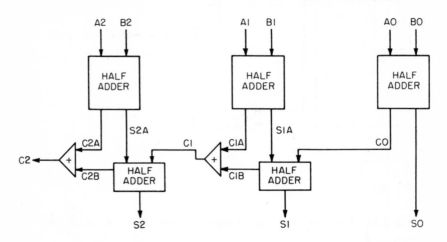

Fig. 2-21. Binary addition using two half adders per binary column.

carry can therefore come from the result of either the first or second addition. To pick up a carry from either source it is necessary to produce an OR operation sensing for carrys at either the first or second half adder output. This is shown symbolically in Fig. 2-21 where a binary number $A_0 \, A_1 \, A_2 \cdot \cdot \cdot \cdot$ is being added to $B_0 \, B_1 \, B_2$. The coefficients here represent the coefficients of the various powers of 2, and not an AND operation.

The addition of the three binary bits, A_N, B_N, and carry, from the n-1th stage does not have to be done in two successive operations with half adders as above. It can be done with a full or three-input adder. Rules for the three-input adder can be visualized by adding two inputs, and then adding the result to the third input. Remembering that in binary arithmetic 1 plus 0 or 0 plus 1 is 1, and 1 plus 1 is 0 with 1 carry, it is seen that a sum term of 1 results for each combination on an odd number of 1's. There are three combinations of one 1, and two 0's, among three variables, and one combination of three 1's. A and B being the binary numbers in a given column and C being the carry from the next lower order column, this is expressed algebraically as

$$\text{Sum} = A\overline{B}\overline{C} + \overline{A}B\overline{C} + ABC + \overline{A}\overline{B}C .$$

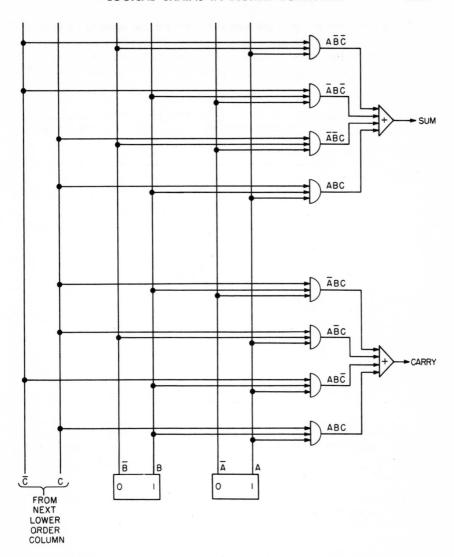

Fig. 2-22.   Binary addition using a three-input, or full adder.

And since a carry results from any combination of two 1's and a 0, or from three 1's, the carry condition is given by

$$\text{Carry} = \overline{A}BC + A\overline{B}C + AB\overline{C} + ABC.$$

If the sum and carry results were mechanized from these expressions symbolically it would appear as in Fig. 2-22. As shown, eight three-input AND gates and two four-input OR gates are required. This may be simplified a great deal by algebraic manipulation of the sum and carry expressions.

2.4. Binary Decoding. One frequently occurring logical operation is the determination of the time at which a particular action is to start or stop. This

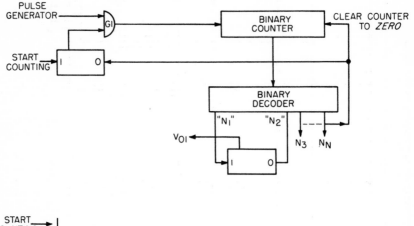

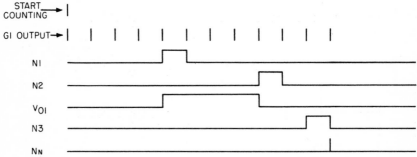

Fig. 2-23. An array of logical building blocks used to time the starting and stopping of a sequence of events.

is performed by counting pulses from a constant frequency pulse generator that serves as a clock. When the counter reaches a predetermined count this is sensed by the binary decoder which emits a signal setting a flip-flop. The flip-flop remains set until *reset* by a decoded count at a later time. By decoding various counts and routing them to set and reset sides of memory flip-flops, control signals starting and stopping at any time may be generated. A typical logical array is shown in Fig. 2-23. Usually pulses are gated into the counter by a control flip-flop set by a start-pulse that may or may not be synchronous with the pulse generator. If nonsynchronous there is generally a time ambiguity

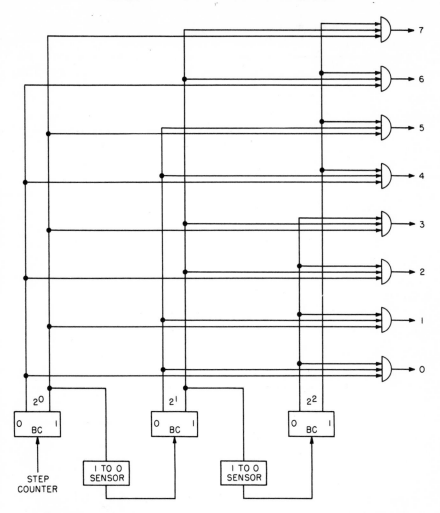

Fig. 2-24. A three-stage counter with AND gate decoders to produce output signals in time sequence on eight output lines.

problem of one pulse period as the start-pulse may occur just after or just before a pulse from the pulse generator.

The binary decoder itself is merely an AND gate that senses for the unique combinations of ones and zeros corresponding to a given count. Figure 2-24 illustrates a decoder that decodes the eight possible counts of a three-stage binary counter. It consists of eight three-input AND gates. The logical interconnections may be shown by the AND gate symbols, and their interconnecting lines as in Fig. 2-24 or more simply, by writing down the Boolean equations

$$0 = \bar{A}_0 \; \bar{A}_1 \; \bar{A}_2$$

$$1 = A_0 \; \bar{A}_1 \; \bar{A}_2$$

$$2 = \bar{A}_0 \; A_1 \; \bar{A}_2$$

$$3 = A_0 \; A_1 \; \bar{A}_2$$

$$4 = \bar{A}_0 \; \bar{A}_1 \; A_2$$

$$5 = A_0 \; \bar{A}_1 \; A_2$$

$$6 = \bar{A}_0 \; A_1 \; A_2$$

$$7 = A_0 \; A_1 \; A_2$$

Fig. 2-25. Algebraic description of the gating operations of Fig. 2-24.

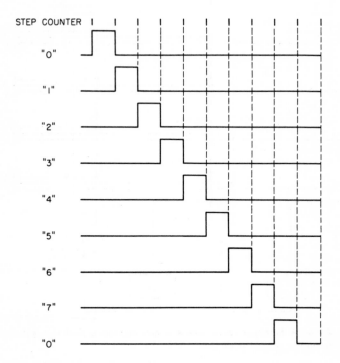

Fig. 2-26. Output waveforms for the gates of Fig. 2-24.

for each count. This is shown in Fig. 2-25 where A_0, A_1, A_2 are the 2^0, 2^1, 2^2 binary column respectively. The output signals for this array of gates are shown in Fig. 2-26.

Frequently it is necessary to decode all binary counts of a counter having considerably more than three binary stages. There are a number of ways in which this may be done logically, each having its own circuit problem relating to economy of components and the feasibility of AND gates driving AND gates in series. For example, in a 6-stage counter, the counter has 2^6 or 64 different possible states. These states could be decoded in the same way as the one above, each input sensing the one or zero side of a binary column. In general a gate input term implies a single component such as a diode or resistor. Consequently

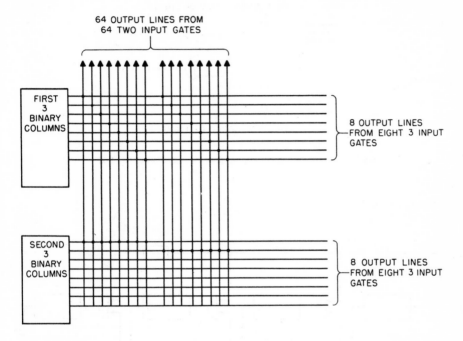

Fig. 2-27. Decoding the 64 possible unique states of a six-stage counter by separately decoding the first and last three binary stages, and mixing these two groups of eight lines in 64 two-input AND gates.

to decode the 64 counts by 64 gates of six inputs each will require 6×64 or 384 components — normally diodes. They could however, be decoded more cheaply in the manner shown in Fig. 2-27.

Here, the first and last three binary columns are decoded in the manner shown in Fig. 2-24, yielding two groups of eight output lines. These two groups of eight are combined in each of 8×8 or 64 unique combinations to give the final 64 output lines. This last mixing has required 64 two-input gates or 128 components — probably diodes. The two groups of eight three-input gates has required $2(8)(3) = 48$ diodes. Consequently this scheme requires a total of $128 + 48$, or 176 diodes compared to 384 in the original arrangement.

The saving however, is not as great as it would seem, because each of the 64 final output lines is the result of the AND gating of a pair of three-input AND gates, one from each of the two groups of eight as shown symbolically in Fig. 2-28. As the load on each of the three-input gates is quite large — each has to feed eight of the 64 final two-input gates — all 16 of the three-input gates would probably require an amplifier at its output. Consequently the cost of

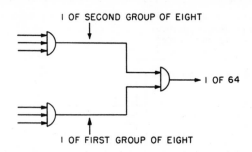

Fig. 2-28.   Generation of each of the 64 output lines of Fig. 2-27.

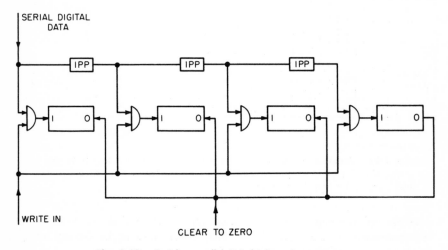

Fig. 2-29.   Serial-to-parallel digital information converter.

176 diodes and 16 amplifiers has to be compared against that of the 384 diodes in the original scheme.

2.5. Serial-to Parallel Converters.   Digital information is frequently available serially as a time sequence of ones and zeros coming from a radio, wire channel, magnetic tape, magnetic drum or other source. Usually in the form of the presence or absence of voltage pulses of a definite time duration and repetition rate, it must be converted to a space sequence of ones and zeros before it can be manipulated digitally. If the time between bits is not very large, this may be done as in Fig. 2-29. The elements *1PP* are delay lines having a delay equal to the time between bits in the input information.

There is one moment when the time spacing of data on the delay line is such that the centers of the ones and zeros in successive bits are at the input terminals of the gates corresponding to the flip-flops in which they are to be stored. At this moment all the "write-in" gates are enabled with a pulse and the entire array of ones and zeros on the delay line is simultaneously dropped into the flip-flops.

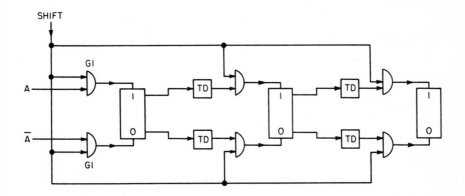

Fig. 2-30.   A serial-to-parallel converter using a shift register.

If the time between successive bits is more than approximately 5 microseconds, the delay line element becomes too large. In this case a shift register is employed as in Fig. 2-30. Here, the input information — which must be supplied in the normal and complemented form and usually from opposite sides of a flip-flop — is fed to the input gates G1. The input data timing must be known so that every time the center of a new bit arrives at the input gates a pulse is generated that feeds all shift gates simultaneously. This pulse writes into the first flip-flop the information on the input line at that moment. It writes into any other flip-flop, the information contained in the flip-flop behind it. In this way the input information is moved bit by bit down the line of flip-flops until the first bit to arrive at the register has been deposited in the last flip-flop in the line.

The elements marked *TD* are short time-delay units, logically necessary to write into any flip-flop the old information stored by the flip-flop behind it just prior to the shift pulse. Without the time delay the possibility would exist of reading into a given flip-flop not the old data of the flip-flop immediately behind it, but the new data being moved into it during the shift pulse. This time delay need be only as long as the duration of the shift pulse itself. It frequently does not require any additional components as the turnover time of the flip-flop itself may suffice.

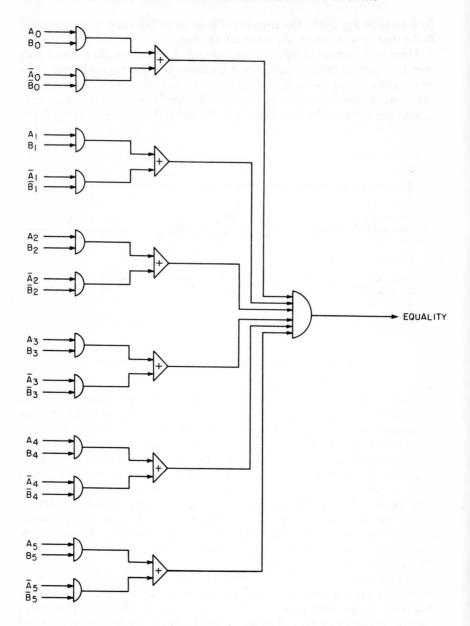

Fig. 2-31.   A binary comparator sensing for the equality of two 6-bit binary numbers.

Information existing as a space sequence of ones or zeros in such a register may be read out to give a time sequence of ones and zeros. The time spacing between the bits at "read out" is fixed only by the frequency of the shift-out pulses, and may be more or less than the spacing at write-in. This is a useful feature as it is often necessary to write in information in a slow or even nonperiodic manner, and then read it out serially at a rapid periodic rate.

2.6. Binary Comparator. As a final example of the type of logical arrays it may be necessary to assemble from building blocks, consider a binary comparator. This device senses when one binary number is equal to another binary number. It does this by sensing for equality, binary column for binary column. A frequent requirement is to sense for the equality of two 6-bit numbers as this usually represents an alphabetic or decimal character. For example, if the binary numbers are $A_0A_1A_2A_3A_4A_5$ and $B_0B_1B_2B_3B_4B_5$, the equality, column for column may be equality of ones or of zeros, and the algebraic condition for equality in all columns is

$$\text{Equality} = (A_0B_0 + \overline{A}_0\overline{B}_0)\ (A_1B_1 + \overline{A}_1\overline{B}_1)\ (A_2B_2 + \overline{A}_2\overline{B}_2)$$

$$(A_3B_3 + \overline{A}_3\overline{B}_3)\ (A_4B_4 + \overline{A}_4\overline{B}_4)\ (A_5B_5 + \overline{A}_5\overline{B}_5)$$

The input terms are of course one or the other sides of the flip-flops of the various binary columns of the two numbers. This algebraic expression would be mechanized by the AND-OR array of gates shown in Fig. 2-31.

TRANSISTOR FUNDAMENTALS

Previous chapters discussed the type of building blocks needed in digital computers and the logical functions required of them. From here on the book deals with the design of these building blocks using diodes, resistors, and transistors, Chapter 3 covering the fundamentals of semiconductors and transistors.

There is a wealth of information available dealing with transistor circuit analysis using the various four-terminal network equivalent circuits. The design and analysis of transistorized computer building blocks makes very little use of these circuits however, as they hold primarily for small-signal operation. Most computer-type circuits are large-signal current-switching circuits with known input currents from high source-impedance generators. Consequently, design can generally best be done from the volt-ampere curves of the transistor. The collector-to-emitter and base-to-emitter volt-ampere curves, together with a knowledge of the transient response characteristics, supply all the information needed.

3.1. Conductors, Insulators, and Semiconductors. The electrical conductivity of a material depends upon the number of movable electrical charges it contains. In the familiar planetary picture of the atom, all matter is composed of atoms consisting of a positively charged nucleus surrounded by electrons rotating in successively larger orbits around it. The sum of the negative charges on the orbital electrons equals the positive charge on the nucleus, making each atom electrically neutral. Each electron orbit or shell requires a unique number of electrons to fill it. When a shell is filled it is relatively stable, and a good deal of energy is required to remove electrons from it. It is primarily the electrons in the outer, unfilled "valence" shells that are detachable from the atom as current carriers.

Atoms of highly conducting metals such as copper or silver, have one planetary electron in excess of a completed number of shells. These metals, in the solid crystalline state, have their nucleii and surrounding planetary electrons of the inner, filled orbits arranged in a fixed, regular array called a crystal lattice. The excess electron of each atom is not tightly bound to the atom, but is free to wander through this structure of relatively fixed positive charges. The motion of these free, valence electrons under the influence of an applied electric field con-

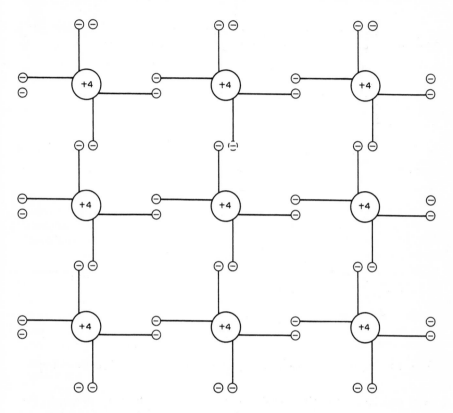

Fig. 3-1. Germanium crystal lattice structure showing adjacent atoms sharing electrons to fill outer orbits.

stitutes a current. Because there is one free electron per atom, the number of current carriers is large, and the electrical resistivity is low — 1.7×10^{-6} ohm cm for copper.

In solid insulating materials, the outer shell valence electrons are not so easily detached from the atoms; consequently there are very few unbound charges for carrying current. The resistivity of insulators ranges from 10^{+11} to 10^{+19} ohm cm.

Semiconductors have a resistivity somewhere between that of conductors and insulators. The resistivity is strongly temperature-sensitive, ranging between

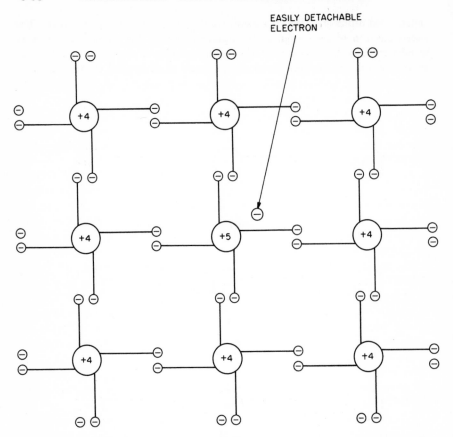

Fig. 3-2. A pentavalent impurity atom replacing a germanium atom in a germanium crystal.

10^{-3} and 10^{+5} ohm cm depending on the purity of the semiconductor. The most important semiconductors for transistor applications are germanium and silicon. Briefly, the conduction process in germanium — taking a typical semiconductor — is as follows.

Germanium has a valence of four, i.e., its outer orbit or shell has four electrons. In the solid crystalline state it arranges itself in the crystal lattice structure shown symbolically in Fig. 3-1.

The nucleii, each with a positive charge of $+32$, and the 28 planetary electrons in the inner, filled orbits, are shown as inert cores with a positive charge of $+4$. These cores are in relatively fixed positions in a diamond cubic lattice structure. The outermost electron orbit of individual atoms contains four electrons, but eight are required to fill it completely.

Each atom completes its outer valence shell by sharing one valence electron with its nearest neighbor as shown in Fig. 3-1. This sharing of electron pairs is called a "covalent" or electron-pair bond. Electrons so shared in covalent bonds are firmly fixed to the lattice structure and are not free to drift through the structure as current carriers. Thermal vibration of the crystal atoms however, breaks a certain fraction of these bound electron pairs, and electrons so liberated are available as current carriers and will move in the direction of an applied positive potential.

The atom that had one of its electron pairs broken is left with a unit positive charge. Thermal vibration of an adjacent atom may break one of its electron pair bonds, and this liberated electron may move into the vacancy left by the original broken bond. Effectively, the positive charge has moved from the first to the second atom, although it is actually a bound electron that has moved from the second to the first atom. This "electron vacancy" moving from atom to atom in the opposite direction from that of the bound electron is called a "hole." It can be treated as if it were an actual free particle with a positive charge equal to that of the electron. Thus the breaking of an electron-pair bond produces two current carriers in semiconductors — the liberated electron and the hole.

The resistivity of the semiconductor depends on the number of such broken covalent bonds per unit volume. For pure germanium at room temperature there is roughly one broken covalent bond for every $3 \times 10^{+9}$ atoms, resulting in a resistivity of 60 ohm cm. As the temperature is increased, the thermal vibration of the atoms increases, resulting in more broken covalent bonds and therefore more current carriers and decreased resistivity. This is in contrast to conductors whose resistivity increases with temperature.

In pure germanium, broken covalent bonds produced by thermal vibration of the atoms are the only source of electrons and holes. A pure semiconductor is referred to as an intrinsic semiconductor.

3.2. Artificially Generated Electrons and Holes. The conductivity of pure germanium can be increased if in some way the number of free electrons or holes in the crystal can be increased. Figure 3-2 illustrates the result of adding to pure germanium, a small amount of an impurity having five valence electrons — arsenic or antimony. The impurity atom displaces a germanium atom in the crystal lattice. Four of its valence electrons are shared with those of four neighboring germanium atoms in covalent bonds. These four electrons are bound tightly to the atom, but the fifth one, not having a place in the symmetrical alignment of forces that hold the crystal together, is easily detached from the atom even at room temperature. It is then available to wander through the crystal much like the free electron in metals.

It should be noted that although a positive charge is left behind on the pentavalent atom when its fifth electron is detached, such a positive charge does not have the properties of a hole. As this pentavalent atom has its outer shell completely filled, it does not have the energy to break down adjacent covalent bonds and rob them of their electron. It is thus a *stationary* positive charge and cannot increase the conductivity of the crystal. Such a germanium crystal with added pentavalent impurities is called N type germanium, as the added current car-

MISSING ELECTRON AT THIS POINT RESULTS IN FORCE WHICH TENDS
TO REMOVE AN ELECTRON FROM AN ADJACENT ATOM
LEAVING IT WITH A POSITIVE CHARGE OR "HOLE"

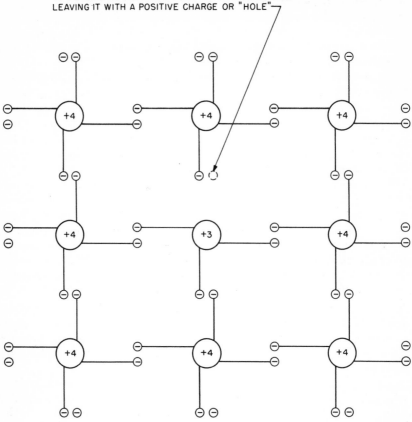

Fig. 3-3. A trivalent impurity atom replacing a germanium atom in a germanium crystal.

riers are the negative electrons. The impurity is called a donor type impurity
as it donates electrons to the crystal.

If the added impurity is an element such as indium or gallium, the situation
shown in Fig. 3-3 results. The impurity atom enters the crystal structure, but
since it has only three valence electrons, one of its covalent bonds is not filled.
This results in a large force tending to break down adjacent covalent bonds,
robbing them of an electron. The removal of an electron from a covalent bond
leaves an electron vacancy or positive charge at that point. The positive charge
produced by the stolen electron in turn breaks a covalent bond adjacent to it.
This process continues. The breaking up of covalent electron pairs, leaving behind a positive charge that in turn can break up another electron pair, constitutes a wandering positive charge, or hole.

The original trivalent atom has acquired one extra negative charge, but as the outer shell is completed, this added negative charge is stationary and cannot increase the conductivity of the crystal. The wandering holes however, have done so.

Such a germanium crystal with added trivalent impurities is called P type germanium as it has an excess of positively charged current carriers. The impurity is called an acceptor type impurity as it accepts electrons from the germanium atoms. Semiconductors doped with either type of impurity are called

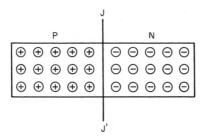

Fig. 3-4. A junction between P and N type germanium.

extrinsic semiconductors. Note that the conductivity of either a P or N type semiconductor is uniform in all directions and consequently has no rectifying properties.

3.3. PN Junctions. Figure 3-4 shows the properties of a junction between P and N type germanium. To the left of JJ′, the germanium has been uniformly doped with a trivalent impurity resulting in P type germanium. To the right of JJ′ a pentavalent impurity has been uniformly added, resulting in N type germanium.

In the absence of an applied voltage, an electrostatic potential builds up across the junction. The P region will be negative with respect to the N region. This comes about in the following way. Holes from the P germanium diffuse across the junction into the N region, and electrons from the N region diffuse across the junction into the P region. This process resembles the diffusion of gases from regions of high, to regions of low concentration. An electron crossing to the P region leaves a fixed, positively charged donor ion immediately to the right of the junction. A hole crossing to the N region leaves a fixed, negatively charged acceptor ion immediately to the left of the junction. Thus a charge is built up on either side of the junction — positive on the right, negative on the left. These charges result in a potential difference of about 0.2 volt across the junction which acts as a barrier to further build up, because additional holes trying to cross the junction region from the P side meet an electric gradient large enough to drive them back, and electrons trying to cross from the N to the P region are similarly forced back.

3.4. Forward and Reverse Biased *PN* Junctions.   The effect of an externally applied potential on such a junction between dissimilar semiconductors is shown in Figs. 3-5A and B. In Fig. 3-5A, the externally applied potential is in such a direction as to make the *P* type germanium positive with respect to the *N* type. This is in the opposite direction to the potential resulting from the diffusion process already discussed. Thus the barrier potential that prevented the further transport of charges across the junction is decreased and a large number

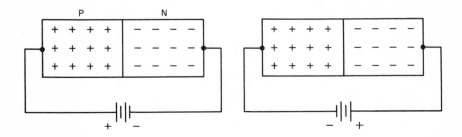

Fig. 3-5A.   A *PN* junction biased in this direction exhibits low impedance.

Fig. 3-5B.   A *PN* junction biased in this direction exhibits high impedance.

of charges can now make the crossing. The battery sees a low impedance, and a relatively high current flow results.

In Fig. 3-5B the applied potential is in the same direction as the potential caused by the diffusion process. This increases the barrier that electrons and holes must scale to cross the junction, and fewer charges make the crossing. The battery then sees a high impedance, and a relatively small current flows. Such a junction then has rectifying properties, it is essentially the structure of a semiconducting diode. The bias of Fig. 3-5A is referred to as a forward bias, that of Fig. 3-5B as a reverse bias.

It is worthwhile looking at this situation in another way. In Fig. 3-5A, the applied potential drives holes in the *P* region to the right, and electrons in the *N* region to the left. Because the *P* region has many holes and the *N* region many electrons, the situation can continue and a large current will flow. In Fig. 3-5B, the holes in the *P* region are drawn to the left, and the electrons in the *N* region to the right. Consequently no carriers are available to cross the junction and the current flow is small. In a way it is similar to exhausting water from both ends of a pipe simultaneously. Once the water is exhausted, the flow ceases.

3.5. Minority-Carrier Injection.   In the forward biased connection of Fig. 3-5A, holes from the *P* region were driven across the junction into the *N* region, and electrons from the *N* region were driven into the *P* region. The carriers injected into both regions are less numerous than the type of carriers normally there, and are called "minority carriers." This process of minority-carrier injection is extremely important, and is responsible for transistor action. Eventually, injected minority carriers recombine with the majority carriers of the region into which they are injected. They may travel as much as .005 inch into the region of injection before recombination occurs.

3.6. Transistors. Using this phenomena of minority-carrier injection, a semiconductor power-amplifying element — a transistor — can be built as indicated in Fig. 3-6. The device shown has a narrow region of N type germanium sandwiched between two regions of P type germanium. This results in two PN junctions of the type shown in Fig. 3-4.

If E_E is disconnected, and the right-hand junction operated in reverse bias —

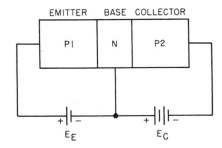

Fig. 3-6. A junction transistor consists of a forward biased PN junction supplying current carriers to a reverse biased PN junction.

P region negative with respect to the N region — the battery E_C will see a high impedance and very little current will flow. The current that does flow will be due to thermally generated minority carriers — holes in the N region and electrons in the P2 region. This process, discussed in Sec. 3-1, occurs whether the germanium has had impurities added, or not. At room temperature, it does not contribute very many carriers and the current flow is quite small, but the number of carriers produced increases exponentially with temperature, and for germanium, this reverse leakage current roughly doubles every 10°C.

If the device is at room temperature and E_C is reconnected with the polarity shown in Fig. 3-6, the *P1-N* junction has a forward bias and a large current will flow in the *P1* region. This current consists of holes from *P1* injected into *N* region, and electrons from *N* injected into the *P1* region. The *N* region is made quite narrow — about .001 inch — but the distance minority carriers travel before recombination is about .005 inch. Consequently the holes injected into the *N* region are available and are of the correct sign to transport current across the *P2-N* junction. The geometry of the structure is such that 90% to 99% of the holes that *P1* injects into the *N* region cross into the *P2* region. An increment of current injected into the *P1* terminal therefore results in an increment of current out of the *P2* terminal, 90% to 99% as large. That fraction of the current injected into *P1* that does not come out through *P2* comes out through the terminal connected to the *N* region.

The *P1-N* junction having a low impedance, a small voltage increment applied to *P1* will produce large current changes in it. But the *P2-N* junction being reverse biased, has a high impedance and can sustain high voltages. Thus E_C can be made high, and large currents injected into *P1* with small voltage changes come out of the *P2* region accelerated by large voltages. Since 90% to 99% of the current injected into *P1* comes out through *P2*, an energy or power gain has been achieved. The source of added power or energy is the battery E_C. To make use of the device as an amplifier, a large load impedance and

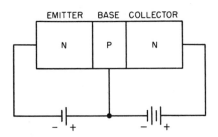

Fig. 3-7.   An *n-p-n* junction transistor.

relatively high voltage is placed in series with the *P2* terminal. Then a small power increment at the input to *P1* (small voltage change — large current change) results in a large power change at the output of *P2* (large voltage change and a current change within 90% to 99% of current input to *P1*).

The device shown in Fig. 3-6 is a *p-n-p* junction transistor. The *P1* region is called the emitter as it emits the current carriers that flow in the *P2-N* circuit. The *P2* region is called the collector because it collects the minority carriers injected into the *N* region. The *N* region is called the base.

Minority electrons injected from the base into the emitter add nothing to the collector current. In actual practice therefore, the emitter is more heavily doped with trivalent impurities than is the base with pentavalent impurities.

The geometry of junction transistors is not quite as simple as Fig. 3-6 suggests, but geometry and building methods are well discussed in the literature and will not be dealt with here.

The first type of transistor devised was a point-contact transistor consisting of two closely spaced metallic "cats-whisker" contacts on a base of *N*-type germanium. The mechanism of its operation was not fully understood and its characteristic volt-ampere curves were not very reproducable. Consequently it has been almost completely replaced by the junction transistor.

In Fig. 3-6, a narrow section of *N* germanium was shown sandwiched between *P*-type germanium. Transistor action can also be achieved by placing a narrow region of *P* germanium between the two outer sections of *N*-type germanium as shown in Fig. 3-7. Such a device is called an *n-p-n* junction transistor. To achieve transistor action the emitter-base junction must operate in forward bias, and the collector-base junction at a reverse bias, as in the *p-n-p* transistor. This requires supply voltages of opposite polarity to those needed for *p-n-p* transistors. Action of the *n-p-n* is similar to the *p-n-p* arrangement. The N-type emitter injects into the P-type base minority carriers — this time electrons — that do not recombine with the holes in the P-type base, but cross into the collector, supplying the carriers needed for the reverse biased base-collector junction.

The symbols commonly used for the two types of transistors are shown in

Fig. 3-8A. Symbolic representation of a p-n-p transistor.

Fig. 3-8B. Symbolic representation of an n-p-n transistor.

Figs. 3-8A and B. In both cases, the terminal with the arrow is the emitter, the direction of the arrow indicating the direction of conventional current flow. Therefore in the *p-n-p* transistor conventional current flows into the emitter; in the *n-p-n* it flows out of it.

In this book the emphasis is on *p-n-p* germanium transistors. Methods of analysis of any *p-n-p* circuits discussed in later chapters are entirely applicable to *n-p-n* circuits as almost all *p-n-p* circuits have their complements with *n-p-n* transistors. In general, by reversing the polarity of supply voltages and therefore the direction of all currents, the *n-p-n* complement of a *p-n-p* circuit may be obtained.

Silicon transistors that are mainly of the *n-p-n* variety will not be dealt with in this book, chiefly because these circuits are merely special cases of general type circuits analyzed in detail for germanium transistors. The main advantage of silicon transistors is their ability to operate at higher temperatures — 150°C instead of 85°C — for germanium units. Ability to operate at such high temperatures is becoming increasingly important because of the many missile and airborne applications where adequate cooling is normally not available.

Silicon transistors generally have lower current gains than germanium units. Also, the minimum junction voltage for a given current is usually higher for silicon than germanium. Since the essential difference between the two types of transistors lies in the magnitudes of various parameters — apart from the fact that silicon units are mainly *n-p-n* and germanium units *p-n-p* — silicon transistors need not be considered in detail, but the methods of analysis developed herein for germanium transistor circuits are in general also applicable to silicon.

3.7. Transistor Circuit Fundamentals. The transistor is a three-terminal device that can be used as an amplifier with either of the three terminals common to the input and output circuits. The three possible connections for both transistor types are shown in Figs. 3-9A, B, and C. These connections are referred to as the grounded or common base, grounded or common emitter, and grounded or common collector connections, respectively.

Since the emitter-to-base junction is operated with a forward bias its volt-ampere characteristic is like that of a diode in the forward direction, and it therefore has a very low, nonlinear input impedance.

As most of the minority carriers injected by the emitter come out again at the collector, the current gain from the emitter to collector is close to unity. And as the collector junction is operated with reverse bias, the collector-to-base volt-ampere characteristic resembles the reverse characteristic of a diode. In general this means that power amplification in the grounded base connection can be obtained only if the load impedance at the collector is greater than the impedance of the generator driving the emitter terminal. This usually requires impedance matching with transformers, or the equivalent of cathode followers at either or both the input and output terminals. The grounded base connection corresponds in general to the grounded grid connection in vacuum tube circuits.

The common emitter connection is capable of large current gains. Since there can be no accumulation of charge in the transistor it must be true that

$$\Delta I_E = \Delta I_B + \Delta I_C$$

where ΔI_E, ΔI_B, ΔI_C are the incremental emitter, base and collector currents respectively. If the incremental collector-to-emitter current gain is defined as

$$\frac{\Delta I_C}{\Delta I_E} = \frac{\beta}{\beta + 1}$$

then

$$\Delta I_B = \Delta I_E - \Delta I_C \tag{3-1}$$

$$= \Delta I_E - \left(\frac{\beta}{\beta + 1}\right) \Delta I_E \tag{3-2}$$

$$= \frac{\Delta I_C}{\beta} \tag{3-3}$$

or

$$\frac{\Delta I_C}{\Delta I_B} = \beta$$

This ratio has the significance of collector-to-base current gain. For a collector-to-emitter current gain $[\beta/(\beta+1)]$ of .98 — a reasonable value for many transistors — β, the collector-to-base current gain, is 49.

The volt-ampere characteristics of the base-to-emitter junction looking into the base will have the same general diode-like shape as that looking into the emitter. The former can be generated with reasonable accuracy from the latter by dividing the current ordinates on the latter curve by $\beta + 1 \cong \beta$. This

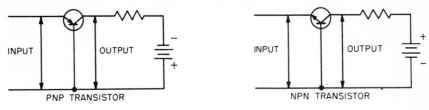

Fig. 3-9A.   Grounded or common-base connection.

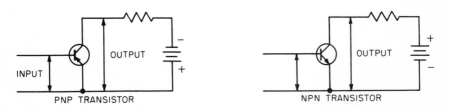

Fig. 3-9B.   Grounded or common-emitter connection.

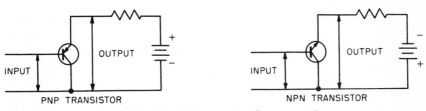

Fig. 3-9C.   Grounded or common-collector connection.

means that the input impedance — the slope of the I-E curve — is roughly β times as large in the grounded emitter as it is in the grounded base stage. This higher input impedance, and the possibility of achieving current gain between input and output without the use of transformers, makes the grounded emitter connection the most useful of the three. This connection corresponds to the grounded cathode connection in vacuum tubes.

The grounded collector connection is used primarily to give impedance transformation. It has high input impedance, low output impedance, a voltage gain of somewhat less than unity and a current gain of approximately that in the grounded emitter stage. Without going into the details of equivalent circuits, the high input and low output impedance can be simply demonstrated as follows.

In Fig. 3-10, assume an applied input voltage change ΔV_I. Then the input impedance is — for a reverse biased high impedance collector junction —

$$R_{INPUT} = \frac{\Delta V_I}{\Delta I_B} = \frac{\Delta V_{EB} + \Delta V_{RL}}{\Delta I_B}$$

But from Eq. 3-2

$$\Delta I_B = \frac{\Delta I_E}{\beta + 1}$$

where β is the collector-to-base current gain. Then

$$R_{INPUT} = \frac{(\Delta V_{EB} + \Delta V_{RL})}{\Delta I_E} (\beta + 1)$$

$$= \left(\frac{\Delta V_{EB}}{\Delta I_E} + \frac{\Delta V_{RL}}{\Delta I_E} \right) (\beta + 1)$$

$$= (R_E + R_L)(\beta + 1)$$

where R_E is the slope of the emitter-base volt-ampere curve looking into the emitter at constant collector-to-base voltage. This is usually given in the manufacturer's data sheets and is about 20 ohms for most germanium transistors. Being in general small compared to R_L it can be neglected. Consequently at the input to a grounded-collector amplifier the impedance is emitter load resistance multiplied by $(\beta + 1)$.

The output impedance of the grounded collector connection can be determined from Fig. 3-11. For an assumed emitter current change ΔI_E, the output impedance is

$$R_O = \frac{\Delta V_E}{\Delta I_E} = \frac{\Delta V_{EB} + \Delta V_{RG}}{\Delta I_E}$$

But from Eq. 3-2

$$\Delta I_E = (\beta + 1) \Delta I_B$$

Therefore

$$R_O = \frac{\Delta V_{EB} + \Delta V_{RG}}{(\beta + 1) \Delta I_B} = \frac{1}{(\beta + 1)} \left(\frac{\Delta V_{EB}}{\Delta I_B} + R_G \right) = \frac{1}{\beta + 1} (R_B + R_G)$$

Here R_B is the slope of the emitter base volt-ampere curve looking into the base at constant emitter-to-collector voltage. This also is given in the manufacturer's data sheets and is about 300 to 500 ohms for most germanium transistors. In comparison with the input signal generator resistance R_G it can usually be ignored. Therefore at the output of a grounded collector stage the impedance seen is that of the generator driving the base reduced by a factor of $1/(\beta + 1)$.

Since the emitter-base terminals act like a diode, they are always separated in potential by a voltage of approximately 0.1 to 0.4 volt. Thus the emitter constantly follows the base in potential and the circuit is generally called an emitter follower. It is in many ways similar to a vacuum tube cathode follower, the main point of difference being that the output impedance of the emitter follower is dependent on the impedance of the input signal generator. In the vacuum tube cathode follower there is no similar dependence.

3.8. Transistor Volt-Ampere Curves. To use the transistor as a circuit element, the designer needs its d-c volt-ampere characteristic curves. The most

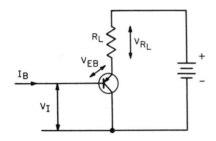

Fig. 3-10. Common-collector or emitter-follower connection.

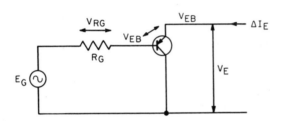

Fig. 3-11. A generator E_G with source impedance R_G driving an emitter follower.

useful for a typical *p-n-p* germanium transistor (Raytheon type CK761), are those shown in Figs. 3-12A and 3-13A and B.

Figure 3-12A gives the collector-current *v.* collector-voltage curves for various values of input emitter current in the grounded base configuration. They resemble very closely the plate characteristics of a vacuum tube pentode. The slope of the curves is very small, indicating a high output impedance, and the running parameter is an input current rather than an input voltage. The knee of the curve, i.e., the collector voltage at which the collector current starts falling off rapidly, is at zero volts rather than at approximately 50, as in a pentode. The entire region to the right of $V_{CB} = 0$, and above $I_E = 0$ is called the active region. Here the collector-to-base junction is in reverse bias and the emitter-to-base junction is in forward bias. The collector volt-ampere curve indicates a high impedance as might be expected of a diode with a reverse voltage.

In this region, at a fixed collector voltage, a given increment of emitter current results in an almost equal increment of collector current, as discussed in Sec. 3.7. This ratio, the incremental collector-to-emitter current gain is spoken of as "alpha", and is defined as

$$\alpha = \left(\frac{\Delta I_C}{\Delta I_E}\right) \text{ Constant } V_C \qquad (3\text{-}4)$$

It is a very important transistor parameter, and for most transistors ranges between 0.90 and 0.99.

From Fig. 3-12A, alpha is seen to be independent of collector voltage, and to decrease only slightly with collector current. The ratio of the d-c collector current to the d-c emitter current at any operating point is often referred to as the "d-c alpha" to that point.

Although not apparent in Fig. 3-12A, there is a finite value of collector current at zero emitter current. This was discussed in Sec. 3.6, and is due to thermally generated minority carriers in the base and collector regions, which are driven across the reverse biased collector junction. At low collector voltages (under approximately 0.5 volt), this current is designated I_{CO}, and is also an important transistor parameter. I_{CO} varies with temperature as

$$I_{CO} = I_{COR} \left[e^{\,0.069\,(T-T_R)} \right] \qquad (3\text{-}5)$$

where I_{CO} and I_{COR} are the collector leakage currents at a temperature T, and at a reference temperature T_R (in °C) respectively. A current varying as in Eq. 3-5 will double every 10°C.

Leakage current is also a function of the collector voltage, but as this voltage-sensitive component is unaffected by temperature it is not as serious as the temperature sensitive component of Eq. 3-5 alone. To a close approximation the total collector leakage (at zero emitter current) at any temperature, and voltage V_C, is given by

$$I_C = I_{COR} \left[e^{\,0.069\,(T-T_R)} \right] + \frac{V_C}{R_C} \qquad (3\text{-}6)$$

where R_C is the slope of the $I_C - V_C$ curve for $I_E = 0$. This slope is normally too small to be read from a curve as in Fig. 3-12A. The manufacturer's data sheets generally give this resistance at some emitter current in the center of the operating range. From Fig. 3-12A it can be seen that this resistance has a maximum value at $I_E = 0$, and it is therefore safe to take the manufacturer's value. This collector slope is usually given as an admittance with the input open-circuited; it is designated h_{OB} or h_{22}, and defined as

$$h_{OB} = \left(\frac{\Delta I_C}{\Delta E_C}\right) \text{ Constant } I_E \qquad (3\text{-}7)$$

It is worthwhile examining the magnitude of the currents in Eq. 3-6. For the CK761, h_{OB} is 1×10^{-6}, and therefore the voltage component of leakage at approximately 5 volts of collector voltage is $5/1 \times 10^{+6} = 5$ microamperes.

I_{CO} at 25°C is quoted by the manufacturer as a maximum of 5 microamperes. Since from Eq. 3-5 it doubles every 10°C, it is 40 microamperes at 55°C. Consequently, at a temperature slightly above room temperature it is the temperature-sensitive component of Eq. 3-6 that predominates.

From Fig. 3-12A it is obvious that a close approximation to the collector current is given by

$$I_C = I_{CO} + \alpha \, I_E \qquad (3\text{-}8)$$

where α is given by Eq. 3-4, and is taken as the average value over the range of currents under discussion.

One final point about Fig. 3-12A is of importance. In the region to the left of the origin, the collector-to-base junction is operating with a forward bias,

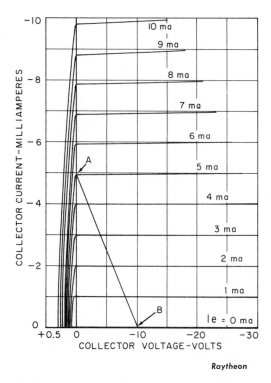

Raytheon

Fig. 3-12A. Collector current v. collector-to-base voltage, common-base connection; type CK761 transistor.

and as expected, the volt-ampere curve resembles a diode in the forward direction. This region where the emitter and collector junctions are both forward biased is called the saturation region. Operation here is to be avoided as it decreases the frequency response of the transistor (see Chapter 4).

Figure 3-12B shows the curve of the input terminals in the common base connection; it resembles that of a diode in the forward direction. The curve shown is that for a collector-to-base voltage of zero. For other collector voltages the curve retains the shape shown but is moved parallel to the emitter base voltage axis. It moves toward $V_{EB} = 0$ for increasingly negative collector voltage. The magnitude of this shift per unit change in collector voltage at a fixed value of

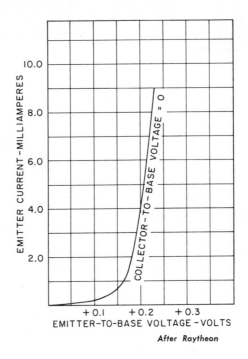

After Raytheon

Fig. 3-12B. Emitter current v. emitter-to-base voltage, common-base connection; type CK761 transistor.

emitter current is another important transistor parameter. Referred to as the feedback voltage ratio, it is generally designated in manufacturers data sheets as h_{12} or μ, and is defined as

$$\mu = h_{12} = \left(\frac{\Delta E_E}{\Delta E_C}\right) \text{Constant } I_E \qquad (3\text{-}9)$$

For most germanium transistors it is a relatively small number, and ranges between 0.1 and 0.7 millivolts of emitter voltage shift per volt of collector voltage change.

The slope of the curve in Fig. 3-12B is a function of the operating point, and can therefore only really be referred to as an input impedance when performing small-signal excursions on the curve. The slope of the tangent to this curve at any point is an important transistor parameter normally designated in the manufacturer's data sheets as h_{ib} or h_{11}, and defined as

$$h_{ib} = h_{11} = \left(\frac{\Delta E_E}{\Delta I_E}\right) \text{Constant } E_C \qquad (3\text{-}10)$$

It is generally quoted in data sheets at the $I_E = 1$ ma point, and ranges between

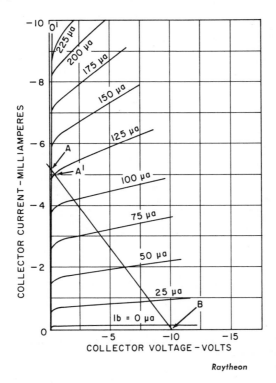

Raytheon

Fig. 3-13A. Collector current v. collector-emitter voltage; common-emitter connection; type CK761 transistor.

20 and 60 ohms for most small — under 150 milliwatts of collector dissipation — transistors.

The curves of Figs. 3-13A and B are the corresponding output and input curves for the common emitter connection. They are more useful than those of Figs. 3-12A and B as the common emitter and common collector connections are most frequently employed in computer circuits. Furthermore, given the common emitter curves, the common base curves can be generated with good accuracy. The reverse however, is not true, as the collector and emitter current are very nearly equal, and consequently their difference, the base current, cannot be read from the curves with any degree of accuracy.

Again, the $I_C - V_C$ curve of Fig. 3-13A has a pentode-like appearance, with input current rather than voltage as the controlling parameter. The slopes of the curves are greater than those in Fig. 3-12A, indicating a lower output im-

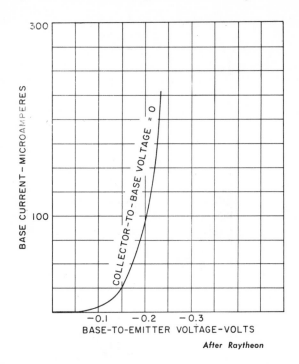

After Raytheon

Fig. 3-13B. Base current v. base-to-emitter voltage, common-emitter connection; type CK761 transistor.

pedance. It will be seen too, that quite large current gains between the collector and base terminals are obtainable. The incremental current gain is usually designated by the symbol β. One of the most important transistor parameters, it is defined as

$$\beta = \left(\frac{\Delta I_C}{\Delta I_B}\right) \text{Constant } V_C \qquad (3-11)$$

The usual range of β is from 10 to 100. The incremental value of β is seen from Fig. 3-13A to vary greatly both with collector voltage and collector current. The ratio of the d-c collector current at the knee of the curves to the d-c base current at that point, is a handy parameter, referred to as "d-c beta".

A useful relationship between the common-emitter and common-base current gain can be obtained from Eq. 3-1. Dividing both sides of this equation by ΔI_B and rearranging, gives

$$\frac{\Delta I_E}{\Delta I_B} = \frac{\Delta I_C}{\Delta I_B} + 1 = \beta + 1 \qquad (3\text{-}12)$$

and dividing both sides of the same equation by ΔI_E and rearranging, results in

$$\frac{\Delta I_B}{\Delta I_E} = 1 - \frac{\Delta I_C}{\Delta I_E} = 1 - \alpha \qquad (3\text{-}13)$$

Muliplying Eqs. 3-12 and 3-13 gives

$$\beta + 1 = \frac{1}{1 - \alpha} \qquad (3\text{-}14)$$

or

$$\beta = \frac{\alpha}{1 - \alpha} \qquad (3\text{-}15)$$

This relationship between common-base and common-emitter current gain is very useful. Since α is normally close to unity — because of the term $(1 - \alpha)$ in the denominator of Eq. 3-15 — a small percentage change in α results in a large percentage change in β. This explains the relatively large variation in incremental β over the operating range in Fig. 3-13A.

From Eqs. 3-1 and 3-8 a relation can be obtained for the d-c collector current as a function of the base input current, i.e., the collector current in the common emitter connection. Therefore if I_E is eliminated between these two equations, there results

$$I_C = \frac{I_{CO}}{1 - \alpha} + \frac{\alpha}{1 - \alpha} I_B = \frac{I_{CO}}{1 - \alpha} + \beta I_B \qquad (3\text{-}16)$$

From this it can be seen that for $I_B = 0$, $I_C = I_{CO}/(1 - \alpha)$. Thus the output current for zero input current is $1/(1 - \alpha)$ times as large in the common-emitter as it is in the common-base connection. For $\alpha = 0.98$, a usual value, $1/(1 - \alpha)$ is as large as 50.

As already mentioned, the collector leakage current at zero emitter current in the common base circuit may be as high as 40 microamperes at 55°C. Consequently with zero input current in the grounded emitter configuration, the output leakage current may be as high as $I_{CO}/(1 - \alpha) = (50)(.04) = 2$ ma.

Ordinarily this could not be tolerated, and a way to decrease it can be found from Eq. 3-16. Instead of reducing the base input current to zero when turning off the collector current, a reverse current of the magnitude of I_{CO} — the collector leakage current with the emitter open in the common base circuit — is forced into the base. Then Eq. 3-16 gives for $I_B = -I_{CO}$

$$I_C = \frac{I_{CO}}{1 - \alpha} + \frac{\alpha}{1 - \alpha} (-I_{CO}) = I_{CO}$$

Thus the collector leakage current has been reduced to the relatively low value existing in the common base connection, as compared to $1/(1 - \alpha)$ times this amount if the input base current were merely reduced to zero.

In digital circuits designed in later chapters, transistors in the common-emitter configuration will be operated mainly as switches, either full on or supposedly completely off. To prevent the collector leakage current from building up to $I_{CO}/(1 - \alpha)$, transistors that are meant to be turned off will be supplied with a reverse base current of I_{CO} at the highest operating temperature. In calculating the value of the components that supply this current, the d-c potential at the base of the transistor can be assumed to be that at the emitter.

The curve in Fig. 3-13B is the input characteristic for the common emitter connection. It is shown for a collector-to-base voltage of zero, and is one of a family for various other collector-to-base voltages. The other curves of the family parallel this one very closely, and are shifted horizontally along the voltage axis. They move away from the origin for increasingly negative collector voltages. The amount of the shift is roughly the same as for the common base input family — about 0.1 to 0.7 millivolt per volt of collector voltage.

To the left of the curves in Fig. 3-13A along the lines 00′, the collector-to-emitter voltage is less than approximately 0.2 volt. From Fig. 3-13B it can be seen that the base-to-emitter voltage corresponding to any point along 00′ in Fig. 3-13A, is greater in magnitude than collector-to-emitter voltage. Therefore the collector is positive relative to the base and both junctions are in forward bias. As already mentioned, this region where both junctions are in forward bias is called the saturation region, and is to be avoided as it decreases transistor frequency response.

At this point in the book it becomes possible to design slow-speed digital circuits with transistors. These types of circuits are usually on-off switch type circuits. The transistor is generally required to force an output node — the collector — to either of two voltage levels. Consequently a transistor will frequently be operating at the extremes of a load line such as AB, in Fig. 3-13A. As discussed above, if the transistor is to be cut off, as at B, to a collector current no greater than I_{CO}, a reverse current of I_{CO} must be delivered to the base. If the transistor is to be turned full on as at point A, Fig. 3-13A indicates that a forward current of about 135 microamperes must be applied to the base. The base-to-emitter voltage at this forward current may be read from the $I_B - V_B$ curve of Fig. 3-13B, and from this base voltage the component values of the input circuit needed to supply the forward base current in the steady-state may be calculated.

Before going into the details of such designs, however, it is necessary to consider the transient response characteristics of transistors, and these are discussed in Chapter 4.

TRANSISTOR TRANSIENT RESPONSE

The d-c value of transistor output currents for specified inputs can be read from the static volt-ampere curves of Figs. 3-12 and 3-13. There is however, a time delay between the application of an input signal and the appearance of the steady-state value of the output called for by the static curve. For some transistors this time delay is already significant in the upper audio range. Chapter 4 discusses this transient response characteristic in the three different circuit configurations; magnitudes of time delays are calculated and methods of reducing them considered.

4.1. Frequency Dependence of Transistor Parameters. In Chapter 3, in discussing the nature of transistor action, it was shown that the emitter injects minority carriers into the base region, and that these carriers move by a diffusion process into the collector region. The collector-to-base voltage drop appears mainly across a very small region on either side of the junction itself. Consequently, there is very little electrical gradient in most of the base region from emitter-to-collector junction. Due to the lack of an accelerating field over most of the base region, the base transit time of the injected minority carriers is quite large, and accounts for the time delay between the output and input signal.

This time delay can be described quantitatively by specifying the common base current gain α as being some unique function of frequency. The inverse Laplace transform of this frequency response characteristic will then give the time response characteristic. The time response characteristic could be specified to conform to the actual transistor behavior, and the frequency-response characteristic derived from this, but since the transistor is more usually employed as an amplifier over a wide frequency band, it is more natural to express its behavior first in terms of frequency.

Experimental measurements of the phase shift and attenuation of the output current relative to the input current with the output short circuited, show that the actual behavior of a transistor is very well approximated by the following expression:

$$\alpha = \left(\frac{-\Delta I_C}{\Delta I_E}\right)_{\text{Constant } V_C} = \frac{-\alpha_0}{1 + j\dfrac{\omega}{\omega_0}} \tag{4-1}$$

Here α_0 is the low-frequency value of α and $\omega_0 = 2\pi\, f\alpha_{co}$ where $f\alpha_{co}$ is the frequency at which the magnitude of α is $1/\sqrt{2}$ times its low-frequency value.

This frequency, $f\alpha_{co}$ (referred to as alpha cutoff frequency), is, next to β, the most important parameter of the transistor. The magnitude and phase of α in Eq. 4-1 are given by

$$|\alpha| = \frac{\alpha_0}{\sqrt{1 + (f/f\alpha_{co})^2}} \tag{4-2}$$

$$\varphi = \tan^{-1} f/f\alpha_{co} \tag{4-3}$$

It must be emphasized that Eqs. 4-1, 4-2 and 4-3 are approximations made to fit experimental data. The magnitude of α is described by Eq. 4-2 to an accuracy of 10% up to a frequency of 10 $f\alpha_{co}$. The phase shift given by Eq. 4-3 may be in error by 10° at $f\alpha_{co}$ and by as much as 50° at 3 $f\alpha_{co}$[1].

Values of $f\alpha_{co}$ range from 500 kc to 30 mc for ordinary transistors. Special types of transistors are available with much higher values of $f\alpha_{co}$. They are referred to as "drift" transistors and achieve their higher cutoff frequency by producing an electrical gradient in the base region. This gradient accelerates the injected minority carriers from emitter to collector and is achieved by a controlled distribution of impurities in the base region. In general these drift transistors have a big drawback in that to operate properly, the collector-to-emitter voltage must not be allowed to drop below 1 to 3 volts. This usually results in higher collector dissipation.

Given the common base current gain described in Eq. 4-1, examining the common emitter current gain shows that since $\beta = \alpha/(1-\alpha)$ (Eq. 3-15),

$$\beta = \left(\frac{\Delta I_C}{\Delta I_B}\right)_{\text{Constant } V_C} = \frac{\dfrac{\alpha_0}{1 + j\omega/\omega_0}}{1 - \dfrac{\alpha_0}{1 + j\omega/\omega_0}}$$

$$= \frac{\alpha_0}{1 - \alpha_0}\left[\frac{1}{1 + \dfrac{j\omega}{\omega_0\,(1-\alpha_0)}}\right] \tag{4-4}$$

---

[1] Arguimbau, L. B., *Vacuum Tube Circuits and Transistors,* Chap. 5, Fig. 32. New York: John Wiley & Sons, Inc., 1956.

or

$$\beta = \frac{\beta_0}{1 + \dfrac{jf}{f\alpha_{co}\,(1 - \alpha_0)}} \qquad (4\text{-}5)$$

where $\beta_0 = \alpha_0/(1 - \alpha_0)$ is the low-frequency common emitter current gain. From Eq. 4-5 the magnitude of β is

$$|\beta| = \frac{\beta_0}{\sqrt{1 + \left[\dfrac{f}{f\alpha_{co}\,(1 - \alpha_0)}\right]^2}} \qquad (4\text{-}6)$$

Consequently in the common emitter connection, the current gain is down to $1/\sqrt{2}$ times its low-frequency value at a frequency of $f\alpha_{co}\,(1 - \alpha_0)$. Thus the low-frequency common emitter current gain is greater than that in the common base connection by a factor of $1/(1 - \alpha_0)$. This gain is obtained at a sacrifice of frequency response. The common emitter-frequency response is now worse than that of the common base connection by the inverse of this same factor.

4.2. Transistor Turn-on Times. In most of the circuits considered in this book, inputs are square-current waveforms from high-impedance genera-tors. Looking back into the transistor driven by a high-impedance generator, the output loads will be small compared to the driving impedance. The output im-pedance of the transistor here, is the slope of the common base I_C, V_C curves for common base connection, and of the common emitter I_C, V_C curves for com-mon emitter connection. Under these conditions of low-load impedance, the output currents are related to the input currents merely by the short-circuit transfer characteristic. These currents are given by Eqs. 3-4 and 3-13 for the common base and common collector connections respectively.

$$\Delta I_C = - \alpha \, \Delta I_E$$

(Common Base)   [3-4]

$$\Delta I_E = \frac{- 1}{1 - \alpha} \, \Delta I_B$$

(Common Collector) [3-13]

And by combining these two,

$$\Delta I_C = \frac{\alpha}{1 - \alpha} \, \Delta I_B$$

(Common Emitter)   (4-7)

In the above three relations the currents are small-signal increments and α is the small-signal incremental current gain at the given operating point.

It has been shown by J. J. Ebers and J. L. Moll[1] that these small-signal relations are adequate to describe — to a good approximation — large-signal switching from complete cutoff to the edge of the saturation region (points B to A on Fig. 3-13A). For such large-signal swings, since the magnitude of α varies with the operating point, its most representative average value is its d-c value to the edge of the saturation region.

The output response for an input step of current can be calculated from Eqs. 3-4, 3-13, and 4-7. Substituting in these relations the value of α given by Eq. 4-1, and including for $j\omega$ the complex variable s $[\alpha = \alpha_0 \, \omega_0/(s + \omega_0)]$, gives

$$I_C \, (s) \; = \; \left[\frac{- \; \alpha_0 \; \omega_0}{s + \omega_0} \right] \; I_E \, (s)$$

$$\text{(Common Base)} \quad (4\text{-}8)$$

$$I_E \, (s) \; = \; \frac{- \; [s + \omega_0] \; I_B \, (s)}{s + \omega_0 \, (1 - \alpha_0)}$$

$$\text{(Common Collector)} \quad (4\text{-}9)$$

$$I_C \, (s) \; = \; \left[\frac{\alpha_0 \; \omega_0}{s + \omega_0 \, (1 - \alpha_0)} \right] \; I_B \, (s)$$

$$\text{(Common Emitter)} \quad (4\text{-}10)$$

And for input current steps of magnitude I_{EF} and I_{BF},

$$I_E \, (s) = \frac{1}{s} \; I_{EF},$$

$$I_B \, (s) = \frac{1}{s} \; I_{BF}$$

and

$$I_B \, (s) = \frac{1}{s} \; I_{BF},$$

the inverse transform of relations given in Eqs. 4-8, 4-9 and 4-10 give

$$I_C = \alpha_0 \, I_{EF} \, [1 - e^{-t/T_{CB}}]$$

$$\text{(Common Base)} \quad (4\text{-}11)$$

where $T_{CB} = 1/2\pi \, f\alpha_{co}$;

$$I_E = \frac{I_{BF}}{1 - \alpha_0} \, [1 - \alpha_0 \, e^{-t/T_{CC}}]$$

$$\text{(Common Collector)} \quad (4\text{-}12)$$

---

[1] Ebers, J. J. and Moll, J. L., "Large-Signal Behavior of Junction Transistors," *Proc. I.R.E.*, Vol. 42, pp. 1761-1784, December 1954.

where $T_{CC} = 1/2\pi\ f\alpha_{co}\ (1 - \alpha_0)$, and

$$I_C = \frac{\alpha_0\ I_{BF}}{1 - \alpha_0}\ [1 - e^{-t/T_{CE}}]$$

(Common Emitter)   (4-13)

where $T_{CE} = 1/2\pi\ f\alpha_{co}\ (1 - \alpha_0)$.

These relations can be very useful. Since they all have the same form and the common emitter connection is that most frequently dealt with here, take, for example, the relation in Eq. 4-13. It is a simple exponentially increasing current and will thus reach 95% of $\alpha_0\ I_{BF}/(1 - \alpha_0)$ in three time constants, $3/2\pi f\alpha_{co}\ (1 - \alpha_0)$. Here $\alpha_0/(1 - \alpha_0) = \beta_0$ is the d-c value of the common emitter current gain (d-c beta), evaluated at the knee of the common emitter I_C—V_C curves at $I_B = I_{BF}$. Consequently, in turning on a d-c current of I_C, if the base is driven with just enough current to do this (as read from static I_C—V_C curves such as Fig. 3-13A), a 0 to 95% rise-time of three common emitter time constants would have to be accepted. If, however, the base is over-driven by having delivered to it a current greater than that needed for the required collector current just at the knee of the curve, it would operate over only a portion of a full exponential, and the rise-time may be many times smaller than three time constants.

As an example, consider the circuit in Fig. 4-1. The transistor is a typical switching transistor — the RCA 2N269. It has an $f\alpha_{co}$ of 4 mc; its characteristic curves are shown in Figs. 4-2 to 4-5A and B.

Assume the minimum load resistor is 1000 ohms and it is desired to switch the transistor from full-off to full-on. The load line for this is shown in Fig. 4-2. Current in the circuit is limited to 10 ma by the 1000-ohm resistor and 10-volt supply. The curves show that to turn on the 10 ma and attain point A on the load line requires a d-c base drive of 0.2 ma. Thus the value of d-c beta is $10/0.2 = 50$, and for this 0.2 ma of base drive, the 0 to 95% rise-time would be

$$3\ T_{CE} = \frac{3}{2\pi\ f\alpha_{co}\ (1 - \alpha_0)}$$

But since $\alpha_0 \cong 1$, take

$$\frac{1}{1 - \alpha_0} = \frac{\alpha_0}{1 - \alpha_0} = \beta_0$$

which can be read directly from the curves in Fig. 4-2. The collector rise to 10 ma will then be

$$\frac{3\ \beta_0}{2\pi\ f\alpha_{co}} = 3\left[\frac{50}{(6.28)\ (4 \times 10^{+6})}\right] = 3(1.99) = 6.0\ \mu sec$$

This would be prohibitively long in many applications.

Consider however, that the base is driven with a current that would give 20 ma of collector current at the knee of the curve if operation were not limited by the 1000-ohm load and 10-volt supply. From Fig. 4-2, this value of base current is seen to be about 0.55 ma (point C), and there is only very little more collector current in the steady-state. The collector bottoms to within about 0.09 volt from the emitter with 0.55 ma of base drive, as compared to 0.2 volt for the

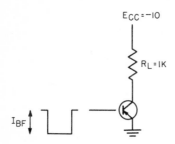

$E_{CC} = -10$

$R_L = 1K$

I_{BF}

Fig. 4-1. A square wave of current applied to the input of a common-emitter amplifier.

0.2 ma base drive. This can be seen more clearly in the expanded curves of Fig. 4-3 as the intersection of an almost horizontal 10-ma load line with the 0.55 ma base current curve. Now, however, the collector current rises from Eq. 4-13 as

$$I_C = 20 \ [1 - e^{-t/T_{CE}}]$$

and it reaches a value of 10 ma at a time

$$t = T_{CE} \ \log_e \left[\frac{20 - 10}{10} \right] = 0.69 \ T_{CE}$$

Here, $T_{CE} \cong \beta_0/2\pi \ f\alpha_{co}$ is evaluated at the base current actually being delivered to the transistor, i.e., the value at the collector current that would have been turned on had there been no limiting by the 1000-ohm resistor and 10-volt supply. Thus

$$\beta_0 = \frac{20}{0.55} = 36$$

and

$$T_{CE} = \frac{36}{2\pi \ 4 \times 10^{+6}} = 1.43 \ \mu sec$$

The rise-time to 10 ma is therefore

$$0.69 \ T_{CE} = 0.69 \ (1.43) = 0.99 \ \mu sec$$

As will be seen, a slight gain has resulted from a decrease in the common emitter rise-time constant ($\beta/2\pi \ f\alpha_{co}$), as β_0 in general decreases for increasing collector currents. Even more however, has been gained in that the turn-on time is now a fraction of a time constant rather than three time constants.

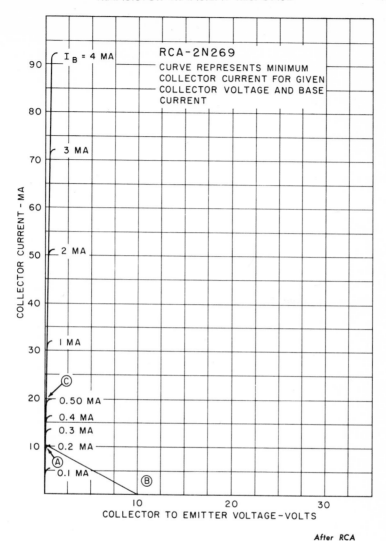

CURVE REPRESENTS MINIMUM
COLLECTOR CURRENT FOR GIVEN
COLLECTOR VOLTAGE AND BASE
CURRENT

RCA-2N269

After RCA

Fig. 4-2. Collector current v. collector-to-emitter voltage; grounded emitter.

If this 0.55 ma base drive is maintained in the steady-state, the collector-to-emitter voltage can be read from Fig. 4-3 as $-$ 0.09 volt (intersection of the 0.55 ma base-current curve and a 1000-ohm load line from V_{CE} $-$ 10). Figure 4-4 shows the base-to-emitter voltage as $-$ 0.31 at I_B = 0.55 ma. Though the curve specifically holds only for V_{CB} = 0, it does not vary much for other collector voltages. Assuming that it still holds, the collector is seen to be 0.31 $-$

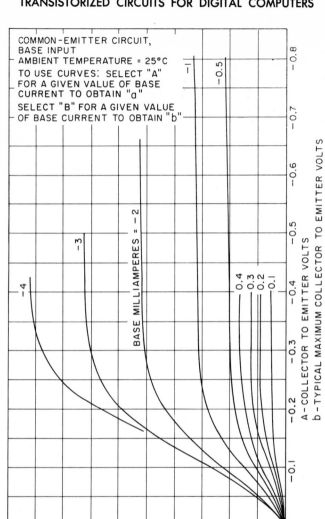

Fig. 4-3. Collector characteristics of RCA 2N269 in vicinity of saturation region.

0.09 = 0.22 volt positive with respect to the base. With this forward bias on the collector, it too commences acting like an emitter and injects minority carriers into the base. This slows up the transistor turn-off process — a problem considered in detail later.

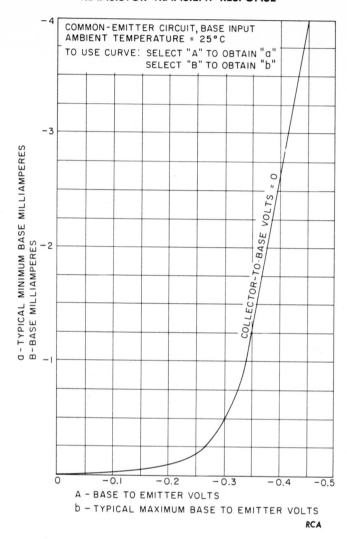

Fig. 4-4. Base characteristic of RCA 2N269 for switching applications.

This turn-on speed-up by overdriving can perhaps be better visualized from the curves in Fig. 4-6. The lower exponential corresponds to unity overdrive, or $\beta_0 I_{B1} = E_{CC}/R_L$.

The current v. time curve follows the path OAB. The upper exponential corresponds to an overdrive factor of two. The current follows the path OC as if it were proceeding to a current of $2E_{CC}/R_L$, but it is limited by the magnitude of supply voltage and load resistor and follows the path OCB.

It would be useful to have universal curves of turn-on time for various over-drive factors as a function of unity overdrive turn-on time for different transistors. The nonuniform variation of β_0 with collector current however, makes this impossible.

As an example of the speed-up attainable, the calculations have been made

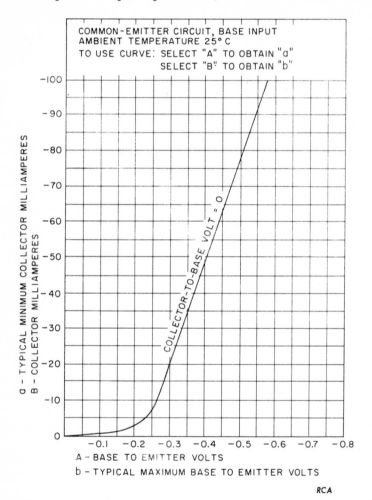

Fig. 4-5A.　Collector current v. base-to-emitter voltage: RCA 2N269.

for the RCA 2N269. The curves in Figs. 4-9 to 4-12 show turn-on times to 5, 10, 15, and 20 ma for various overdrive factors as calculated from Eq. 4-13. At each point $\alpha_0/(1-\alpha_0) = \beta_0$ has been taken as the d-c beta to the collector current at the knee of the curve to which the transistor would turn on for the given base current, if not limited by the load resistor. The time constant T_{CE} has been taken as $\cong \beta_0 / 2\pi\, fa_{co}$ where $fa_{co} = 4$ mc. The turn-on time for unity overdrive has been taken as the 0 to 95% rise-time. For other overdrive factors it has been taken as the 0 to 100% rise-time as in the example above (rise-time

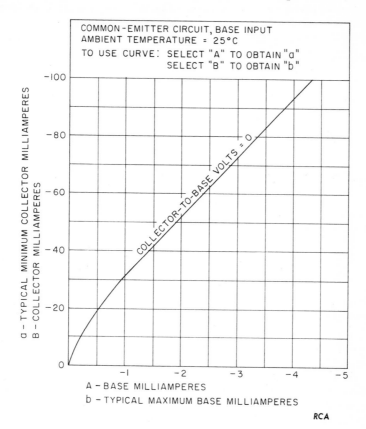

Fig. 4-5B. Current transfer characteristic of RCA 2N269 for switching applications.

$= t_r = T_{CE} \log_e N/(N-1)$ where $N = 2, 3, 4, 5$ for overdrive factors of 2, 3, 4, 5). The ratio $t_r/T_{CE} = \log_e N/(N-1)$ has been plotted in Fig. 4-7 for various values of N [$N = (\beta_0 I_B)/(E_{CC}/R_L)$].

The value of d-c beta (measured to the knee of the collector current curves) and the common emitter time constant for the 2N269, have also been plotted in Fig. 4-8 as they are useful in the calculations for the graphs of Figs. 4-9 to 4-12. The values of d-c beta plotted in Fig. 4-8 were read from the curve of Fig. 4-2.

The curves in Figs. 4-9 to 4-12, are the results calculated from Eq. 4-13. The question arises as to how closely these calculated values may be expected to approximate actual measured values. As a check on this, measurements were made on a random sample of 25 2N269's. The amplitude of base current steps needed to turn-on a collector current of 10 ma and 20 ma in 0.5 μsec were measured. The results are given in Fig. 4-13.

The major sources of error in the calculation are in the assumed value of $f\alpha_{co}$ and the reading of β_0 from the transistor curves in Fig. 4-2.

The value of 4 mc is given in the manufacturer's data sheet as the minimum value of $f\alpha_{co}$ for this type of transistor. Production spread is not quoted, but

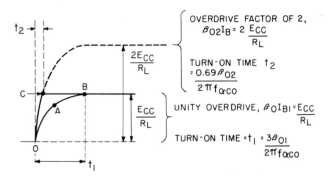

Fig. 4-6.   Speeding up turn-on time by forward overdriving.

a maximum value of two to three times the minimum value for such a transistor type is not unusual. The curves in Fig. 4-2 represent the minimum collector currents obtainable at given collector voltages and base currents. Again, production spread is not quoted in the data sheet, but a maximum collector current two to three times the minimum is not unusual for such a transistor type. Since the calculation was based on a worst-case transistor the calculated drive currents are, as would be expected, larger than the measured values. The fact that the error is larger for the 20 ma turn-on case than for the 10 ma case is probably due to the fact that the curve of Fig. 4-2 is more pessimistic in the high-current region than it is in the low-current region.

A useful relation can be derived from Eq. 4-13 for the figure of merit for a transistor. Differentiating this equation gives

$$\frac{dI_C}{dt} = \frac{\alpha_0 \, I_B}{(1 - \alpha_0) \, T_{CE}} \, e^{-t/T_{CE}}$$

$$= \frac{\alpha_0 \, I_B \, 2\pi \, f\alpha_{co} \, (1 - \alpha_0)}{1 - \alpha_0} \, e^{-t/T_{CE}}$$

$$\cong 2\pi I_B f\alpha_{co} \, e^{-t/T_{CE}}$$

In most cases the base will be overdriven and operation will be on the linear

part of the exponentially rising collector current (Fig. 4-6) for the total duration of the rise-time. Over this range of time $e^{-t/T_{CE}} \cong 1$, and gives

$$\frac{dI_C}{dt} \cong 2\pi I_B \, f\alpha_{co} \tag{4-14}$$

This result is interesting in that it shows that the initial rate of rise of collector

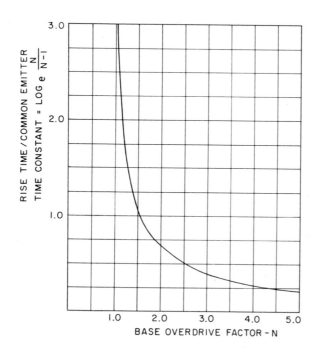

Fig. 4-7. Ratio of rise-time/common-emitter time constant v. base overdrive factor.

current for an input step of base current is independent of β, and depends only
on $f\alpha_{co}$ and the amplitude of the base input current step. The ratio

$$\frac{\dfrac{\Delta I_C}{\Delta t}}{\Delta I_B} = 2\pi f\alpha_{co} \tag{4-15}$$

is a useful figure of merit for a transistor. Having the physical significance of
rate of change of collector current per unit step of base current, it is consequently
similar to an a-c gain parameter, and provides a good rough estimate of the
capabilities of the transistor. The steps of base current required to turn on 10
or 20 ma of collector current in 0.5 μsec could therefore have been roughly
calculated from Eq. 4-15 as $\Delta I_B = \Delta I_C/\Delta t/(2\pi f\alpha_{co}) = 0.8$ ma for 10 ma, and

$\Delta I_B = 1.60$ ma for 20 ma for an assumed value of $f\alpha_{co} = 4$ mc. These values compare quite well with the average of the 25 measured values in Fig. 4-13. Calculations from Eq. 4-15 can only be made however, when operation is on the linear part of the exponentially rising collector current for a calculated base

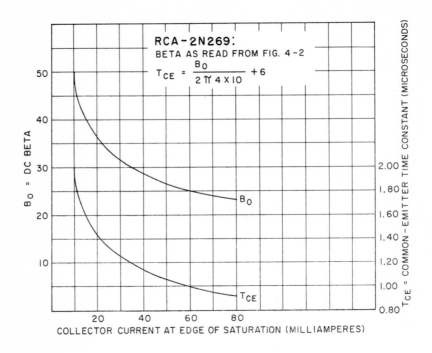

Fig. 4-8. D-c beta and common-emitter time constant v. collector current at edge of saturation.

current, i.e., when the calculated ΔI_B is greater than two to three times the d-c value of base current needed for the specified collector current.

Another way of looking at Eq. 4-15 is that it specifies the operating current gain necessary to achieve given values of collector current turn-on times. The d-c operating gain to turn on 10 ma is therefore 50 as read from Fig. 4-2. But from Eq. 4-15, to turn on 10 ma in 0.5 and 0.25 μsec (20 ma in 0.5 μsec), requires base drives of 0.8 ma and 1.6 ma. Consequently, the effective operating gains necessary to turn on the same 10 ma in 0.5 and 0.25 μsec are $10/0.8 = 12.5$ and $10/1.6 = 6.3$, respectively.

Later chapters show that in general, computer circuits are cascades such as in Fig. 4-14. Assume that there is no current loss between the output and input of the passive diode networks, and transistor amplifiers Nos. 1 and 2 are exactly alike. The problem in such cascades is usually to drive from the output of a given

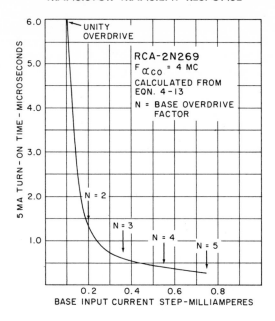

Fig. 4-9. Turn-on time to 5 ma v. base input current step.

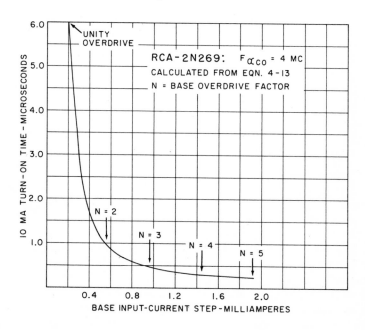

Fig. 4-10. Turn-on time to 10 ma v. base input current step.

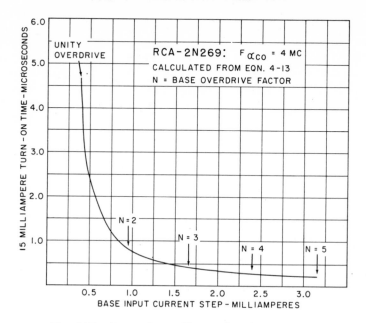

Fig. 4-11. Turn-on time to 15 ma v. base input current step.

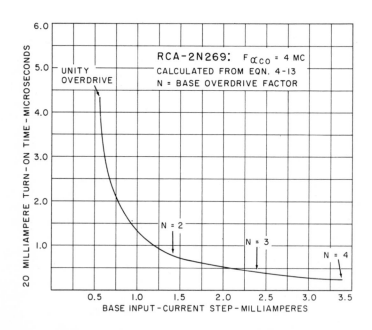

Fig. 4-12. Turn-on time to 20 ma v. base input current step.

transistor No. 1 amplifier as many networks in parallel as possible, each driven network being in turn capable of driving the inputs of transistor amplifier No. 2. Normally, amplifiers 1 and 2 are required to have equal switching times. Obviously then, these current gains of 12.5 and 6.3 — for switching 10 ma in 0.5 or 0.25 μsec, respectively — represent the maximum number of units it is possible to drive in parallel from the output of a given amplifier at those speeds. As explained later, it is far from true that the passive networks produce

FORWARD BASE CURRENT STEP FOR 0.5 MICROSECOND
TURN-ON TIME
RCA2N269

COLLECTOR CURRENT	CALCULATED	MEASURED VALUES		
	FROM EQUATION 4-13	AVERAGE OF 25 TRANSISTORS	MINIMUM	MAXIMUM
10MA	0.92MA	0.72MA	0.44MA	0.99MA
20MA	2.0MA	1.2MA	0.62MA	1.69MA

Fig. 4-13. Forward base current step for 0.5 μsec turn-on time: RCA 2N269.

no current loss. Consequently the maximum number of units it is possible to drive in parallel is considerably fewer than the 12.5 and 6.3 for this transistor type at the given switching speeds. This number of units that an amplifier is capable of driving in parallel at its output is important in computer circuitry, and is usually referred to as the pyramiding or fan-out factor. It is obvious that keeping the total transistor count down requires as large a pyramiding factor as possible. Equation 4-15 is useful in providing a preliminary estimate of the absolute maximum pyramiding factor for a given switching speed and $f\alpha_{co}$. Actual values will be closer to one-half this maximum value, depending on the current loss from the output of one transistor to the input of the next.

4.3. Transistor Turn-off Time. Assume that a transistor has been turned on but has not been permitted to enter the saturation region, i.e., the region where the collector-to-base junction has a forward bias. There are a number of ways this may be done, but as the exact manner in which it is accomplished does not matter here, take it as having been achieved by simply controlling the input so that on the load lines in Figs. 3-12A and 3-13A operation is just at point A. If the input is suddenly reduced to zero, the collector current does not immediately follow it to zero, because as previously shown, minority carriers that have been injected into the base region by the emitter are not subject to an accelerating field there, but move by a slow diffusion process to the collector. Consequently these minority carriers that had been in transit to the collector at the moment the input current was reduced to zero, must be swept out before the collector current can be reduced to zero. The simplest way to sweep out these trapped charges is to reverse the direction of the input current rather than reduce it to zero. In calculating the nature of the reverse base-current driver, assume that the base-to-emitter potential is exactly what it had been just prior to the onset of the pulse of reverse current (as read from the I_E — V_{EB} or I_B — V_{BE} curves of Figs. 3-12B and 3-13B), because until the trapped

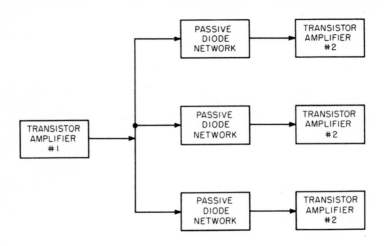

Fig. 4-14. A typical computer array of passive diode gates and transistor amplifiers.

charges are swept out, the emitter-to-base junction remains in forward bias and has a low impedance, even though current is being driven through it in the direction opposite to that in which it normally conducts.

Ebers and Moll have shown that so long as the starting point is other than saturation, this large-signal switching response (from A to B in Figs. 3-12A and 3-13A) can be adequately described by the small-signal transistor parameters. In most cases operation will be with loads small compared to transistor output impedances. In this case output and input currents are related to one another by the short-circuit current transfer characteristics of Eqs. 4-8, 4-9 and 4-10. The same equations must then be solved as for the turn-on case, except that the initial currents are not zero as they were for turn-on, but are equal to the currents just at the edge of saturation.

Introduce these initial conditions into Eqs. 4-8, 4-9 and 4-10 by writing them in the differential form. Set $s = d/dt$ and take the Laplace transform of the result. Recall that

$$\mathscr{L} [dI/dt] = sI (s) - I (0 +)$$

where $I (0 +)$ is the current in question immediately after $t = 0$. Equations

4-8, 4-9 and 4-10 then give

$$I_C(s) = \frac{I_C(0+) - \alpha_0 \, \omega_0 \, I_E(s)}{s + \omega_0}$$

(Common Base)   (4-16)

$$I_C(s) = \frac{I_C(0+) + \alpha_0 \, \omega_0 \, I_B(s)}{s + \omega_0 \, (1 - \alpha_0)}$$

(Common Emitter)   (4-17)

$$I_E(s) = \frac{I_E(0+) - I_B(0+) + (s + \omega_0) \, I_B(s)}{s + \omega_0 \, (1 - \alpha_0)}$$

(Common Collector)   (4-18)

For reverse steps of current of magnitude I_{ER} and I_{BR}

$$I_E(s) = \frac{1}{s} \, I_{ER}$$

$$I_B(s) = \frac{1}{s} \, I_{BR}$$

and

$$I_B(s) = \frac{1}{s} \, I_{BR}$$

we get from Eqs. 4-16, 4-17, and 4-18,

$$I_C(s) = \frac{sI_{C1} - \alpha_0 \, \omega_0 \, I_{ER}}{s \, (s + \omega_0)}$$

(Common Base)   (4-19)

$$I_C(s) = \frac{sI_{C1} + \alpha_0 \, \omega_0 \, I_{BR}}{s \, [s + \omega_0 \, (1 - \alpha_0)]}$$

(Common Emitter)   (4-20)

$$I_E(s) = \frac{sI_{E1} + \omega_0 \, I_{BR}}{s \, [s + \omega_0 \, (1 - \alpha_0)]}$$

(Common Collector)   (4-21)

where I_{C1}, I_{E1} are the initial currents flowing just prior to the applied reverse current step. Solving the above three relations gives

$$I_C = I_{C1} \, e^{-t/T_{CB}} - \alpha_0 \, I_{ER} \, [1 - e^{-t/T_{CB}}]$$

(Common Base)   (4-22)

where $T_{CB} = 1/2\pi \, f\alpha_{co}$;

$$I_C = I_{C1} e^{-t/T_{CE}} - \frac{\alpha_0 I_{BR}}{1 - \alpha_0} [1 - e^{-t/T_{CE}}]$$

(Common Emitter)   (4-23)

where $T_{CE} = 1/2\pi f\alpha_{co} (1 - \alpha_0)$, and

$$I_E = I_{E1} e^{-t/T_{CC}} - \frac{I_{BR}}{1 - \alpha_0} [1 - e^{-t/T_{CC}}]$$

(Common Collector)   (4-24)

where $T_{CC} = 1/2\pi f\alpha_{co} (1 - \alpha_0)$.

Equations 4-22, 4-23 and 4-24 being of the same form, examine the common emitter relation as it is that most frequently used. Here, the current decay relation is the difference between two exponentials as shown in Fig. 4-15.

The term $I_{C1} e^{-t/T_{CE}}$ in Eq. 4-23 describes how the transistor would turn off if the input current were merely reduced to zero ($I_{BR} = 0$). The current would fall exponentially towards zero with a time constant $T_{CE} = 1/2\pi f\alpha_{co} (1 - \alpha_0)$, and would therefore come down to within 5% of its equilibrium value in three $T_{CE} = 3/2\pi f\alpha_{co} (1 - \alpha_0) \cong 3\beta/2\pi f\alpha_{co}$. Consequently, the fall-time would equal the unity overdrive rise-time, and would in most cases be prohi-

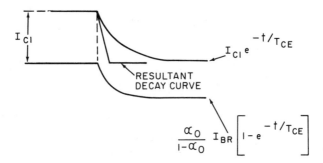

Fig. 4-15. The active-region decay time expression is the sum of a term describing the zero reverse base drive decay time, and a term representing the effect of reverse base current alone.

bitively long. With a reverse current I_{BR} the actual fall-time is the difference between the above exponential and an exponentially increasing current that starts from zero and builds up to $\alpha_0 I_{BR}/(1 - \alpha_0)$ with a time constant of T_{CE}.

This second term is a negative current of exactly the same form as the turn-on build-up relation of Eq. 4-13. Figure 4-15 shows that turn-off time is now considerably less than three T_{CE}. Exact turn-off time is calculated by setting Eq. 4-23 equal to zero. Again there is the question of where to evaluate $\alpha_0/(1 - \alpha_0) = \beta_0$. Best agreement with actual measurements is obtained by evaluating

β_0 in the second term of Eq. 4-23 at the edge of saturation at a forward base current of I_{BR}. In the first term, β_0 in the term of $T_{CE} \cong \beta_0/2\pi \, f\alpha_{co}$ should be evaluated at the edge of saturation at a collector current of I_{CI}. In actual cases, since calculations from Eq. 4-23 will not be relied upon for accurate result but will only be used as a guide, β_0 will be evaluated in the first term at the same point as for the second term.

The following example shows how much can be gained by reverse base drive. Assume the circuit of Fig. 4-1, with 10 ma of collector current and a base drive just enough under 0.2 ma to prevent saturation (see Fig. 4-2). If the input is reduced to zero, the 0 to 95% fall-time would be three $T_{CE} = 6$ μsec as calculated for the unity overdrive turn-on time. But if a reverse drive of 0.1 ma is provided, Eq. 4-23 gives (since $I_C = 5$ ma for $I_{BR} = 0.1$ ma),

$$0 = I_{C1} \, e^{-t/T_{CE}} - \frac{\alpha_0 \, I_{BR}}{1 - \alpha_0} \, [1 - e^{-t/T_{CE}}]$$

or

$$10e^{-t/T_{CE}} = 5 \, [1 - e^{-t/T_{CE}}]$$

$$e^{-t/T_{CE}} = 0.33$$

$$t = 1.1 \, T_{CE}$$

$$= \frac{1.1 \, \beta_0}{2\pi \, f\alpha_{co}}$$

$$= \frac{1.1 \, 50}{2\pi \, 4 \times 10^{+6}}$$

$$= 1.1 \, (2) = 2.2 \text{ μsec.}$$

Obviously this can be bettered with more reverse drive.

For purposes of illustration, the calculation of Eq. 4-23 has been performed for turning off 10, 15 and 20 ma from a point just at the edge of saturation for the RCA 2N269 transistor. The results are shown in Figs. 4-16, 4-17 and 4-18. In these calculations $f\alpha_{co}$ has been taken as 4 mc, and T_{CE} in both terms of Eq. 4-23 has been calculated from the d-c beta at the specified reverse base drive using the transistor characteristic of Fig. 4-2. Since Fig. 4-2 and a value of $f\alpha_{co}$ of 4 mc represent the worst transistor of this type, most transistors are in general better than indicated in Figs. 4-16 to 4-18.

4.4. Transistor Storage Time. Given a large enough input drive in either the common base, emitter or collector connection, the operating point on the load line extends beyond the knee of the collector curves (see Figs. 3-12A and 3-13A). At such points the collector-to-base junction has a forward bias (collector positive relative to the base in *p-n-p* transistors, and negative with respect to base in *n-p-n* transistors). This is the region of saturation referred to in Chapter 3. In this region the collector emits minority carriers into the base and is in many ways indistinguishable from a true emitter. To shut the transistor off, it is now necessary to sweep out of the base region the minority carriers in-

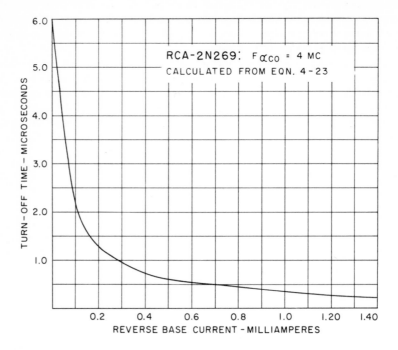

Fig. 4-16.   Turn-off time from 10 ma — unsaturated v. reverse base current.

jected by the true emitter, and also those injected by the collector acting as an emitter.

Ebers and Moll have shown in the following manner how transistor behavior may be calculated in this so-called saturation region. They assume that the total transistor current may be divided into two components. One is the normal component with the true emitter emitting and the true collector collecting. These currents are still related to each other as in the unsaturated region by Eq. 4-1:

$$I_{CN} = \frac{\alpha_N I_{EN}}{1 + j\omega/\omega_N} \qquad [4\text{-}1]$$

Here, α_N is the normal low-frequency current gain measured with the emitter acting as an emitter and the collector acting as a collector, and $\omega_N = 2\pi f\alpha_{CON}$ where $f\alpha_{CON}$ is the frequency at which α_N is 70% of its low-frequency value.

The second component of the total transistor current is a current emitted by the collector — possible now it is forward biased — and collected by the emitter.

The fact that the emitter is forward biased does not prevent it from collecting current emitted by the collector. The collector emission current moves by

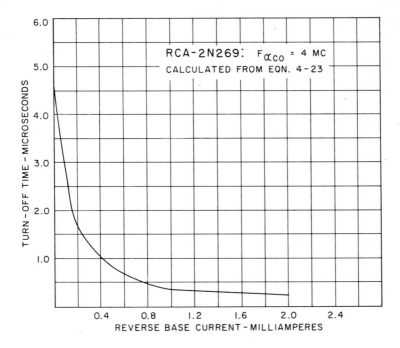

Fig. 4-17. Turn-off time from 15 ma — unsaturated v. reverse base current.

diffusion toward the emitter where some fraction of it is picked up by the emitter acting as a collector. This inverse current is given by an equation of the same form as that which describes the normal current component,

$$I_{EI} = \frac{\alpha_I \, I_{CI}}{1 + j\omega/\omega_I} \qquad (4-25)$$

Here, I_{CI} is the current emitted by the collector, and I_{EI} is that fraction of it collected by the emitter; α_I is the low-frequency current gain measured as one measures the normal emitter-to-collector current gain in the unsaturated region, but with the emitter and collector connections interchanged; $\omega_I = 2\pi \, f\alpha_{COI}$ where $f\alpha_{COI}$ is that frequency at which α_I is 70% of its low-frequency value. In most transistors, high forward gain is desirable, and transistor geometry is so arranged as to achieve this. But the geometry giving highest forward gains, leads in general to an unsymmetrical transistor, i.e., one in which $\alpha_N > \alpha_I$, and $\omega_N >$

ω_I. For special purposes, transistors are sometimes made symmetrical in forward and reverse current gain and alpha cutoff frequency.

Ebers and Moll have derived relations for the above component currents in terms of the total external terminal currents. The current I_{EI} is the inverted current being collected by the emitter, and represents a current due to an excess of charges driven into the base region by the emitting collector. Until I_{EI} drops to zero, the charge in the base region exceeds that corresponding to the edge of the saturation region (point A Figs. 3-12A, and 3-13A). Consequently the total external collector current (emitter current in the common collector connection) cannot change until I_{EI} drops to zero. This time for I_{EI} — the collector's emission current — to drop to zero is referred to as storage time.

The current I_{EI} for the common base, emitter and collector connections are given as:

Common Base —

$$I_{EI} = \frac{-\alpha_I}{1 - \alpha_N \alpha_I} [I_C + \alpha_N I_{E1} e^{-t/T} + \alpha_N I_{E2} (1 - e^{-t/T})]$$

$$(4\text{-}26)$$

where I_{E1} = forward emitter current just before the beginning of the turn-off step
I_{E2} = reverse emitter current just after beginning of turn-off step
I_C = collector current just at edge of saturation = V_{CC}/R_L.

Common Emitter —

$$I_{EI} = \frac{\alpha_I}{1 - \alpha_N \alpha_I} \left[I_C - \frac{\alpha_N}{1 - \alpha_N} I_{B1} e^{-t/T} - \frac{\alpha_N I_{B2}}{1 - \alpha_N} (1 - e^{-t/T}) \right]$$

$$(4\text{-}27)$$

where I_{B1} = forward base current just before the beginning of the turn-off step
I_{B2} = reverse base current just after beginning of turn-off step
I_C = collector current just at the edge of saturation = V_{CC}/R_L

Common Collector —

$$I_{EI} = \frac{\alpha_I \alpha_N}{1 - \alpha_I \alpha_N} \left[I_E + \frac{I_{B1}}{1 - \alpha_N} e^{-t/T} + \frac{I_{B2}}{1 - \alpha_N} (1 - e^{-t/T}) \right]$$

$$(4\text{-}28)$$

where I_{B1} = forward base current just before beginning of the turn-off step
I_{B2} = reverse base current just after beginning of the turn-off step
I_E = emitter current just at the edge of saturation = V_{CC}/R_L

In the above three equations the sign convention is that a current into a transistor terminal is positive, out of a transistor terminal it is negative. Accordingly in Eq. 4-27 for a *p-n-p* transistor I_C and I_{B1} are negative, I_{B2} is positive.

In all three relations $T = (\omega_N + \omega_C)/\omega_N \, \omega_I \, (1 - \alpha_N \, \alpha_I)$, where α_N, α_I, ω_N, ω_I have been defined above as the normal and inverted current gains and angular alpha cutoff frequencies.

Since Eqs. 4-26, 4-27 and 4-28 are of the same form, take as an example Eq. 4-27, and examine particularly to see the physical significance of its terms. It

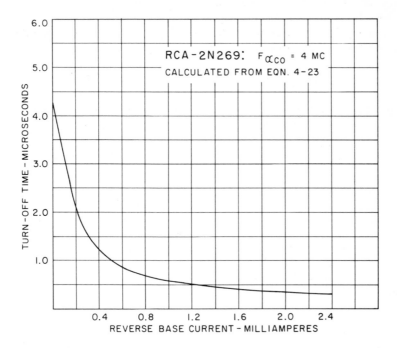

Fig. 4-18. Turn-off time from 20 ma — unsaturated v. reverse base current.

has been shown that the end of the storage period comes at the time that I_{EI} drops to zero. This occurs when the terms inside the bracket drop to zero. Assume that $I_{B2} = 0$, i.e., that to turn the transistor off the input current has merely been dropped to zero, not reversed in direction. Then because of the sign convention, the situation is as shown in Fig. 4-19, where $\alpha_N \, I_{B1}/(1 - \alpha_N)$ exceeds V_{CC}/R_L and our turn-on rise-time has been speeded up. It is a small fraction of a time constant instead of three time constants. But on turn-off, the output current commanded to turn off at t_2 does not start decreasing until t_3, which is the moment when

$$I_C = \frac{V_{CC}}{R_L} = \frac{\alpha_N \, I_{B1}}{1 - \alpha_N} \, e^{-t/T}$$

Obviously then, the more overdriving to speed up turn-on time, the longer the storage time. After the time t_3, operation is again in the active region, and the collector current commences to fall as if it had never been in saturation. It falls in accordance with the relations in Eq. 4-23.

If however, the third term in Eq. 4-27 is considered as not being zero, i.e., instead of dropping the input current to zero its direction has been reversed to some value I_{B2}, the situation is as shown in Fig. 4-20.

Since I_{B2} is directed into the transistor it has a positive sense, and the third term of Eq. 4-27 is an exponentially increasing negative current (exponential PQR in Fig. 4-20). Consequently, the resultant current

$$\left[\frac{\alpha_N I_{B1}}{1 - \alpha_N} e^{-t/T} - \frac{\alpha_N I_{B2}}{1 - \alpha_N} (1 - e^{-t/T}) \right]$$

decays from a peak of $\alpha_N I_{B1}/(1-\alpha_N)$ towards I_C at a much more rapid rate, and operation in saturation ends sooner at t'_3 instead of at t_3. Thus the second

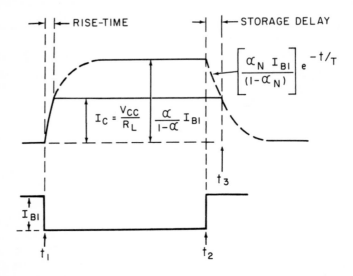

Fig. 4-19. Forward overdriving to speed up turn-on time, results in a storage delay when turning the transistor off.

term of Eq. 4-27 represents the coming out of saturation without reverse drive, and the third term represents the help derived from the reverse current in coming out of saturation. After the time t'_3, the external collector current starts falling — as if it had never been in saturation — in accordance with the relations of Eq. 4-23, where the reverse current is still I_{B2}.

The pulse of reverse current I_{B2} must last for the sum of the storage time delay $(t'_3 - t_2)$, plus the active-region decay time given by setting Eq. 4.23 equal to zero.

Equating the bracketed terms in Eqs. 4-26, 4-27 and 4-28 gives the storage time delays for the three connections as

$$T_{SD} = T_S \log_e \frac{\alpha_N (I_{E2} - I_{E1})}{I_C + \alpha_N I_{E2}}$$

$$\text{(Common Base)} \qquad (4\text{-}29)$$

$$T_{SD} = T_S \log_e \frac{[\beta_N I_{B1} - \beta_N I_{B2}]}{I_C - \beta_N I_{B2}}$$

$$\text{(Common Emitter)} \qquad (4\text{-}30)$$

$$T_{SD} = T_S \log_e \frac{[I_{B2} - I_{B1}]}{[I_{B2} + I_{E1} (1 - \alpha_N)]}$$

$$\cong T_S \log_e \frac{[\beta_N I_{B2} - \beta_N I_{B1}]}{[I_{B2} + I_{E1}]}$$

$$\text{(Common Collector)} \qquad (4\text{-}31)$$

In the above three relations, the sign convention is again that currents into the transistor are positive, and out of the transistor are negative. Consequently for a *p-n-p* transistor I_{B1}, I_C and I_{E2} are negative, and I_{B2} and I_{E1} are positive. For the above three relations $T_S = (\omega_N + \omega_I)/\omega_N \omega_I (1 - \alpha_N \alpha_I)$.

For unsymmetrical transistors, $\omega_N > \omega_I$ and $\alpha_N > \alpha_I$, so that

$$T_S \cong \frac{1}{\omega_I (1 - \alpha_I)} \cong \frac{\beta_I}{\omega_I}$$

where β_I is the inverted beta, i.e., beta measured with the collector and emitter connections interchanged. T_S is best derived not from β_I/ω_I, which would have to be measured individually, but by measuring the inverted time constant by applying a pulse of forward base current and measuring the time to rise to 63% of its equilibrium value. This would be done with the collector and emitter connections interchanged and in the active region. For symmetrical transistors (those in which $\omega_N = \omega_I$ and $\alpha_N = \alpha_I$),

$$T_S \cong \frac{1}{\omega_N (1 - \alpha_N)} \cong \frac{\beta_N}{2\pi f\alpha_{coN}}$$

One final point about relations in Eqs. 4-29 to 4-31: For best results β_N is taken as the d-c beta to the edge of saturation at the base current of the term in which it is involved. Thus, for $\beta_N I_{B1}$ evaluate β_N at I_{B1}, and at I_{B2} for $\beta_N I_{B2}$.

The total time delay on turn-off is therefore seen to be the sum of the storage delay given by Eqs. 4-29 to 4-31 and the active-region decay time given by setting Eqs. 4-22 to 4-24 equal to zero.

4.5. Capacitive Overdrive for Reducing Switching Time. From the foregoing discussion it is obvious that the optimum input current waveshape for fully switching a transistor is as in Fig. 4-21. The current shown is for a common-emitter amplifier. Similar waveshapes apply for the other two connections. The current I_{BDC} should be just enough to bring the transistor to the edge of saturation (point A of Fig. 3-13A). Provided it is no larger than this, only active-region decay time need be considered as there will be no storage time. The current I_{BF} should be sufficiently large that the overdrive results in

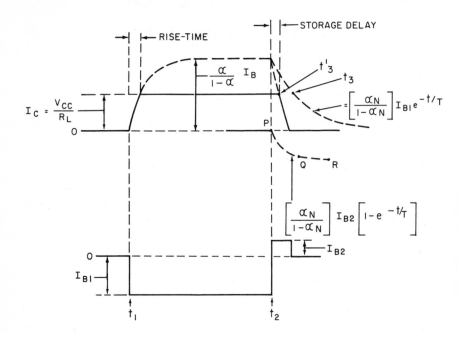

Fig. 4-20. Forward overdriving to speed up turn-on time, and reverse base current driving to decrease storage and active-region decay time.

the desired turn-on time as calculated from Eq. 4-13. The duration t_1, of this overdrive spike need only be as long as the required turn-on time.

The amplitude of the reverse current spike I_{BR} should be large enough to supply the required active-region decay time as calculated from Eq. 4-23. Its duration t_2 also, need only equal the required turn-off time.

An approximation to such an input current waveform is given by the circuit shown in Fig. 4-22. The required spikes at the leading and trailing edge of the input waveform are contributed by the capacitor C_1. The input driver must have an internal impedance, low compared to R_1. Assume that V_1 switches between ground and $-V_1$ with rise and fall time of t_S, and that the collector current is also to switch with rise and fall times of t_S. As explained in Chapter 3, p. 53, to cut off a common-emitter transistor in the steady-state, it is not sufficient to reduce the base current to zero. A reverse base current of I_{CO} must be delivered at the highest temperature or the collector leakage current will build up to βI_{CO}. Therefore V_A and R_A are chosen so that $V_A/R_A = I_{CO}$ at the highest temperature.

Assume the transistor is to be turned on to the edge of saturation, at which point $V_C \cong -0.3$ volt (see Fig. 4-3). Consequently, $I_C = (V_{CC} - 0.3)/R_L$. The base current required for this collector current, designated I_{BDC}, can be read from Fig. 4-3. Then $I_{R1} = I_{BDC} + I_{RA}$ is chosen. For the required I_{BDC}, read the base voltage from a curve such as Fig. 4-4 — assume V_{B1}. Then choose $R_1 = (V_1 - V_{B1})/(I_{BDC} + I_{RA})$. The required d-c current to turn on the

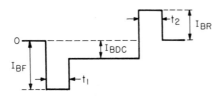

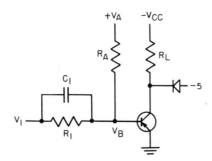

Fig. 4-21.   Ideal base current waveform for fast turn-on and turn-off times.

Fig. 4-22.   A circuit that gives an approximation to the ideal base current waveform of Fig. 4-21.

transistor is now being supplied. I_{BF}, the peak base drive necessary to turn on the specified collector current with the required speed can be found from curves such as those in Figs. 4-9 to 4-12. The difference, $I_{BF} - I_{BDC}$ must then be supplied through C_1.

To a first approximation the base voltage remains fixed during the switching transient, so that the current through C_1 can be calculated from $I = C_1 \Delta V/\Delta t$. Therefore C_1 is selected as $C_1 = [I_{BF} - I_{BDC}] t_S/V_1$. As equal rise and fall times were assumed at V_1, there is a reverse current of $I_{BF} - I_{BDC}$ through C_1 on the positive-going edge of the signal.

Figures 4-16 to 4-18 show that for equal turn-on and turn-off times I_{BF} is larger than I_{BR}. Therefore selecting C_1 to meet the turn-on time requirement also meets the turn-off time requirement. Voltage and resistance tolerances and the production spread of β, must however, be taken into account. This is dealt with in detail in Chapter 6.

In general, the input at V_1 does not switch up to ground. It usually is a collector output point, and is consequently about -0.1 to -0.3 volt at its upper level. R_1 and R_A must then be recalculated so that such a potential at V_1 results

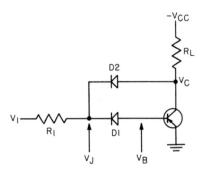

Fig. 4-23. Preventing saturation by negative feedback which commences just at the edge of saturation.

in a zero, or somewhat positive potential at V_B to ensure transistor cutoff. This also, will be considered later.

The main difficulty with the above procedure, however, is that sufficient d-c current must be provided to bottom the lowest gain transistor. Since the production spread in β may be as large as two or three to one, the current that just bottoms the lowest gain transistor will also drive the highest gain transistor heavily into saturation, causing storage, in addition to turn-off delay. The amplitude of the reverse base drive spike must therefore be sufficient to make the sum of the resulting storage and decay time equal to the specified minimum value. The amplitude of this turn-off spike can be increased by increasing C_1 and decreasing R_A. Now R_A serves to supply not only I_{CO} — the d-c shut-off bias — but also supplies additional current which is available as reverse base drive when V_1 switches to its upper level. R_1 must now be decreased so that $I_{R1} - I_{RA} = I_{BDC}$ still supplies the current needed to bottom the lowest gain transistor. Consequently, unless there are rather tight upper and lower limits on current gain and also on $f\alpha_{co}$, unreasonably large current spike requirements result. This makes the design of the input driver inefficient. In general, the solution to this is a compromise between a driver capable of producing large switching spikes, and setting tight incoming inspection limits on transistor gain and $f\alpha_{co}$.

It is useful to acquire a feel for the magnitudes involved in calculating a circuit such as Fig. 4-22 for a nominal transistor, and nominal voltages and resistors. Assume, for example, that it is desired to switch 10 ma of collector current with rise and fall times of 0.5 μsec, using an RCA 2N269 transistor. Take it that V_1 switches between ground and -5 volts, with rise and fall times of 0.5 μsec. From the manufacturer's data sheets I_{CO} at approximately 80°C is 60 microamperes. Based on Fig. 4-2 a d-c base current of 0.2 ma is required to turn on 10 ma of collector current. Figure 4-4 shows the base voltage at 0.2 ma of base current to be -0.25 volt. Consequently, $R_A = V_A/60 \times 10^{-6}$, and

$$R_1 = \frac{V_1 - 0.25}{I_{BDC} + I_{RA}} = \frac{5 - 0.25}{0.26 \times 10^{-3}} = 18,200 \text{ ohms}$$

is chosen.

Turning on 10 ma in 0.5 μsec requires, by Fig. 4-10, a base current of 0.92 ma. Since R_1 supplies only 0.2 ma to the base, the difference of 0.72 ma must come through C_1. Therefore

$$C_1 = \frac{i\Delta t}{\Delta V} = \frac{0.72 \times 10^{-3}\ 0.5 \times 10^{-6}}{5} = 72 \text{ mmf,}$$

is selected. Actually the nearest standard capacitor above this value would be chosen. If there is collector-to-base capacity the input circuit must supply the current to charge it. Suppose therefore, that the collector is permitted to fall 5 volts before it is caught by a diode as shown in Fig. 4-22. Then if the collector to base capacity is 10 mmf — a reasonable value for this transistor — C_1 must supply an additional current,

$$\frac{C\Delta V}{\Delta t} = \frac{(10 \times 10^{-12})5}{0.5 \times 10^{-6}} = 0.1 \text{ ma}$$

Consequently, C_1 would be recalculated to deliver 0.82 ma instead of 0.72 ma. According to Fig. 4-16, turning off 10 ma in 0.5 μsec requires a reverse current of 0.66 ma. Since C_1 is designed to deliver 0.82 ma on the turn-on transient, it will also deliver a reverse current of this amount on the positive excursion of the input signal, thus meeting the turn-off requirement.

It should be noted that during the turn-on transient the input driver must be able to absorb a current of approximately $I_{R1} + I_{C1} = 1.08$ ma. During the steady-state it must absorb only $I_{R1} = 0.26$ ma. During the turn-off transient the input driver must emit a current of $I_{C1} = 0.82$ ma. If the input driver is a zero impedance source, these currents are automatically supplied. As a rule the input driver has different impedances at the leading and trailing edges of the signal and this must be taken into account (see Chapter 6).

4.6. Avoiding Storage Delay by Negative Feedback. A more effective scheme for avoiding storage delay, than that outlined has been devised by R. H. Baker[1]. It is shown in Fig. 4-23. Here, diode D2 is a germanium diode, and

---

[1] Baker, R. H., "Boosting Transistor Switching Speed," *Electronics*, p. 190, March 1957.

D1 is a silicon diode. The circuit depends on the volt-ampere characteristic of the silicon diode D1 in the forward direction. It does not break down and become a low impedance until it has a forward voltage of approximately 0.5 volt (see Fig. 5-4). From 0.5 volt up, it has a very steep characteristic — its impedance is under 50 ohms.

The diode D2 may be almost any type of germanium diode. For such a diode the forward drop is of the order of 0.3 volt for currents under 1 ma. The d-c

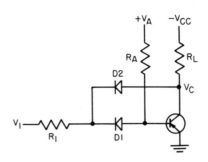

Fig. 4-24. Negative feedback to prevent saturation, and reverse base drive to speed up active-region decay time.

current through R1 is chosen large enough to give the required turn-on speed (for V_1 at its lower level), from Eq. 4-13 or one of the curves of Figs. 4-9 to 4-12. Therefore, as indicated by Fig. 4-10, turning on 10 ma in 0.5 μsec, requires 0.92 ma of base current. Consequently for the first 0.5 μsec, all the 0.92 ma demanded by R_1 is supplied by the base (as the voltage across D2 is in the reverse direction), and a turn-on speed of 0.5 μsec is achieved. For 0.92 ma of base current, the potential of the base $\cong -0.34$ volt with respect to ground (see Fig. 4-4), and for a forward drop of 0.5 volt across D1 the potential at V_J is -0.84 volt. During the fast 0.5 μsec turn-on therefore, D2 is disconnected and V_C is racing up towards ground from $-V_{CC}$. With 0.92 ma of base current V_C would bottom to -0.08 volt (Fig. 4-3 — intersection of a 10-ma load line with $I_B = 0.92$ ma). But as soon as V_C becomes slightly positive with respect to V_J (-0.84 volt with respect to ground), D2 starts turning on and permits V_C to go no more positive than 0.3 volt relative to V_J (-0.54 volt relative to ground). Since the drop across D1 is 0.5 volt however, V_B is -0.34 volt and consequently the collector is always 0.2 volt negative relative to the base. Under these conditions the collector base junction always has a reverse bias and storage delay is avoided. So long as the drop across D2 is less than that across D1 the collector cannot take on a forward bias.

Immediately after D2 starts conducting, the current into the base changes. R_1 still demands 0.92 ma, but now D1 and the base supply slightly more than 0.2 ma. The collector still supplies roughly 10 ma to R_L [actually $(V_{CC}-0.54)/$

R_L], plus the 0.70 ma through D2 to R_1 to satisfy its total requirement of 0.92 ma. If on turn-on, V_1 is at − 5 volts, then R_1 is chosen as

$$R_1 = \frac{5 - V_J}{0.92} = \frac{5 - 0.84}{0.92} = 4600 \text{ ohms.}$$

Thus the nature of the input driver is somewhat different. It must be able at − 5 volts to absorb a d-c current of 0.92 ma rather than as in the capacitive overdrive case, a pulse of 0.92 ma that could relax to 0.20 ma in the steady-state. Under these conditions, operation never enters saturation, whatever the gain of the transistor. A high-gain transistor will merely share its 0.92 ma differently in the steady-state between the base and D2. Therefore if a transistor required only 0.1 ma to turn on 10 ma in the steady-state, R_1 would take 0.1 ma from the base and 0.82 ma from D2 via the collector.

To turn the transistor off with the required speed it is necessary to supply the reverse current calculated from Eq. 4-23, or read from a curve such as Fig. 4-16. Consequently, to turn the 10 ma off in 0.5 μsec requires a reverse drive (see Fig. 4-16) of 0.66 ma. This can be supplied through R_A as shown in Fig. 4-24. Throughout the turn-off transient the base remains roughly at the potential it had (− 0.34 volt), during the transistor on time, as there are trapped charges in the base region. Assuming that V_1 switches rapidly up to ground, this results in a reverse potential across diode D1, and it consequently disconnects. The current being drawn through R_A is then available as reverse base current to speed up the active-region decay time. Set $(V_A+0.34)/R_A$ at 0.66 ma to provide the required turn-off speed. This means for 0.5 μsec turn-on, R_1 must draw 0.92 ma initially from the base, plus 0.66 ma normally supplied by R_A into the base during the turn-off transient. Therefore R_1 is calculated (for $V_1 = - 5$ volts as before), as

$$\frac{5 - 0.84}{0.92 + 0.66} = 2600 \text{ ohms}$$

This circuit is called a "current demand" circuit, because the current through R_1 reapportions itself so that only sufficient passes through the base to supply the current demanded by R_L to bottom the collector to about − 0.5 volt, whatever the value of R_L may be. The current through R_1 must therefore be greater than $I_{RA} + (V_{CC}-0.5)/\beta R_L$. The scheme does not necessarily require the silicon diode D1. It can be done with a split-base resistor as in Fig. 4-25.

Here R_1 must be chosen so that for the highest gain transistor, in the steady-state, the drop across R_1 is always greater than the drop across D2. The calculations are much more complex; it is extremely difficult to always satisfy this requirement under worst-case conditions of diode drops, resistance tolerance and transistor gain tolerance.

4.7. Avoiding Storage Delay by Collector Clamping. The easiest way to prevent the collector junction from assuming a positive bias and thus causing storage delay, is the brute force method shown in Fig. 4-26. In this case, R_1 is first selected to be a sink for I_{RA} and to turn on the required current in the specified time. Take again a turn-on of 10 ma in 0.5 μsec. As shown in Fig. 4-10 this requires a base current of 0.92 ma. From the intersection of a 10-ma load line with the 0.92-ma base current curve in Fig. 4-3 it is seen that if the collector is not stopped it will bottom to −0.08 volt. As Fig. 4-4 shows the base potential for 0.92 ma of base current to be − 0.34 volt, a forward bias of 0.26 volt on the collector junction would consequently result. The diode stopper connected as shown to a low impedance source of − 0.8 volt, however, prevents this, be-

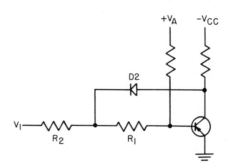

Fig. 4-25. Negative feedback antisaturation method of Fig. 4-24, with germanium diode replaced by resistor.

cause as shown in Fig. 4-3, 0.92 ma would turn on 30 ma of collector current in the steady-state at the knee of the collector current curve. If R_L demands only 10 ma [$(V_{CC}−0.40)/R_L=10$ ma], then D_S must carry away the remaining 20 ma. Choosing for D_S a diode with forward characteristic such as T_{7G} of Fig. 5-2, the forward drop at 20 ma is 0.4 volt. As the supply voltage is −0.8 volt, V_C is stopped at − 0.4 volt, and since the base potential is − 0.34 volt, the collector has a reverse bias of − 0.06 volt which is enough to prevent storage delay.

Obviously such a system is sensitive to production tolerances in the forward drop of D_S, the base-to-emitter potential of the transistor, and the source impedance and potential at V_S. For a high-gain transistor, the 0.92 ma may well turn on 50 to 60 ma of collector current; D_S would then have to carry away as much as 60 ma. At this point its forward drop is 0.7 volt and the transistor would have a forward bias. If V_S is made more negative to avoid saturation in the worst-case (high-gain transistor, high forward-drop diode D_S), the result would be to stop the collector at close to − 1 volt with respect to the emitter. For high-gain transistors where 0.92 ma of base current may turn on approximately 50 ma, this results in 50 milliwatts of collector dissipation which exceeds the rated value at temperature only slightly above room temperature.

Furthermore, to switch off, the reverse base drive (from R_A) must now be enough to turn off not approximately 10 ma, but anything from 30 to 60 ma, with the required speed. In most cases this would call for a prohibitively large reverse drive.

It will be seen therefore, that this scheme, though the easiest, is quite impractical. It has been discussed here only to illustrate the types of difficulties that may be encountered.

4.8. Avoiding Storage Delay by Emitter-Current Limiting. Another way in which storage delay may be avoided is shown in Fig. 4-27A. Here, the collector potential is limited by limiting the collector current. The collector

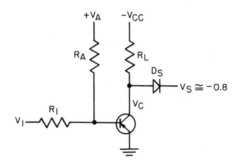

Fig. 4-26. An attempt to avoid saturation by an upper-level collector clamp.

potential then is $-V_{CC} + I_C R_L$, and I_C, R_L, V_{CC} are so chosen that the collector never goes positive in relation to the base. This requires a different type of switching. It requires that V_1 be a voltage rather than current source — i.e., a generator of very low internal impedance is necessary — for if a positive bias on the collector-to-base junction is to be prevented the base potential must be very clearly defined. Suppose the input generator has an open circuit voltage V_1, and a not negligible source impedance, R_S. Then, when it drives the base, the actual base potential is $V_1 + I_C R_S/\beta$. Consequently, for different values of β, the actual base potential will vary, and the upper limit to which the collector potential may be permitted to rise cannot be precisely designed.

However, if a low-impedance source at V_1 is assumed, with consequent well-defined base voltages, saturation can be avoided in the following manner (see Fig. 4-27B). Assume that a current of approximately 10 ma is to be switched in and out of R_L. This can be done with base voltage swings of ± 0.5 volt. For $V_1 = + 0.5$ volt, assume that T1 is cut off, and all the current from R_A flows into D1. If D1 is a diode as T_{7G} in Fig. 5-2, the potential at its anode is $+ 0.3$ volt. And since the base of the transistor is at $+ 0.5$ volt, the emitter junction of T1 has 0.2-volt reverse bias, and the assumption that T1 is cut off is true. To switch the 10 ma into R_L, all that need now be done is to move V_1 down far enough to put a reverse voltage across D1. Figure 4-3 shows that at 10 ma of collector current 0.2 ma of base current would be required, and Fig. 4-4 indicates that at 0.2 ma of base current, the base-to-emitter voltage is 0.25 volt. Therefore for $V_1 = -0.5$ volt, V_E is -0.25 volt, there is a reverse voltage across D1, and all the current through R_A flows through the transistor into R_L.

To ensure that with all the resistor and voltage tolerances off in the worst direction the collector potential is never positive with respect to the base, design

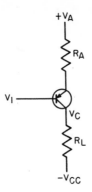

Fig. 4-27A. An attempt to avoid saturation by emitter-current limiting.

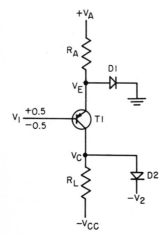

Fig. 4-27B. An upper-level collector clamp to provide unique upper-level output voltage.

to permit a maximum potential at V_C of -0.6 volt, which is still a 0.1-volt reverse bias on the collector. It is then necessary to see whether with T1 on, and voltage and resistor tolerances off in the opposite direction, the emitter-to-collector voltage is so large as to exceed the rated transistor dissipation.

Assume $\pm 5\%$ resistor and voltage tolerances. Select V_A large compared to the base voltage swing so that I_{RA} is roughly a constant current source. A value of 5 volts for V_A is adequate. Let us arbitrarily select $-V_{CC}$ as -10 volts.

(It will be seen later that this is not unreasonable.) Then for a nominal emitter current of close to 10 ma choose $R_A = 500$ ohms. If $\overline{R}_A$, $\overline{R}_L$, $\overline{V}_A$, $\overline{V}_{CC}$, $\underline{R}_A$, $\underline{R}_L$, $\underline{V}_A$, $\underline{V}_{CC}$ are designated as the values these parameters have at the upper and lower limits of their expected 5% tolerance variation, the first condition for no saturation is

$$- 0.6 = - \underline{V}_{CC} + \overline{I}_E \, \overline{R}_L$$

assuming $I_C \cong I_E$, where $\overline{I}_E$ is the upper limit emitter current resulting from $\overline{V}_A$ and $\underline{R}_A$. From Figs. 4-3 and 4-4 at 10 ma of collector current the emitter-to-base voltage is $- 0.25$. Consequently, for V_1 at $- 0.5$ volt

$$\overline{I}_E = \frac{\overline{V}_A + 0.25}{\underline{R}_A} = \frac{1.05(5) + 0.25}{0.95(500)} = 11.6 \text{ ma}$$

Therefore

$$\overline{R}_L = 1.05 \; R_L \,(\text{nominal}) = \frac{\overline{V}_{CC} - 0.6}{\overline{I}_E} = \frac{(0.95)(10) - 0.6}{11.6} = 7670 \text{ ohms}$$

or R_L (nominal) $= 7310$ ohms. If the resistor and voltage tolerances are off in the opposite direction, the maximum negative collector potential is given by

$$\overline{V}_C = - \overline{V}_{CC} + \underline{I}_E \, \underline{R}_L$$

where

$$I_E = \frac{\underline{V}_A + 0.25}{\overline{R}_A} = \frac{(.95)(5) + .25}{1.05(500)} = 9.05 \text{ ma}$$

Therefore

$$\overline{V}_C = - (1.05)(10) + 9.05(.95) \; (R_L \,(\text{nominal}) \,)$$

$$= - 10.5 + 6.26 = - 4.2 \text{ volts}$$

Consequently, in designing to avoid saturation when tolerances are off in the direction that tends to cause saturation, a large amount of collector dissipation must be accepted if the tolerances are off in the opposite direction. Since the emitter rides about 0.25 volt above the base, the emitter-to-collector voltage is 3.95 volts, and for a current of 9.05 ma, the transistor dissipates 36 milliwatts. This exceeds the rated value at 55°C. In addition there is the further nuisance that the collector potential at its upper level is ambiguous. It may be as high as $- 0.6$ volt or as low as $- 4.2$ volts. This could be remedied by the upper clamp diode D2, which would prevent the collector from ever going more positive than V_2, which would be set at $- 4.2$ volts.

In general, however, it is obvious that antisaturation by a large resistor to limit the emitter current causes as much difficulty as it solves.

4.9. Limiting Duration of the Turn-on Pulse to Reduce Storage Delay.
In dealing with pulses of relatively short duration, saturation is less of a problem. Figure 4-6 shows that if the duration of a turn-on pulse is T2, benefit is derived from turn-on speed-up by overdrive. But if the input pulse is removed at point C, no excess of charges is injected into the base region beyond that just

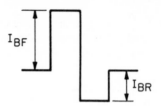

Fig. 4-28. If the transistor "on" time is sufficiently short, the forward base drive can be large to provide fast turn-on, and yet the reverse base drive need only be large enough to provide the required active-region decay time.

at the edge of saturation. Then, if the input pulse has the waveshape of Fig. 4-28, the amplitude of the reverse current spike I_{BR} need only be sufficient to give the required active-region decay time (Eq. 4-23). There will be no storage effects. I_{BF} however, must be sufficient as calculated from Eq. 4-13, to give the required turn-on time.

Chapter *5*

DIODE GATING

This chapter commences the design of some of the most basic building blocks — diode AND and OR gates. Diode gates are passive networks performing the logical function of AND and OR gating. As their output power is less than the input required to drive them, when they are used in a "logical" chain, a power amplifying element such as a tube, transistor or magnetic amplifier must be interposed at various points in the chain. Until recently most large-scale computers used a system of diode gating and vacuum tube amplifiers. In some cases, logic and power amplification were both done by tubes, but this was not very satisfactory. With the advent of transistors and magnetic devices, it became more efficient to have these devices perform both the logic and power amplification. Even today however, diode gating followed by transistors or magnetic amplifiers is a widely used technique in the computer field.

The design of such diode gates and chains of diode gates using a worst-case design procedure is the subject of this chapter. Worst-case designing is designing so that the circuit will still work when all supply voltages and active and passive components are simultaneously at those extremes of their tolerance limits, that will tend most to make the circuit inoperative.

5.1. Diode Characteristics. Diode-gating circuits can be built with any one of a multitude of germanium, silicon, selenium or even vacuum diodes. Germanium diodes are most frequently used. They are available in a great variety of types each having some particularly useful property such as high forward conductance, high peak-inverse voltage, low inverse leakage, or low back-impedance recovery time. There are available the conventional whisker type, or the newer gold-bonded germanium diodes. The gold-bonded diode has a lower forward impedance, lower reverse leakage, and is considerably more uniform in its characteristics than the conventional whisker diode. This is shown in Figs. 5-1 and 5-2. Figure 5-2 gives the volt-ampere curves for a number of gold-bonded diodes showing the wide variety of forward and reverse properties available. Figure 5-3 shows the characteristics of some typical whisker-type diodes.

Silicon diodes are used where low reverse leakage at high temperature, high peak-inverse voltage or high forward-current-carrying capability is required.

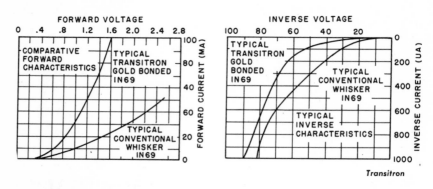

Fig. 5-1. Comparison of forward and reverse characteristics of gold bonded and conventional whisker type diodes.

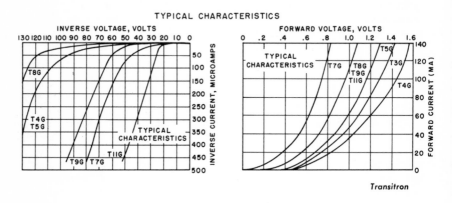

Fig. 5-2. Typical characteristics of germanium diodes.

They have the odd property of a very high forward impedance for forward voltages less than approximately 0.5 volt, and breaking down to a low impedance value thereafter. This makes possible a number of useful circuit tricks such as d-c level shifts without attenuation, transistor emitter biasing without degeneration, and signal clipping. Typical characteristics for silicon diodes are shown in Fig. 5-4.

Selenium area diodes have been used in computer circuitry.[1] Their principal advantage is low price, low reverse leakage for a given forward-current-carrying capability, and the fact that they can be cheaply stacked in series to achieve higher peak-inverse voltage. If the area of a selenium diode is chosen to give only the required forward current capability desired, and the number of cells in

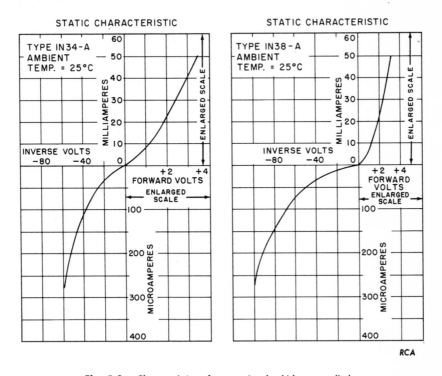

Fig. 5-3. Characteristics of conventional whisker-type diodes.

series is chosen to sustain the maximum inverse voltage, it is possible to achieve less reverse leakage than in a conventional whisker-type germanium diode selected for the same forward current.

In this respect however, it is not better than the gold-bonded germanium diode or the silicon diode. Another drawback with selenium area diodes is that they have a relatively high capacitance varying from .01 to .05 mf per square inch, depending on the reverse voltage at which they operate. Increasing the number of series cells to reduce capacitance results in increasing the already large forward voltage drops. Selenium diodes also lose their rectifying properties if operated for long periods of time with forward current without being sub-

[1] Masterson, E. and Pressman, A. I., "A Self-Checking High-Speed Printer," *Proc. Eastern Joint Computer Conference,* pp. 22-29, December 1954.

jected to inverse voltage. This precludes their use in many types of computer circuits. But in applications where price — as already mentioned — is an important factor, and relatively high forward voltage drops and large input capacitance are unimportant, they are useful. A typical volt-ampere curve for selenium is shown in Fig. 5-5. From this curve one can tailor-make a diode, choosing

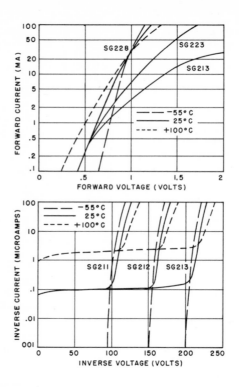

Fig. 5-4. Forward and reverse characteristics of some silicon diodes.

cell area for required forward current, and a number of series cells for required peak inverse voltage and permissible diode capacitance.

5.2. Positive AND Gates. Figure 5-6 shows the structure of a diode AND gate for positive-going signals. The inputs are V_1, V_2, and V_3, and the output is at V_O. A three-input gate is shown for illustration only; the gate can be designed for any number of inputs desired. The input signals may assume either of two voltage levels, an upper level, usually ground, and a lower level, $-V_L$. The output, V_O will be at ground only when all three inputs are simultaneously at ground, in which case the gate is said to be enabled. If any one input is at $-V_L$, the output is at $-V_L$, and the gate is said to be inhibited. The gate works in the following manner.

When the gate is inhibited, it may be inhibited by either one or all three of the inputs being at $-V_L$. This forces V_0 to $-V_L$, (for the balance of this chapter diode forward voltage drops will be neglected), and any inputs at ground level are disconnected from V_0 and from the driver at $-V_L$ by the high back-impedance of their input diodes. R_A now delivers into V_0 node a cur-

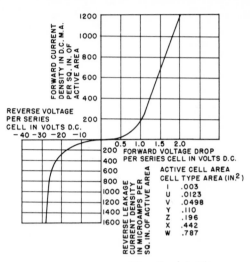

International Rectifier

Fig. 5-5. Forward and reverse characteristics of selenium rectifier cells.

rent $I_G = (E_A+V_L)/R_A$. If all three inputs are at V_L, then this current divides almost equally, and each driver at V_1, V_2 or V_3 must be a sink for $I_G/3$. (The nature of the input drivers is discussed later, but in passing, they have such low internal impedance that the output voltage they assume, ground or V_L, is independent of the magnitude of the current they absorb or emit.)

If two inputs are at $-V_L$ and the third is at ground, then V_0 is at $-V_L$, and a current, $(E_A+V_L)/R_A$ pours into the gate output node from R_A. The node must also absorb I_{BL}, the reverse leakage current (at a reverse voltage, V_L), from the diode at ground. Consequently, each driver at V_L must in this case be a sink for

$$\frac{1}{2}\left[\frac{E_A + V_L}{R_A} + I_{BL}\right]$$

Since the logic of an AND gate requires that a single input at $-V_L$ keeps the output at $-V_L$, then for the case of two inputs at ground and the third at $-V_L$, the driver at $-V_L$, must be a sink for a nominal current of $2I_{BL} + (E_A + V_L)/R_A$. In the case where one driver is at ground and one driver or more is at $-V_L$, the output is at $-V_L$, and the driver at ground must now be a source rather than a sink for current of magnitude I_{BL}.

The gate design has thus become a problem of designing drivers capable of absorbing, or being adequate current sinks, at the lower voltage level, or emitting current or being adequate current sources, at the upper level. This chapter discusses only the current absorption and emission requirements of drivers, and not their design.

These current requirements are nominal. The gate must work for all voltages and resistors being off their nominal value by the expected tolerance in the

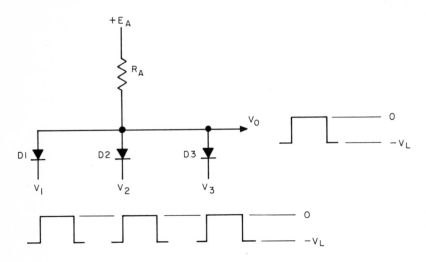

Fig. 5-6.   A diode AND gate for positive signals.

worst direction, and all diode reverse leakages being at their maximum value. In this chapter a line above a term indicates the upper limit value resulting from it, or the variables upon which it depends, being at the extreme tolerance limit in that direction that would make the variable a maximum. Similarly, a line below a term indicates its lower limit value resulting from tolerances being off in that direction that would tend to minimize it.

As the gate emits a positive output signal, it normally does its useful work at ground level. This is generally to emit a specified output current at ground level for charging wiring capacitance in a given time, driving other AND or OR gates, or turning transistors on or off. Whatever the work, gate design commences by specifying a minimum current output capability when the output voltage is at ground. The minimum output current occurs for minimum voltage across R_A with R_A at the upper limit of its tolerance. Therefore

$$\underline{I_{EA}} \text{ (read I emission lower limit)} = \frac{(1 - .01t_v) E_A}{(1 + .01t_r) R_A} \qquad (5\text{-}1)$$

where t_v is maximum expected percentage voltage variation, and t_r is the maximum expected percentage resistance variation. For a previously selected E_A (which is usual), this fixes the nominal value of R_A.

To inhibit the gate, assume the voltage and resistance tolerances are off in the opposite directions. Each driver must then have a current absorption capability in the steady-state of

$$\overline{I}_i \text{ (read I inhibit upper limit)} = \frac{[1 + .01t_v]\ E_A + V_L}{[1 - .01t_r]\ R_A} + (n - 1)\ I_{BL} \tag{5-2}$$

where n is the number of diodes in the gate, and I_{BL} is the maximum expected diode leakage at the highest operating temperature (with allowance made for diode aging). Consequently, as can be seen, the inhibiting driver must have a current absorption capability greater than the minimum output current capability of the gate when it is enabled. The ratio

$$\frac{\overline{I}_i}{I_{EA}} = \frac{[1 + .01t_r]}{[1 - .01t_v]} \left[\frac{(1 + .01t_v)}{(1 - .01t_r)} + \frac{1}{(1 - .01t_r)\ E_A/V_L} \right.$$

$$\left. + (n - 1)\ \frac{I_{BL}}{E_A/R_A} \right] \tag{5-3}$$

is a measure of the gate loss. Most efficient gating requires this to be as small as possible. It is obvious that the larger the ratio of the source voltage E_A to the gate voltage swing, i.e., the more accurately resistor R_A connected to E_A can be regarded as a constant current source whose output current is independent of whether V_O is at the ground level or at the $- V_L$ level, the more efficient is the gate. This is shown in Fig. 5-7, where gate loss $\overline{I}_i/I_{EA}$ has been plotted as a function of the ratio E_A/V_L for various ratios of $I_{BL}/(E_A/R_A)$, (the ratio of a single diode back-leakage to the nominal gate output current). This has been done for $n = 3$ — the average type of gate in computer circuitry — and for an assumed $\pm 5\%$ voltage and resistance tolerance.

Figure 5-7 shows that above an E_A/V_L ratio of approximately 5, little gain in gating efficiency results from further increasing this ratio. Although a large ratio gives greater efficiency, it is obtained at a cost of increased d-c power dissipation in the form of a large value of R_A connected to a large source voltage E_A. This means a somewhat more expensive d-c power supply, higher operating temperature, and a more expensive cooling method.

In general, however, for a machine with a large number of gates it is preferable to have good gating efficiency, (E_A/V_L equal to 5 or more), even at the increased cost and nuisance of d-c power dissipation and higher operating temperatures, because it is even more expensive in cost and space to build a large number of higher power gate drivers. For a machine with a small number of gates, a ratio of E_A/V_L in the vicinity of 2 to 4 tends to be optimum.

EXAMPLE. Design a three-input AND gate to deliver a 5-volt signal to a 100-mmf wiring-capacitance load, and capable of driving the load to full output in 1 μsec. The resulting gate is shown in Fig. 5-8. Assuming V_2 and V_3 are already up at ground level, when V_1 goes up to ground all three diodes are disconnected from the output node. Then the output voltage rises as

$$V_O = (E_A + V_L) \ [1 - e^{-t/R_A C_A}]$$

From this relation, R_A and E_A can be fixed to achieve a 5-volt rise in 1 μsec.

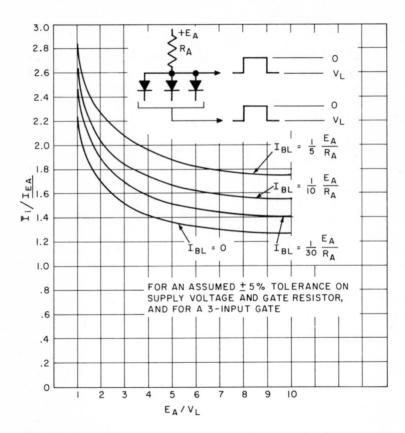

Fig. 5-7. Diode AND gate current loss v. ratio of gate supply voltage to output voltage swing. Calculated from Eq. 5-3.

But the same answer can be obtained more conveniently by considering the average current required from R_A to give the necessary output. Therefore to put a 5-volt charge on C_A in 1 μsec requires an average current of

$$I_{AV} = \frac{C_A \ \Delta V}{\Delta t} = \frac{100 \times 10^{-12} \times 5}{1 \times 10^{-6}} = 0.5 \ \text{ma}$$

If this is set to equal I_{EA} of Eq. 5-1, the gate is capable of delivering the required output at the extremes of the voltage and resistance tolerance. From Fig. 5-7, choose $E_A/V_L = 5$ as a suitable compromise between gating efficiency and d-c power dissipation. This fixes E_A at $+ 25$ volts. Then for voltage and resistance tolerance of 5%, R_A from Eq. 5-1 has a nominal value of

$$R_A = \frac{(1 - .01)\ t_V\ E_A}{(1 + .01)\ t_r\ I_{EA}} = \frac{(.95)\ 25}{(1.05)\ 0.0005} = 45,300\ \text{ohms}$$

This is a slightly conservative value as it gives the required 0.50 ma at the top of the voltage swing when there is a nominal 25 volts across R_A, rather than

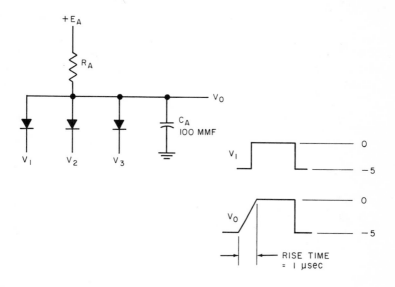

Fig. 5-8. A diode AND gate driving a capacitive load.

at the center of the voltage swing when there is a nominal 27.5 volts across R_A. Another way of looking at it is that the lower limit average current is .95 (27.5)/ 1.05 (45.3) = 0.55 ma, rather than 0.50 ma.

To inhibit the gate then, from Eq. 5-2, the driver must be a sink in the worst-case for a current of magnitude

$$I_i = \frac{[1 + .01\ t_V]\ E_A + V_L}{[1 - .01\ t_r]\ R_A} + (n - 1)\ I_{BL}$$

$$= \frac{(1.05)\ (25) + 5}{(0.95)\ (45.3)} + 2\ I_{BL}$$

$$= 0.73 + 2I_{BL}$$

Here, I_{BL} is the back-leakage of the worst diode (at 5 volts of reverse voltage), at the highest operating temperature, with a conservative allowance made for aging. In actual practice, a diode would either be purchased to preset specifications, or a stock diode used and life tested to determine this upper limit of back-leakage. Assume here, the value of 0.1 ma — there are innumerable diodes that meet this specification. Therefore the gate driver to inhibit the gate must be a sink when its output voltage is -5 volts for

$$\bar{I}_i = .73 + 2 \ (0.1) = 0.93 \text{ ma}$$

This could have been read from the curves of Fig. 5-7. In our example $E_A/V_L = 5$, $I_{BL} = 1/5 \ (E_A/R_A)$, for which

$$\bar{I}_i/I_{\underline{E}} = 1.87$$

and for I_{EA} of 0.5 ma, $\bar{I}_i = 1.87 \ (0.5) = 0.93$ ma.

Therefore a driver with 0.93 ma of absorption current capability will be able to inhibit the gate in the steady-state. The output voltage rise-time is fixed by the current available through R_A from E_A. Additional current due to back-

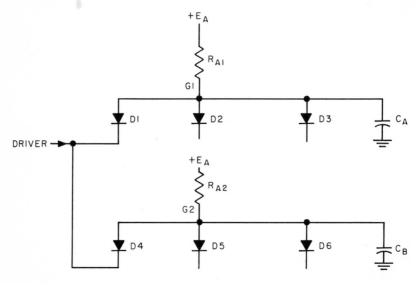

Fig. 5-9. A gate driver feeding two AND gates with capacitive loads. At the fall-times, the driver need not necessarily supply the sum of two d-c and two a-c drives.

leakage through the input diodes cannot be depended upon. There may be a situation of low temperature ($25°C$), and high back-resistance diodes, in which case the diode back-leakage may be .02 to .01 of the assumed worst-case values. The output voltage fall-time will be fixed by the absorption current capability of the gate driver.

In general, here, in considering a positive AND gate concern is primarily with the rise-time of the positive-going signal rather than its fall-time. But in the instances where fall-time is important, additional current absorption capability must be provided in the driver, as all the 0.93 ma provided for will be supplied by the 45,300-ohm resistor. To produce a 1 µsec fall-time another 0.5 ma must be provided to discharge the capacitor, as it had been calculated that 0.5 ma in the capacitor drove it 5 volts positive in 1 µsec. Normally, this does not neces-

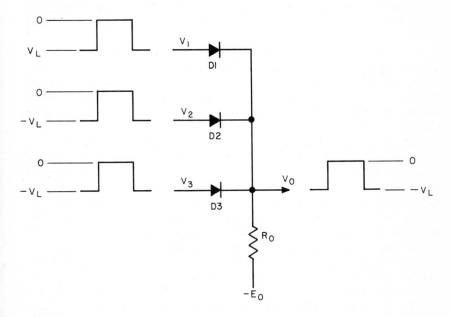

Fig. 5-10. A diode OR gate for positive inputs.

sitate increasing the sink current capability of the driver, because a driver usually feeds more than one gate as shown in Fig. 5-9.

The driver designed provided for an absorption current capability sufficient to inhibit G1 and G2 in the steady-state. For $R_{A1} = R_{A2}$, this would be twice the calculated 0.93 ma. Only if G1 and G2 were required to go from the enable to the inhibit state *simultaneously* would the driver need the added 0.5 ma of absorption current capability. Generally, one gate, say, G1, will be enabled with the drivers at D1, D2, D3 at ground, and G2 inhibited by a driver at D5 or D6, at the $- 5$ volt level. Then during the transition from 0 to $- 5$ volt the driver at D1 has available the 0.93 ma of sink current capability (normally used to inhibit G2 in the steady-state), to discharge the output capacitance at G1. During this transition G2 is being kept inhibited by the driver at D5 or D6. Where a single driver must move all its gates from the enable to the inhibit state simultaneously, however, if fall-times are important, the driver must have the added current capacity to discharge the output capacitance on all its gates.

5.3. Positive OR Gates. Figure 5-10 shows the structure of a three-input diode OR gate for positive-going signals. Like the AND gate, an OR gate can be built for any number of inputs.

The output at V_O is at ground if any input at V_1, V_2 or V_3 is at ground. If one input is at ground and some of the others are at $-V_L$, then the drivers at $-V_L$ are disconnected from V_O and from the driver at ground by the high back-impedance of their input diodes. At the moment the last of the three inputs falls to $-V_L$, V_O begins to fall towards $-E_O$ and is caught at $-V_L$ by the diodes latching in.

As in the AND gate, the drivers at V_1, V_2, V_3 are such low-impedance sources that the voltage levels they assume are independent of the amount of current emitted or absorbed. The function of the diodes is to provide isolation between the drivers. If the diode back-leakage is negligible, then the load on the drivers is whatever current E_O draws through R_O, and whatever load there is external to the gate.

Such an OR gate usually drives capacitive loads, inputs to diode AND gates, or inputs to transistor amplifiers. During the transition from $-V_L$ to ground, one of the input diodes is conducting in the forward direction, and since zero source impedance drivers have been assumed, the output rise-time is fixed by driver rise-time. During the transition from ground to $-V_L$, if the driver fall-time is very fast and there is sufficient capacitive load to slow up the output fall-time, the input diode disconnects, and thereafter the output fall-time is determined only by the average current being provided from $-E_O$ through R_O. Thus the prime purpose of R_O is to be a sink for a current large enough to produce the required fall-time in a capacitive load.

In considering the positive AND gate, it was seen that to inhibit the AND gate a sink must be provided for current when the output voltage is at $-V_L$. Therefore, if the OR gate drives an AND gate, the resistor R_O must be a sink for the calculated $\overline{I_i}$ of Eq. 5-2. When it drives a transistor amplifier, again the prime purpose of R_O is to be a sink for current at the $-V_L$ level. The amount of current absorption capability that must be built into the combination of R_O and $-E_O$ depends on the nature of the amplifier and required speed of response.

Thus whatever the type of load, the first thing to be fixed in an OR gate design is the current absorption capability for the output at $-V_L$. Worst-case driver requirements must then be calculated to force the output up to the ground level. Consequently, if a minimum absorption capability of $\underline{I_{AO}}$ is required, then $-E_O$ and R_O are fixed by

$$\underline{I_{AO}} \text{ (read I absorption lower limit)} = \frac{[1 - .01\ t_v]\ E_O - |V_L|}{[1 + .01\ t_r]\ R_O}$$

$$(5\text{-}4)$$

where again t_v and t_r are the worst-case voltage and resistance tolerances.

To enable the OR gate in the steady-state, again assume the voltage and resistance tolerances are off in the opposite directions, and the driver must be able to emit, when at the ground level, the current demanded by R_O plus the back-leakage current demanded by $n - 1$ diodes that may be at the $-V_L$ level. This current is

$$\bar{I}_{EO} \text{ (read I emission upper limit)} = \frac{[1 + .01\ t_v]\ E_O}{[1 - .01\ t_r]\ R_O} + (n - 1)\ I_{BL}$$

(5-5)

where n is the number of OR inputs, and I_{BL} the worst-case diode back-leakage at a reverse voltage of V_L.

An expression for the current loss in the OR gate is derived as for the AND gate; the ratio

$$\frac{\bar{I}_{EO}}{\underline{I}_{AO}} = \frac{[1 + .01\ t_v]\ [1 + .01\ t_r] \left[\dfrac{E_O}{V_L}\right]}{[1 - .01\ t_v]\left[\dfrac{E_O}{V_L}\right] - 1}$$

$$+ \frac{[n - 1]\ [1 + .01\ t_r] \left[\dfrac{E_O}{V_L} - 1\right]}{[1 - .01\ t_v]\left[\dfrac{E_O}{V_L}\right] - 1} \left[\frac{[I_{BL}]}{\dfrac{(E_O - V_L)}{R_O}}\right] \qquad (5\text{-}6)$$

This is plotted in Fig. 5-11 for a three-input OR gate for $\pm$ 5% in voltage and resistance tolerances, and for various ratios of a single diode back-leakage to the nominal absorption current capability of R_O, when $V_O = - V_L$. Again as for the AND gate, Fig. 5-11 shows no significant gain from increasing the ratio E_O/V_L much above approximately 5.

EXAMPLE. Design a three-input OR gate to deliver a 5-volt signal to a 100-mmf capacitive load, rise and fall-times of output signal to be not worse than 1 µsec. The resulting gate is shown in Fig. 5-12.

In the OR gate, the input diodes during the rise-time are conducting in the forward direction, and consequently the output voltage rise-time will be fixed by the input driver rise-time. During the fall-time, if the input driver is sufficiently fast, the diode disconnects, and sufficient average current must be provided through R_O to produce the required fall-time. This average current can be fixed by

$$I_{RO} = \frac{C\Delta V}{\Delta t} = \frac{(100 \times 10^{-12})\ 5}{1 \times 10^{-6}} = 0.5\ \text{ma}$$

It can be provided under worst conditions of voltage and resistor tolerances by setting $\underline{I}_{AO}$ of Eq. 5-4 equal to 0.5 ma. As for the AND gate, this is conservative in that it provides the required current at the bottom of the voltage swing rather than at the center. From Fig. 5-11, choose a ratio of E_O/V_L of 5 as a good compromise between gating efficiency and power dissipation. This sets E_O at -25, and for 5% voltage and resistance tolerances, gives from Eq. 5-4

$$R_O = \frac{.95 \ (25) - 5}{1.05 \ (0.0005)} = 35,800 \text{ ohms}$$

To enable the OR gate in the steady-state, the driver in the worst-case (for diodes of 0.1 ma back-leakage), must have an emission current capability from Eq. 5-5 of

$$\overline{I}_{EO} = \frac{(1.05) \ (25)}{(.95) \ (35.8)} + 2 \ (0.1) = 0.97 \text{ ma}$$

This could also have been read from the curves of Fig. 5-11, where for $E_O/V_L = 5$, and $I_{BL} = 1/5 \ [\ (E_O - V_L)/R_O]$,

$$\overline{I}_{EO} = 1.93 \ (\underline{I_{AO}}) = 1.93 \ (0.5) = 0.97 \text{ ma}$$

Note that during the rise-time a situation similar to that of the AND gate driver during its fall-time, exists. If the OR driver fed only one gate, and had an emission current capability of only 0.97 ma, it could not charge the 100 mmf 5 volts positive in 1 μsec, as all the 0.97 ma would be demanded by R_O, leaving no current to charge the ouput capacitance. Usually however, the driver feeds a number of gates, and it must therefore be designed to have an emission current capability adequate to feed all the d-c loads. If — as is usual — some of the d-c loads have already been forced up to the ground level by other inputs to the OR gates, the emission current capability normally used for those d-c loads is available to drive the capacitance of the remaining load. But again, as in the AND gate, if at any time all the loads on a given driver must simultaneously be driven positive, there must be added to the driver's emission current capability, a current of magnitude $I_{AC} = C_T \ \Delta V/\Delta t$, where C_T is the total capacitive load on the OR gate outputs, and ΔV is the required voltage swing in the time Δt. Therefore in this case the total lower limit emission current requirement for the OR gate driver is

$$\underline{I'_{EO}} = \overline{I}_{EO} + C_T \ \frac{\Delta V}{\Delta t} = 0.00097$$

$$+ \frac{(100 \times 10^{-12}) \ (5)}{1 \times 10^{-6}} = 1.47 \text{ ma}$$

5.4. Positive AND Gate Driving Positive OR Gate.   The circuit of a positive AND gate driving a positive OR gate is shown in Fig. 5-13. Three input gates of each type are shown, but there is no restriction on the number of inputs to either gate. It is limited only by the available emission and absorption current capability of the drivers at the input to the AND gate.

The problem here is to select E_A, R_A, E_O, and R_O, and calculate drive requirements at the input to G1 for specified output signal amplitude, rise and fall times.

Assume the AND gate load is that of the OR gate input plus an additional stray capacitance C_A. Assume also, that the load on the OR gate output is a capacitance C_O. Again, this OR gate load may be of any nature, but whatever it is, the first

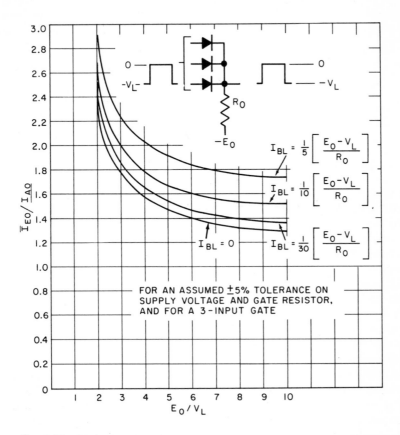

Fig. 5-11. Diode OR gate current loss v. ratio of gate supply voltage to output voltage swing. Calculated from Eq. 5-6.

step is to fix the absorption current requirement of R_O at the $-V_L$ level. With a capacitive load, fix it to produce the specified fall-time. Thus from Eq. 5-4

$$\underline{I_{AO}} = C_O \frac{V_L}{\Delta t} = \frac{[1 - .01\ t_v]\ E_O - V_L}{[1 + .01\ t_r]\ R_O} \tag{5-7}$$

As before, choose $E_O/V_L = 5$ for adequately efficient gating. This fixes E_O for specified V_L, and with a specified rate of fall and assumed C_O, R_O is fixed by Eq. 5-7. With R_O fixed, $\bar{I}_{EO}$, the upper limit emission requirement for driving R_O alone, is fixed by Eq. 5-5. Then since R_A must also supply the current to drive C_A and C_O with the specified rise-time, the lower limit emission current requirement is set from R_A as

$$I'_{EA} = \bar{I}_{EO} + [C_A + C_O]\frac{V_L}{\Delta t} \qquad (5\text{-}8)$$

With E_A/R_A also set at 5, Eq. 5-1 fixes R_A where I_{EA} is the I'_{EA} of Eq. 5-8.

With R_A fixed, calculate from Eq. 5-2, $\bar{I}_i$, the upper limit absorption current requirement of the AND gate driver to inhibit G1 in the steady-state. Here, how-

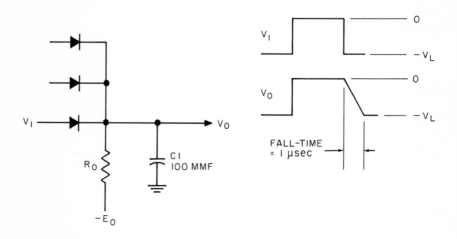

Fig. 5-12.   A diode OR gate driving a capacitive load.

ever, in Eq. 5-2, n is now one more than the total number of diodes in the AND gate. This is because the AND gate driver at the $-V_L$ level must now absorb in the worst-case, back-leakage from $(n - 1)$ diodes in the AND gate, and one back-leakage from the input to the OR gate. (A driver at the input to D1 may have to absorb back-leakage from D2, D3, D4, as shown in Fig. 5-13.)

Finally, since the current to discharge C_A with the required fall-time must come from the AND gate driver, the total upper limit absorption current required of the AND driver is

$$\bar{I'}_i = \bar{I}_i + C_A\frac{\Delta V}{\Delta t} \qquad (5\text{-}9)$$

where $\bar{I}_i$ has already been calculated above.

EXAMPLE.   Design the structure of Fig. 5-13 to swing V_O between -5 and 0 volts with rise and fall times of 1 μsec, and assuming diodes of 0.1 ma of back-leakage at -5 volts. Assume $C_A = C_O = 100$ mmf, $\pm 5\%$ for voltage and resistance tolerances. From Eq. [5-7]:

$$\underline{I_{AO}} = \frac{100 \times 10^{-12} \ (5)}{1 \times 10^{-6}} = 0.0005 = \frac{(.95) \ (25) \ -5}{1.05 \ R_O}$$

from which

$$R_O = 35,800 \text{ ohms}$$

From Eq. [5-5]:

$$\bar{I}_{EO} = \frac{1.05 \ (25)}{.95 \ (35.8)} + 2 \ (0.1) = 0.77 + .2 = 0.97 \text{ ma}$$

and from Eq. [5-8]:

$$\underline{I'_{EA}} = 0.00097 + \frac{(200 \times 10^{-12}) \ (5)}{1 \times 10^{-6}} = 1.97 \text{ ma}$$

From Eq. [5-1]:

$$R_A = \frac{.95 \ (25)}{1.05 \ (.00197)} = 11,500 \text{ ohms}$$

and from Eq. [5-2]:

$$\bar{I}_i = \frac{1.05 \ (25) \ +5}{.95 \ (11.5)} + 3 \ (0.1) = 2.66 + 0.3 = 2.96 \text{ ma}$$

Finally, from Eq. [5-9]:

$$\bar{I'}_i = .00296 + \frac{(100 \times 10^{-12}) \ (5)}{1 \times 10^{-6}} = .00296 + .0005 = 3.46 \text{ ma}$$

Thus, to drive a 100-mmf capacitive load at the OR gate output, 5 volts, with a fall-time of 1 μsec, requires an OR gate sink of 0.5 ma. And to produce 1 μsec rise and fall times at the OR gate output requires a driver at the AND gate input that must be a sink for 3.46 ma.

It is this severe current attenuation that makes long chains of diode logic prohibitively expensive. In actual practice, attenuations are not as bad as in the example given, for a number of reasons. First, cascades of diode logic are usually packaged very close together so that there is no capacitance at junctions between gates, but only at the input and output of a logical chain. Second, only infrequently must both rise and fall time be equally fast. And third, rarely does a gate driver have to supply the sum of the d-c and a-c driver requirements of all its loads simultaneously. Consequently, as mentioned on pp. 103 and 106, it can usually be designed to supply only the d-c requirements of all its loads.

5.5. Positive OR Gate Driving Positive AND Gate. The structure of a positive OR gate feeding a positive AND gate is shown in Fig. 5-14.

Here too, although only three inputs are shown for each gate, the only restriction on the number of inputs is the driver capability at the input to the OR gate. Capacitive loads are shown at both gate outputs. Whatever the nature of the load at the G2 output, the design procedure is unchanged: the first step is to specify a lower limit emission current requirement from R_A to force the output up to ground. The problem is to choose E_A, R_A, E_O, and R_O, and calculate driver requirements at the input to G1 for specified output signal amplitude, and rise and fall times. Assume the output signal is to swing between $-V_L$

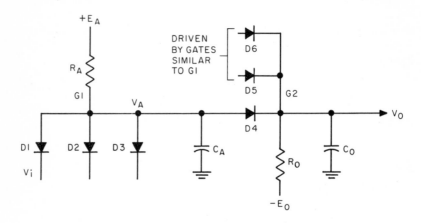

Fig. 5-13.   A positive AND gate driving a positive OR gate.

and ground, with rise and fall times at Δt. Again $E_A/V_L = E_O/V_L = 5$ is chosen to give adequate gating efficiency. Then Eq. 5-1 fixes R_A to give the required output voltage rise-time. Thus

$$\underline{I_{EA}} = \frac{C_A\,V_L}{\Delta t} = \frac{[1 - .01\,t_v]\,E_A}{[1 + .01\,t_r]\,R_A} \qquad (5\text{-}10)$$

To inhibit the AND gate in the steady-state, R_O must be a sink for $\bar{I}_i$ calculated from Eq. 5-2. During the fall-time it must also supply the current required to discharge C_A and C_O in the required time, because all the OR gate drivers have disconnected through their input diodes. Consequently, the lower limit absorption current requirement of R_O is

$$\underline{I_{AO}} = \bar{I}_i + \frac{[C_A + C_O]\,V_L}{\Delta t} \qquad (5\text{-}11)$$

This value of $\underline{I_{AO}}$ substituted into Eq. 5-4 fixes R_O. With R_O fixed, calculate from Eq. 5-5. $\bar{I}_{EO}$, the upper limit emission current required of the OR gate driver to force the OR gate output up to ground in the steady-state. But here again in Eq. 5-5, n is one more than the number of diodes in the OR gate, as the OR driver, in the worst-case, may have to supply back-leakage current to the $(n-1)$ diodes in the OR gate, and the one diode input to the AND gate (D2, D3, D4 in Fig. 5-14). In addition, the OR driver during the rise-time must supply the current to charge C_O in the required time. Therefore the total upper limit emission current required of the OR driver is:

$$\bar{I}'_{EO} = \bar{I}_{EO} + \frac{C_O\ \Delta V}{\Delta t} \tag{5-12}$$

EXAMPLE. Design the structure of Fig. 5-14 to swing the output between -5 and 0 volts with 1 µsec rise and fall times, assuming $\pm\ 5\%$ voltage and resistance tolerances, and diodes of 0.1 ma back-leakage at a reverse voltage of 5 volts. Assume $C_A = C_O = 100$ mmf.
From Eq. [5-10]:

$$\frac{C_A\ V_L}{\Delta t} = \frac{(100 \times 10^{-12})\ (5)}{1 \times 10^{-6}} = 0.0005 = \frac{.95\ (25)}{1.05\ R_A}$$

from which

$$R_A = 45,300 \text{ ohms}$$

And from Eq. [5-2]:

$$\bar{I}_i = \frac{(1.05)\ (25) + 5}{.95\ (45.3)} + 2\ (0.1) = 0.73 + 0.2 = 0.93 \text{ ma}$$

From Eq. [5-11]:

$$\underline{I_{AO}} = 0.00093 + \frac{(200 \times 10^{-12})\ (5)}{1 \times 10^{-6}} = 0.93 + 1.00 = 1.93 \text{ ma}$$

and from Eq. [5-4]:

$$R_O = \frac{.95\ (25)\ -5}{1.05\ (.00193)} = 10,400 \text{ ohms}$$

From Eq. [5-5]:

$$\bar{I}_{EO} = \frac{1.05\ (25)}{(.95)\ (10.4)} + 3\ (0.1) = 2.65 + 0.3 = 2.95 \text{ ma}$$

and from Eq. [5-12]:

$$\bar{I}'_{EO} = 0.00295 + \frac{100 \times 10^{-12} \times 5}{1 \times 10^{-6}} = 2.95 + 0.5 = 3.46 \text{ ma}$$

Here again, it takes a driver of 3.46 ma of emission current capability at the OR gate input to produce 0.5 ma of emission current capability at the AND gate output, under the above assumptions.

In a manner similar to that in the above examples, any array may be strung together. The array need not be a single chain. At any gate output node any number of outputs may be driven in parallel if the driving capability is available. The procedure is to start at the output and calculate backwards towards the original driving point.

This method of thinking in terms of current absorption capabilities (current sinks), and current emission capabilities (current sources), is quite useful, as in most of the digital-type circuits discussed in this book, the generators are more

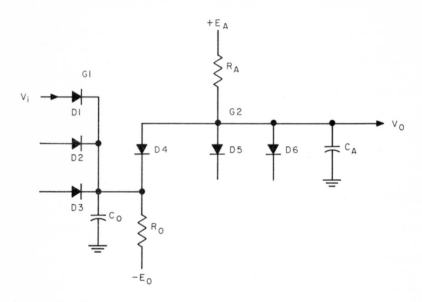

Fig. 5-14.   A positive OR gate driving a positive AND gate.

nearly constant-current, than constant-voltage generators. The loads are frequently of very low impedance compared to generator impedance, in which case the load current is relatively independent of the load impedance. Or the loads are large resistors connected to large and known voltages, in which case load currents are accurately known, and current sources can be designed so that the minimum current available from a source is always adequate to supply the maximum demanded by a load or current sink.

5.6. Negative AND Gate.   By its logic, the structure of Fig. 5-10 is an AND gate for negative-going signals. When discussing it as an OR gate for positive signals, it was seen that any one of the inputs being positive (at ground level), forced the output up to ground level. Therefore it requires all its inputs to be simultaneously negative (at the $-V_L$ level), for the output to be at $-V_L$. Thus, if the true signal being sought is a positive signal (ground level), the structure is an OR gate; if the true signal is a negative one, $(-V_L$ level), then the structure is an AND gate. The design calculations are the same whether it is an AND or an OR gate. When it is a negative AND gate, a positive signal (ground level), at the input, is spoken of as inhibiting the gate. When it is a positive OR gate a positive level (ground), is referred to as enabling the gate.

5.7. Negative OR Gate. Similarly, by its logic, the structure of Fig. 5-6 is an OR gate for negative-going signals. Since it requires all its inputs to be simultaneously at ground for the output to be at ground, an input level of $-V_L$ at V_1, V_2 or V_3, will force the output to $-V_L$. Therefore, if the true signal being looked for is a positive signal (ground level), the structure is an AND gate, and if the true signal is a negative signal ($-V_L$ level), the structure is an OR gate. Again, if it is an OR gate, a $-V_L$ signal at any of its inputs is said to enable it; if it is an AND gate, the same signal is said to inhibit it. The design calculations are again the same whether it is an AND or an OR gate.

5.8. Cascade of Negative Gates. From the preceding discussion it is obvious that the array of Fig. 5-13 described as a positive AND gate driving a positive OR gate is, (if our true signals are negative), a negative OR gate driving a negative AND gate. Similarly, Fig. 5-14 for true negative signals, is a negative AND gate feeding a negative OR gate.

5.9. Choice of Positive or Negative Gates. A logical block diagram describes only the logical interconnections between AND and OR gates. In circuitizing a logical block diagram, whether one uses a positive or negative AND or OR gate in a specific instance, generally depends on which polarity signal is directly available without interposing a phase inverter. In the usual case, only one or the other polarity of input signal is directly available. The choice is then either to use the type of gate corresponding to the polarity of the available signal, or to phase invert the available signal and use the opposite type of gate. Frequently, it may be more desirable to add the phase inverters so as to have only standard gates of one polarity. This has the advantage that a building block can generally then be devised, that consists of a number of AND and OR gates packaged on one plug-in unit. The inputs and outputs of these gates can be brought out to pins on the package, and the same plug-in unit can be used to generate many combinations of AND and OR gating merely by altering the wiring between gate inputs and outputs external to the package. This is not so easily done if both positive and negative polarity gates are used.

Chapter 6

VOLTAGE-SWITCHING DIODE GATE LOGIC WITH TRANSISTOR INVERTING AMPLIFIERS

In the previous chapter it was shown that current attenuation is suffered in transmitting signals through diode gates. If information is propagated through a long chain of gates, the power or current available at each level of gating decreases progressively from the start of the chain towards its end. Eventually, a point is reached at which a gate output cannot do the work required of it — setting flip-flops, driving other gates, or even driving the unavoidable stray capacitive loads on the signal buses with the required speed. In such instances, a power amplifier must be interposed.

This chapter discusses and performs worst-case design calculations on a number of different possible methods, using such cascades of diode gates and voltage-switched transistor amplifiers. P-N-P transistors are used, as most fast-response transistors are of this type.

6.1. Logical Building Blocks. As already noted, normal digital computer logic calls for series cascades of AND and OR gates. The end of a cascade usually drives one or more flip-flops. Frequently, at junctions between AND and OR gates, it may be necessary to drive more than one logical element — for example, the situation shown in Fig. 6-1.*

This array could be done with diodes alone. Starting at the various output points and using the idea of current sources and current sinks as in Chapter 5, the magnitudes of the AND and OR gate resistors could be calculated at intermediate points. This would finally provide the current emission or absorption requirement of the input drivers. There are however, two main objections to this procedure: (1) the current requirements indicated for the input drivers would probably be prohibitively large; (2) each such piece of logic would re-

---

* Explanation of the symbols is given in Chapter 1.

quire its own laborious calculations, which would have to be done anew if changes or additions were made.

What would be preferable, would be a set of building blocks with known input-drive requirements and output load-driving capability. These building blocks could then be interconnected in any desired array, observing a set of previously calculated rules for maximum load on any building block output, and

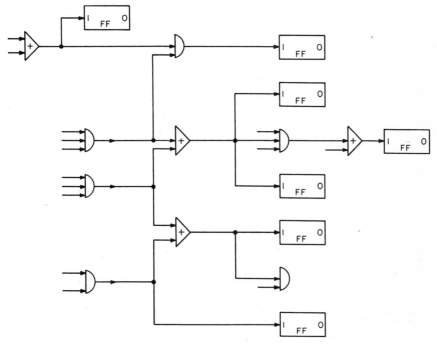

Fig. 6-1.   A possible interconnection of AND gates, OR gates and flip-flops.

required drive for any block input. Logical changes or additions could be easily made by altering the wiring between the standard building blocks.

Obviously for maximum flexibility, the building block should perform a single logical operation and provide power gain. Thus a building block might be a diode OR gate or a diode AND gate, and amplifier. This would permit a number of logical operations at *each level* of logic as in Fig. 6-1, where *each* logical AND or OR gate drives other logical elements. Such a system where power gain is provided at the output of each logical AND or OR gate, is called single-level gating. It is flexible, and has few redundant components, but it is expensive in amplifiers.

Frequently, computer logic will call for multiple operations to be performed only after two levels of logic — usually after a cascade of an AND and an OR gate — such as the array shown in Fig. 6-2.

If the logic calls for such arrays frequently — and usually the logical design can be made to do so — then the best building block is a diode AND gate driving a diode OR gate, driving a power amplifier. Such an arrangement is often referred to as double-level gating. If this is the basic building block, and it is to

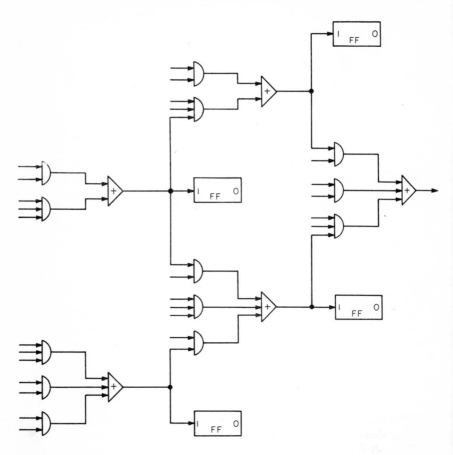

Fig. 6-2. Logic in which a multiplicity of output drives is only required after two levels of gating.

be used where an operation is to be performed at the output of an AND gate, it is employed as a standard AND-OR amplifier cascade, but only one of the input AND gates is used.

In designing with building blocks, the basic building block, or multiples of it, are usually packaged on one plug-in chassis. Thus, a two-level gating building block may be as shown in Fig. 6-3. Only the AND gate inputs and amplifier output are brought out to the chassis output pins. Any array of logical AND and OR gating may then be set up by interconnecting inputs and outputs of such building blocks. It is obvious that the larger, two-level building block is more apt to have redundant components than a single-level gating block. If it contains enough diode gates to perform complex logical operations, and it is universally used throughout a computer, it will naturally have many unused diodes in the simpler logical configurations. The usual type of computer logic will need, in

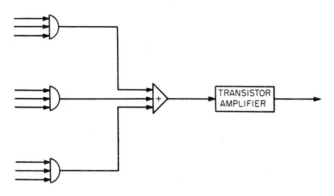

Fig. 6-3.   A basic building block with power gain after two levels of passive gating.

addition, flip-flops, phase-inverting, power-amplifying, and delay-element building blocks.

6.2. Single-Level Gating with Positive Diode AND Gate using Transistor Inverting Amplifier.   Figure 6-4 shows a possible configuration for a single-level positive AND gate building block. Diodes D1, D2, and D3, and resistor R_1, form the positive AND gate that drives the transistor amplifier through the input-coupling network R_2, R_3, and C_1. The diode gate inputs are driven from the collector of transistors similar to T2. The collector circuits of the driving transistors are exactly the same as those of T2. The transistor is operated in the common emitter connection, as a current gain is required to permit gate G1 to drive many other similar gates through the amplifier T2.

When the transistor is cut off, its collector falls toward $-V_2$ but is caught by the diode D_C at the voltage $-V_3$. This is to provide at the gate input, a unique lower-level voltage independent of the number of gates driven by any collector. The transistor input circuit consisting of R_2, C_1, and R_3, are similar to that shown in Fig. 4-22 to achieve good, high-frequency response. The value of R_2 will be set to bottom the lowest gain transistor, but not to saturate too heavily, as this would require too large a reverse drive to get out of saturation. The value of C_1 will be chosen to transmit enough forward and reverse current to the transistor base to achieve the required turn-on and turn-off times. R_3 will be chosen to provide a reverse base current of I_{CO} at the highest operating temperature to achieve good d-c turn-off, as discussed in Chapter 3, p. 53. R_1 is the source of reverse base current flowing through C_1 that provides the required turn-off speed.

As an example, calculate the values of the components in Fig. 6-4 for a specified switching speed, and then calculate the pyramiding factor, i.e., the number of gates similar to G1 that an output node such as V_C can drive.

First step is to see how such a building block will be used logically. A positive (ground level) coincidence at all the gate inputs turns the transistor off, and its collector falls to $-V_3$. Thus the building block produces phase inversion with

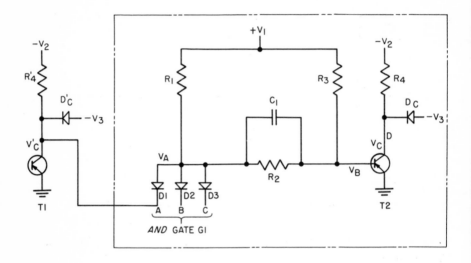

Fig. 6-4. A basic building block consisting of a single-level positive AND gate driving a transistor inverting amplifier.

positive coincidence. If the input signals are designated A, B and C, and the output D, then logically it performs the operation $ABC = \overline{D}$ (for positive true signals). Therefore, if the block is used in a logical chain of AND and OR gates in series, the output of such a block is of the correct polarity for driving an exactly similar block as an OR gate. It has been shown that the structure of R_1 and its input diodes is an AND gate for positive signals, and an OR gate for negative signals. The same building block is then used for AND or OR gating. If the true input signals are positive, then the block produces a logical AND operation; if negative, a logical OR operation.

Assume a need to perform the logical operation $ABC + DEF = G$. (This is shown symbolically and circuitwise in Fig. 6-5.) If the logical cascades are always alternating AND and OR gates, only this one type of building block is required. There may however, be frequent instances of AND — AND combinations, or where for some reason the signal is available, but is of the wrong polarity. Such a case calls for a phase-inverting building block that may be either the same building block used as a single-input AND or OR element, or a different block that simply omits the gate consisting of R_1 and its three input diodes.

Now consider the detailed design of the structure of Fig. 6-4. Assume RCA-

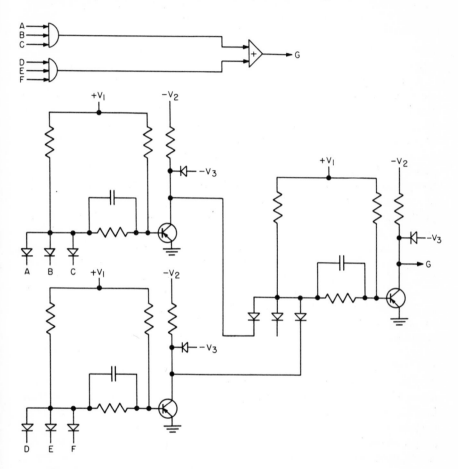

Fig. 6-5. The basic building block of Fig. 6-4 used as a positive AND gate, and a negative OR gate.

type 2N269 transistors that when turned on, with the collectors bottomed, provide nominal collector currents of 10 ma. This current choice is arbitrary, but is close to an optimum value. If much larger currents are switched on, operation is inefficient as β decreases with increasing current (see Fig. 4-8), and more power is dissipated in collector load and gate resistors. At lower currents operation moves into the region where the diode back-leakage currents are an appreciable percentage of total available output currents. Thus, currents in the range of 10 to 20 ma represent the best operating point, and 10 ma is arbitrarily chosen.

When a transistor is turned on, bottom it to beyond the knee of the collector-current curve in order to speak of somewhat unique upper-level voltages of about 0.1 volt below ground. When a transistor is cut off, allow the collector to fall to a voltage well within the maximum collector voltage rating, and relatively close to ground. This is to avoid wasting current in charging stray capacity to large voltages on collector output buses.

A relatively unique d-c turn-on current is also necessary, to indicate how much reverse base current is required to bring it out of saturation. This current is given by the d-c drop across R_2 in Fig. 6-4, and is the voltage difference $(V_A - V_B)$ when transistor T1 is off. The potential V_A is not unique because of the production spread in the forward drops of diodes D'_C and D1, and the variation in the drop across diode D'_C, with current. If diodes such as that shown in Fig. 6-6 (Transitron 1N270), are used, it will be seen that the forward drop at 25°C varies by about 0.2 volt from a forward current of 0.1 to 10 ma. Production spread will account for approximately another 0.1 volt ambiguity in each of D'_C and D1. For a transistor collector current of 10 ma operation will be at a base voltage of approximately 0.26 volt (Fig. 4-5).

From experience a maximum variation of 0.1 volt may be expected in this base voltage. Therefore, the total ambiguity in the d-c transistor turn-on voltage $(V_A - V_B)$ is about 0.5 volt. Choose $(V_A - V_B)$ so that this ambiguity is a relatively small percentage of its nominal value. Then, when $(V_A - V_B)$ is at its maximum value operation does not move too far into the saturation region, and at its minimum value there is still sufficient current to turn on the lowest gain transistor. If $(V_A - V_B) \cong 5$ volts is chosen, then the ambiguity in turn-on voltage due to variation in diode drops and base voltage drops, is only $\pm$ 5%, which can be tolerated. Figures 6-6 and 4-5 show that D'_C and D1, and the transistor base, will absorb close to 1 volt (assuming a maximum of 10 ma through D'_C, and taking a preliminary guess of about 1 ma through D1). This fixes V_3 at -6 volts to give $(V_A - V_B) \cong 5$ volts.

Now fix V_1 and V_2. Chapter 5 showed that above a ratio of supply voltage to gate-swing voltage of approximately 5, there was little gain in gating efficiency. Therefore choose V_1 as $5 \times 6 = 30$ volts. A positive voltage source is needed to supply I_{CO} through R_3 (Chapter 3, p. 53), to the base of the transistor. Since the bottom end of R_3 only moves about 0.25 volt, a positive voltage a good deal lower than $+ 30$ will still supply an adequately constant current through R_3. But to save the expense of an added supply voltage, use V_1 to supply both R_1 and R_3.

The choice of V_2, is dictated by the following considerations. Turning on the transistors to a nominal current of 10 ma as assumed, fixes R_4 and R'_4 as soon as V_2 is fixed. It was shown in Chapter 5 that a driver for a positive AND gate is designed primarily on the basis of its current absorption capability. Consequently, when T1 is cut off, the combination of R'_4, V_2 and the diode D'_C is a sink for current poured into the V'_C node by R_1, R_2, and the back-leakages of D2 and D3. If this sink is to inhibit many AND gates such as G1, as large a sink as possible is desirable. The magnitude of this current sink is fixed by the voltage across R'_4 when T1 is cut off. Obviously, when T1 is cut off, if the collector voltage is permitted to change by a given percentage, the current sink capability of R'_4 will change by the same percentage from the 10 ma that it draws when T1 is on. Therefore the larger the ratio of V_2 to V_3, the greater the chances of having a full 10 ma of absorption current capability with the transistor off.

This of course, means a large value for V_2, and increased d-c dissipation in R'_4. As a reasonable compromise between d-c dissipation and loss of absorption current capability, permit the voltage across R'_4 to change by 20% from the T1-on, to T1-off case. Then, when T1 is off, R'_4 will be current sink (nominally) for 0.8 (10) = 8 ma. This fixes V_2 at $6/0.2 = -30$ volts.

With these voltages fixed, calculate R_1, R_2, R_3, R_4, C_1, and finally the number of gates such as G1 that a transistor may drive, all for a preassigned switching speed. As in Chapter 5, worst-case calculations are performed to make the circuit work when all voltages and resistors are off their nominal values by $\pm$ 5% in the worst direction. Assume a need to switch a transistor from full-on to full-off, or vice versa, in a maximum of 0.5 μsec. (The method of calculation is the same for any selected switching speed.) Exact values will be calculated on the assumption that resistors will be purchased to within 1% of those values, and that aging, humidity and temperature will bring them at worst, to never more than 5% of their nominal value.

In the calculations that follow, as in the previous chapter, a line over a term designates its upper limit value resulting from all component and voltage tolerances being off in the direction that makes the term a maximum. A line under a term designates its lower limit value resulting from all component and voltage tolerances being off in the direction that makes the variable a minimum.

First, choose R_3 (Fig. 6-4). The manufacturer's data sheet gives the maximum value of I_{CO} at 80°C, as 50 μa. Assume a desire to operate at this temperature, and use a factor of 2 for safety to allow for aging and production spread. Then select R_3 so its lower limit current output for V_B at ground, is 0.1 ma. Therefore

$$\underline{I_{R3}} = \frac{[1 - .01 \ t_v] \ V_1}{[1 + .01 \ t_r] \ R_3} \tag{6-1}$$

For 5% resistance and voltage tolerances (t_r and t_v),

$$0.0001 = \frac{(0.95) \ (30)}{(1.05) \ R_3}$$

$$R_3 = 270,000 \text{ ohms}$$

At this point the upper limit value of I_{R3} will be calculated for later use.

$$\bar{I}_{R3} = \frac{[1 + .01 \ t_v] \ V_1}{[1 - .01 \ t_r] \ R_3} \tag{6-2}$$

$$= \frac{(1.05) \ (30)}{(0.95) \ (270)} = 0.12 \ ma$$

Assume that a nominal collector current of 10 ma is to be turned on. This fixes R_4 at

$$R_4 = \frac{30}{0.01} = 3000 \ ohms$$

Then the upper limit collector current will be

$$\bar{I}_{R4}(\text{Transistor on}) = \frac{[1 + .01 \ t_v] \ V_1}{[1 - .01 \ t_r] \ R_4}$$

$$= \frac{(1.05) \ (30)}{(0.95) \ (3)} = 11.1 \ ma$$

The d-c base current through R_2 to turn on the transistor must now be selected. Allow for production spread, aging and general deterioration. Figure 4-5B, which represents the worst transistor of this type, shows that to turn on a collector current of 10 ma requires 0.2 ma of base drive. Double this, using 0.4 ma to give a safety factor of 2 for a nominal collector current of 10 ma. Then, when the collector current is at its upper limit value of 11.1 ma — which according to Fig. 4-5B requires a base drive of about 0.25 ma — a safety factor of 60% still exists. This should be adequate, as R_2 is to be designed so that its lower-limit current is 0.4 ma.

R_2 then, is selected so that in the worst-case a base drive of 0.4 ma is provided. But R_2 must also be a sink for the base current plus the upper-limit current through R_3. Therefore

$$\underline{I_{R2}} = \bar{I}_{R3} + \underline{I_B}$$

$$= 0.12 + 0.40 = 0.52 \ ma$$

The lower limit current $\underline{I_{R2}}$ is obtained when V_3 is at its minimum negative value, the drop across D'_C is a minimum, the drop across D1 is a maximum, the base-to-emitter voltage of T2 is a maximum, and R_2 is at its upper limit.

$$\underline{I_{R2}} = \frac{(\underline{V_A} - \underline{V_B})}{\bar{R}_2}$$

$$= \frac{[1 - .01 \ t_v] \ V_3 + \underline{V_{D'_C}} - \bar{V}_{D1} - \bar{V}_{BE}}{[1 + .01 \ t_r] \ R_2} \tag{6-3}$$

Assume a diode such as in Fig. 6-6. It may be a case where the clamp diode D'_C

is barely conducting as all the current demanded by R'_4 is being supplied by external loads, leaving only enough current — say, 0.1 ma — to be supplied by D'_C. From Fig. 6-6, the forward drop at 0.1 ma is 0.27 volt. An educated guess of about 1.0 ma was taken as the gate current in R_1 and therefore in diode

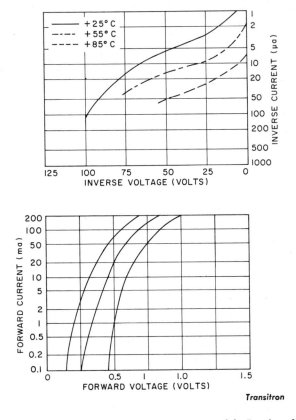

Fig. 6-6. Typical forward and reverse characteristics of the Transitron 1N270.

D1. At this current the forward drop is 0.35 volt, and the base-to-emitter drop is read from Fig. 4-5A as −0.26 volt for 10 ma. Assume ± 0.05 volt variation about this, giving $V_{BE} = 0.31$ volt. Therefore, from Eq. 6-3

$$I_{R2} = \frac{(0.95)\ (6)\ +\ 0.27\ -\ 0.35\ -\ 0.31}{1.05\ R_2} = 0.52 \text{ ma}$$

or

$$R_2 = \frac{5.31}{0.52} = 9800 \text{ ohms}$$

It is now desired to select R_1. When the gate inputs at A, B, and C go up to ground, it is the current available from the combination of R_1 and V_1, and which flows through C_1 during the transient rise at V_A, that supplies the reverse base current needed for fast turn-off. By supplying a forward d-c base current

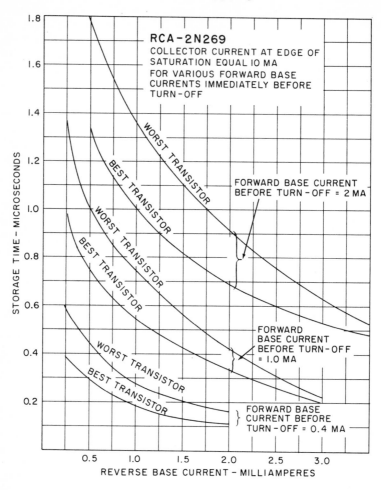

Fig. 6-7. Storage time v. reverse base current: RCA 2N269.

of more than 0.2 ma through R_2, operation enters the saturation region. Consequently, the reverse current available from R_1 must suffice to provide the permitted storage plus turn-off delay, for the tolerance conditions that would make the d-c current through R_2 a maximum. For a total of 0.5 µsec turn-off time, allot 0.25 µsec for storage delay and 0.25 µsec for active-region turn-off delay.

The reverse base drive for 0.25 μsec active-region turn-off delay after saturation ends, can be chosen from Fig. 4-16.

Coming out of saturation in 0.25 μsec would require the calculation of Eq. 4-30. This is cumbersome. In the first place, the inverted β and ω are not given by the manufacturer. Secondly, as there is a wide spread in the measured values of these parameters, the relation would give only approximately correct results. Consequently, rather than measure β_1 and ω_1 and calculate from Eq. 4-30, the reverse current versus storage-time relation can be measured directly. This has been done for a random selection of 25 RCA-type 2N269 transistors, and the result is shown in Fig. 6-7. (The circuit used in this measurement is discussed in the Appendix.) The Figure gives storage time versus reverse base drive for a number of different base currents just prior to the onset of the reverse current pulse. This is done for a collector load and supply voltage that limits the collector current to 10 ma at the edge of saturation. Upper and lower limits that bracket all the sample 25 transistors are shown for each reverse base drive.

To use the curve, Fig. 6-7, it is necessary to know the maximum or upper limit d-c base drive just before the pulse of reverse current, as this will result in maximum storage time. This current occurs when V_3 is at its maximum negative value, the drop across D'_C is a maximum, the drop across D1 is a minimum, the base-to-emitter voltage of the transistor is a minimum, and R_2 is at its lower limit.

Therefore

$$\overline{I}_{R2} = \frac{(\overline{V_A} - V_B)}{\underline{R_2}}$$

$$= \frac{[1 + .01 \ t_v] \ V_3 + \overline{V}_{D'C} - \underline{V}_{D1} - \underline{V}_{BE}}{[1 - .01 \ t_r] \ R_2} \qquad (6\text{-}4)$$

Assume $\overline{V}_{D'C}$ occurs at a forward current of 8 ma. (In cases where only one gate is delivering current to R'_4, the rest of the current demanded comes from diode D'_C.) Then $\overline{V}_{D'C}$ from Fig. 6-6 is 0.45 volt. Take $\underline{V}_{D1}$ as the forward drop at 0.3 ma on the assumption that roughly 1 ma from R_1 divides equally between the three gate diodes. Thus $\underline{V}_{D1}$ is 0.30 volt from Fig. 6-6. And if, as stated above the minimum base-to-emitter voltage V_{BE}, is taken as 0.21 volt ($\pm$ .05 volt tolerance on Fig. 4-5A), we have

$$\overline{I}_{R2} = \frac{(1.05) \ (6) + 0.45 - 0.30 - 0.21}{(0.95) \ (9.8)} = 0.67 \ \text{ma}$$

Some of this current however, is supplied by R_3, and therefore the upper limit base current is given by

$$\overline{I}_B = \overline{I}_{R2} - \underline{I}_{R3} = 0.67 - 0.10 = 0.57 \ \text{ma}.$$

Thus, in guaranteeing in the worst-case a minimum forward d-c base drive of 0.4 ma, it is necessary when turning off, because of component tolerances, to supply a reverse drive sufficient to give the permitted storage time for a forward current just prior to shut off, of 0.57 ma. According to Fig. 6-7, interpolation between the worst-case transistor curves shows that to give 0.25 μsec of storage time for 0.57 ma of forward current just prior to shut off, requires a reverse current of about 1.7 ma.

If this 1.7 ma of reverse current is permitted to flow beyond 0.25 μsec, the turn-off time from the edge of saturation can be read from Fig. 4-16, which shows that only 1.3 ma of reverse drive is necessary for 0.25 μsec of turn-off time. It is better, however, to retain the 1.7 ma of reverse drive as the interpolation in Fig. 6-7 is rather inaccurate.

R_1 can now be selected. It must be chosen to be in the worst-case, a source of average current during the rise-time of 1.7 ma. The average current from R_1 occurs at the moment V_A is midway between its upper and lower levels. Assume −3 volts. Therefore

$$\underline{I_{R1}} \text{ (During rise-time)} = \frac{[1 - .01 \, t_v] \, V_1 + 3}{[1 + .01 \, t_r] \, R_1} = 1.7 \text{ ma} \qquad (6\text{-}5)$$

or

$$\frac{(0.95) \, (30) + 3}{(1.05) \, R_1} = 1.7 \text{ ma}$$

or

$$R_1 = 17{,}600 \text{ ohms}$$

Now select C_1. When the gate G1 is enabled by the last of the three-input diodes going from its lower level to its upper level, the current flowing from R_1 through the input diodes to the current sinks (such as R'_4), now switches through C_1 into the transistor base. In addition, C_1 carries its own circulating discharge current which flows through R_2. At the start of the rise-time this maximum discharge current is $(\overline{V_A - V_B})/R_2$, calculated above as 0.67 ma. At the end of the rise-time, the voltage across R_2 being zero, this discharge current is also zero. Consequently, it is possible to speak of an average circulating discharge current during the rise-time of one half the maximum, or $0.67/2 = 0.34$ ma. This means that during the rise-time the total average current through C_1 is the average current from R_1, plus the average circulating current, or

$$I_{C1} = \underline{I_{R1}} \text{ (During rise-time)} + \tfrac{1}{2} \frac{(\overline{V_A - V_B})}{\underline{R_2}}$$

$$= 1.7 + 0.34 = 2.04 \text{ ma}$$

C_1 needs to be sufficiently large that it does not charge up sooner than the sum of the storage plus decay time, or 0.5 μsec. If it did, delivery of reverse base current would cease before all the charges stored in the base had been cleared out. Therefore

$$C_1 = \frac{I\,\Delta t}{\Delta V} = \frac{\left[\dfrac{I_{R1} + \frac{1}{2}\dfrac{(V_A - V_B)}{R_2}}{}\right]\left[t_s + t_D\right]}{(V_A - V_B)} \tag{6-6}$$

$$= \frac{(2.04 \times 10^{-3})\,(0.5 \times 10^{-6})}{5.31} = 191 \text{ mmf}$$

The lower limit voltage ($V_A - V_B$) in the denominator of Eq. 6-6 has been selected, because this condition requires the largest value of C_1. The lower limit value for I_{R1} in the numerator is chosen, because it is for this value that ($t_s + t_D$) = 0.5 μsec.

The calculated capacitance will also satisfy the 0.5 μsec turn-on time requirement, because from Fig. 4-10, to turn on 10 ma in 0.5 μsec requires a forward base drive of 0.92 ma. On page 127 R_2 and R_3 were calculated to give a minimum d-c forward base drive of 0.4 ma when V_A was at its lower level. Hence the average value of forward base current drawn through R_2 during the fall-time is one half the d-c value, or 0.2 ma. C_2 must then supply the balance of (0.92 − 0.20), or 0.72 ma to achieve 0.5 μsec of turn-on time.

As calculated above, 191 mmf of capacitance requires 2.04 ma to pick up a 6-volt charge in 0.5 μsec. Thus the minimum of 0.72 ma the capacitor must carry during fall-time will not charge it too quickly. The actual current through C_1 during fall-time depends on the sink current capability of the V'_C node when T1 is off. The sink current capability of the node during the fall-time must be enough to drive R_1, R_2, and at least an additional 0.72 ma, through C_1 to the base of T2.

This completes the calculation of all components. Finally it is necessary to decide the number of gates such as G1 that transistor T1 and its associated load resistor R'_4 can drive.

First, calculate the steady-state situation. With T1 off V'_C falls towards $-V_2$ and is caught by diode D'_C at about $-V_3$. Then R'_4 is in the worst-case a sink for a minimum current of

$$I_{R'_4} \text{ (T1 off)} = \frac{(V_2 - V'_C)}{R'_4}$$

$$= \frac{[1 - .01\,t_v]\,V_2 - [1 + .01\,t_v]\,V_3 - V_{D'_C}}{[1 + .01\,t_r]\,R'_4} \tag{6-7}$$

For $V_{D'_C}$, take the forward drop with D'_C barely conducting — say, 0.1 ma, for once D'_C has ceased conducting (a situation spoken of as the clamp having been broken), the impedance looking into V'_C is R'_4, and small current changes result in large voltage changes. As long as D'_C is conducting operation is effectively looking into the forward impedance of a diode under 100 ohms. Then

$$I_{R'_4} \text{ (T1 off)} = \frac{(0.95)\ (30) - (1.05)\ (6) - 0.27}{(1.05)\ (3)}$$

$$= 6.95\ \text{ma}$$

To inhibit a gate such as G1 in the steady-state, the V'_C node must in the worst-case be a sink for a current

$$\overline{I}_{\text{INHIBIT}} = \overline{I}_{R1} + \overline{I}_{R2} + 2\ I_{BL}$$

where $\overline{I}_{R2}$ has been calculated above as 0.67 ma, and I_{BL} is the back-leakage from diodes D2 and D3, which may be at ground. From Fig. 6-6, this is seen to be about 15 μa at 6 volts, at 80°C. If, because of the notoriously large production spread in diode back-leakages, a more conservative figure of 100 μa is taken, then

$$\overline{I}_{\text{INHIBIT}} = \frac{(\overline{V_1 - V_A})}{R_1} + 0.67 + 0.2$$

where

$$\frac{(\overline{V_1 - V_A})}{R_1} = \frac{[1 + .01\ t_v]\ V_1 + [1 + .01\ t_v]\ V_3 + V_{D'C} - V_{D1}}{[1 - .01\ t_r]\ R_1}$$

$$= \frac{(1.05)\ (30) + (1.05)\ (6) + 0.27 - 0.35}{(0.95)\ (17.6)} = 2.21\ \text{ma}$$

Therefore

$$\overline{I}_{\text{INHIBIT}} = 2.21 + 0.67 + 0.2$$

$$= 3.08\ \text{ma}$$

Since R'_4 has a minimum absorption current capability (with V'_C at its lower level), calculated above as 6.95 ma, a transistor output may not be loaded with more than $6.95/3.08 = 2.26$, or two gates such as G1.

Finally, consider what happens at the leading and trailing edges of signals passing through such cascades. During the fall-time at the V'_C node, R'_4 must be a sink for current through R_1, R_2, and C_1, and for back-leakages through D2 and D3. As the behavior during transition from the upper to the lower level is being considered, average currents during the transition are also of interest. Calculate these average currents at the moment when V'_C is at -3 volts — roughly midway in its swing. The minimum value of the average current R'_4 can drain out of the node V_C during the fall-time is

$$I_{OF} = \frac{[1 - .01\ t_v]\ V_2 - 3}{[1 + .01\ t_r]\ R'_4}$$

$$= \frac{(0.95)\ (30) - 3}{(1.05)\ 3} = 8.1\ \text{ma}$$

Then calculate the average current being drawn from R_1 and R_2 during fall-time as the value when V_A is at -3 volts. Hence

$$\overline{I}_{R1} \text{ (Average)} = \frac{[1 + .01 \ t_v] \ V_1 + 3}{[1 - .01 \ t_r] \ R_1}$$

$$= \frac{(1.05) \ (30) + 3}{(0.95) \ (17.6)} = 2.06 \text{ ma}$$

and

$$\overline{I}_{R2} \text{ (Average)} = \frac{3}{[1 - .01 \ t_r] \ R_2}$$

$$= \frac{3}{(0.95) \ (9.8)} = 0.32 \text{ ma}$$

Consequently, for each gate a transistor output drives, there flows into the V'_C node during the fall-time, an upper limit resistive current of

$$\overline{I}_{IFR} = \overline{I}_{R1} \text{ (Average)} + \overline{I}_{R2} \text{ (Average)} + 2 \left(\frac{I_{BL}}{2} \right)$$

$$= 2.06 + 0.32 + 0.1 = 2.48 \text{ ma}$$

During the fall-time, therefore, R'_4 has left for charging the capacitors C1, and any capacitance on the transistor output bus, a minimum current of

$$\underline{I_{CF}} = \underline{I_{OF}} - \overline{I}_{IFR}$$

$$= 8.1 - 2.48 = 5.6 \text{ ma}$$

If the transistor output is loaded with two gates such as G1, the current available for charging the two capacitors C_1, will be $8.1 - 2 \ (2.48) = 3.14$ ma. The output V'_C will then fall from ground to its lower level (assume its lower level has a nominal value of -6 volts), in a time

$$t_F = \frac{C\Delta V}{I} = \frac{(2 \ C_1) \ 6}{I_{CF}}$$

$$= \frac{2 \ (190 \times 10^{-12}) \ (6)}{.0031} = 0.73 \text{ µsec}$$

Assuming an additional 100 mmf of wiring capacitance on the transistor output bus, the capacitance the 3.14 ma must charge is $2 \ C_1 + 100 = 480$ mmf. Calculated as above, the fall-time is 0.92 µsec.

This leads to the odd situation that V_C may turn full-on to its upper level before V'_C has gone all the way down to its lower level, because the 0.92 µsec fall-time calculated above commences almost immediately after the end of the 0.25 µsec storage delay in T1. Consequently, V'_C will come down to its lower level approximately $0.25 + 0.92 = 1.17$ µsec after the start of the turn-off pulse at the base of T1. But it was seen that during the fall-time of V'_C, R'_4 has available to discharge two capacitors such as C_1 and a 100 mmf stray wiring capacitance, a total of 3.14 ma. Therefore there is available for each C_1, a current

$$3.14 \left[\frac{C_1}{2C_1 + 100} \right] = 3.14 \left[\frac{190}{480} \right] = 1.24 \text{ ma}$$

and according to Fig. 4-10, a current of 1.24 ma will turn on 10 ma in 0.35 μsec. Since the base current pulse through C_1 into the base of T2 commences close to

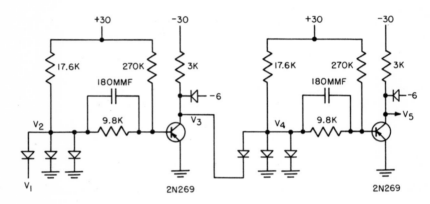

Fig. 6-8. Single-level positive AND gate building blocks on which the waveforms of Fig. 6-9 were measured.

the end of the storage time delay in T1, (which is 0.25 μsec after the start of the turn-off pulse to T1), V_C may come up to ground at $(0.25 + 0.35) = 0.60$ μsec after the start of the turn-off pulse to the base of T1. This compares to the 1.17 μsec it takes for V'_C to come down to its lower level. Capacity at V_C may slow its rise-time, but in general it will reach its upper level before V'_C reaches its lower level.

This relative timing has been discussed in detail because as intended, an 0.5 μsec switching time, has been achieved. Switching time however, is an ambiguous term here. In most logical situations it would be satisfactory for V_C to reach its upper level before V'_C reaches its lower level, but in some instances this could result in logical troubles. Consequently, each case should be individually considered to see whether this may be permitted.

For purposes of illustration, two such blocks as Fig. 6-4 have been connected in series (Fig. 6-8), and measured waveforms thereon are shown in Fig. 6.9. These waveforms were taken with V_3 and V_5 loaded with one additional, exactly similar building block each, to simulate the calculated limit of one block output driving two block inputs. The diodes used were not quite as good as the 2N170. They were type 1N34 diodes, which have a forward voltage drop of 1 volt at 10 ma of forward current. All resistors and voltages were set at their

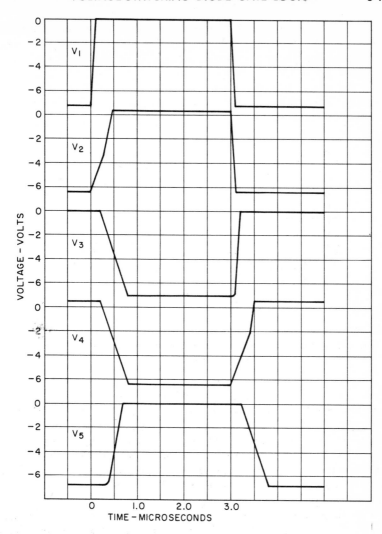

Fig. 6-9. Measured waveforms for circuit of Fig. 6-8, with V_3 and V_5 loaded with one additional building block.

nominal values except the 9800-ohm, which were set 10% low to simulate the condition that would give worst storage effects. The transistor outputs at V_3 and V_5 were loaded with 100 mmf to simulate the assumed wiring capacitance.

The measured rise and fall times in Fig. 6-9 are slightly less than the calculated values that could be expected, as resistors R_1 and R_4 were at their nominal, and not their lower or upper limit values. The waveforms shown are somewhat idealized; the waveshape at the transition times are actually more rounded, but the end points of each rise and fall are exactly as measured.

Circuits of this type with collector clamps such as D'_C, sometimes exhibit a "wait" time before the output voltage starts rising. This wait-time is merely part of the normal collector current rise-time, because if there is no external load on a transistor when it is off, all the current demanded by the load resistor is supplied by the clamp diode [nominally this current is $(30-6)/3 = 8$ ma].

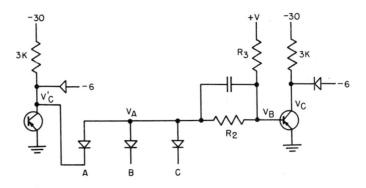

Fig. 6-10. Alternative single-level positive AND gate building block, cheaper in components, but slower than structure of Fig. 6-4.

The collector is then below the clamp voltage by the diode forward drop at 8 ma of forward current, or about 0.45 volt. Then on turn-on, the collector only moves upwards 0.45 volt for the time it takes the transistor to turn on to 8 ma. Thereafter, the "clamp has been broken"; the collector sees a 3000-ohm impedance, and it takes only another 2 ma of collector current to move the collector 6 volts upwards. Therefore, this apparent wait-time at turn-on depends on how heavily the output is loaded. This effect can be seen in the rise-times in trailing and leading edges of V_3 and V_5 of Fig. 6-9.

As an alternative, the reverse current for turn-off may be entirely derived from R_3 (Fig. 6-4), by making it smaller, as shown in Fig. 6-10, and eliminating R_1 altogether. This is a workable scheme for low speed, but it is not practical for switching times of the order of 0.5 µsec. It is instructive to see why.

The design would proceed as follows. Take the same lower limit current — 1.7 ma — through R_3 as was assumed in the previous scheme through R_1 (Fig. 6-4). This reverse current was capable of yielding a sum of storage plus decay time of 0.5 µsec, if the maximum base current just prior to the start of the turn-off pulse was 0.57 ma (Chapter 6, p. 126). Then choose R_2, so that just as previously, the lower-limit d-c base current is 0.4 ma (Chapter 6, p. 122). This lower-limit base current is given by the difference between two large currents. When these large currents go from their tolerance limits in one direction to

the tolerance limits in the other direction, their difference increases by a large percentage.
Thus

$$\underline{I_B} = \underline{I_{R2}} - \overline{I}_{R3}$$

and

$$\overline{I}_B = \overline{I}_{R2} - \underline{I}_{R3}$$

To a close approximation (for I_{R2} and I_{R3}), the difference between an upper limit and a lower limit current is 20%, as the 5% resistance and voltage tolerances are roughly additive. Then

$$\underline{I_{R2}} = \underline{I_B} + \overline{I}_{R3}$$

$$= \underline{I_B} + 1.2 \ \underline{I_{R3}}$$

$$= 0.4 + 1.2 \ (1.7) = 2.44 \ \text{ma}$$

Now

$$\overline{I}_{R2} = 1.2 \ \underline{I_{R2}} = 1.2 \ (2.44) = 2.92 \ \text{ma}$$

This gives

$$\overline{I}_B = \overline{I}_{R2} - \underline{I}_{R3} = 2.92 - (1.7) = 1.22 \ \text{ma}$$

Consequently, in the worst-case the d-c base current just prior to the turn-off pulse, is 1.22 ma, instead of 0.57 ma as in the previous scheme, and according to Fig. 6-7, by interpolation, a reverse base drive of 1.7 ma just after a d-c base current of 1.22 ma, will give approximately 0.6 μsec of storage time rather than the 0.25 μsec previously obtained (interpolating between the worst-case transistors of Fig. 6-7). The situation cannot be improved by going to larger values for I_{R3}, because this would mean a d-c base drive that is a difference between two larger currents than before. A 20% change in these larger currents would result in a d-c current just before turn-off, of even more than 1.22 ma. If however, the greater storage time can be tolerated, the method of Fig. 4-10 is workable. Figure 6-4 does not present this difficulty because it does not derive its forward d-c base current as a small difference between two large currents.

6.3. Double-Level Gating with Positive AND-OR Diode Cascade using Transistor Inverting Amplifier. Figure 6-11 shows a configuration that performs a logical AND and OR operation before an amplifier is interposed. Diodes D1, D2, D3, and resistor R_1, comprise a three-input positive AND gate that drives one input of a three-input positive OR gate. The OR gate G2, made up of diodes D4, D5, D6, and resistor R_2, drives the transistor amplifier through an input coupling network — R_3, R_4 and C_1. Although three inputs are shown for both the AND and OR gates, the circuit can be calculated for any number of inputs.

First, see how the circuit is used logically, then calculate the component values. If the input signals are designated as A, B, C, D, E, and the output F, the circuit performs the logical operation $\overline{F} = D + E + ABC$ (for positive true signals). Thus, it gives a polarity reversal after a cascade of an AND and OR gate. But if

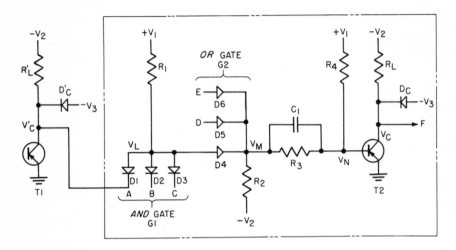

Fig. 6-11. Basic building block consisting of two-level positive AND, positive OR gates, driving transistor inverting amplifier.

the output is to drive another AND gate, since it is now a negative signal, either of two courses are open. First, the AND gate can be designed after T2 as a negative diode AND gate such as that discussed in Chapter 5, (p. 112), or another polarity inverting amplifier can be added after T2 and only the positive diode gates used. As the structures are usually AND-OR-AND-OR, choosing the first way out would lead to the awkward situation that, say, odd numbered AND gates in a chain would be positive AND gates, and even numbered ones would be negative AND gates. Very frequently the correct polarity for a given gate would not be available, and a phase inverter would have to be added. A building block with a second stage phase-inverting amplifier already built in is therefore better; the signal and its complement are always available, and in many cases both are required. This provides two amplifiers per two stages of logic, as in Fig. 6-4, but the scheme is nevertheless more economical.

Assume a need to perform a frequently appearing logical operation such as $ABC + DEF + GHI = J$. Using Fig. 6-11, this would be done as shown in Fig. 6-12 (the gates shown are diode gates). Using Fig. 6-4, it would be done as in Fig. 6-13. Consequently, the method given in Fig. 6-12 requires 12 diodes and two transistor amplifiers. The arrangement of Fig. 6-13 requires 12 diodes and four transistor amplifiers. Also, the arrangement of Fig. 6-12 has both J and $\bar{J}$ available, which is very desirable.

Now calculate the component values for worst-case operation for Fig. 6-11. Use the same supply voltages as in single-level gating, and choose a nominal

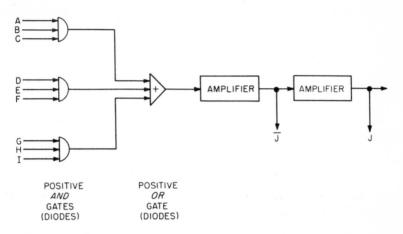

Fig. 6-12. The building block of Fig. 6-11 used to circuitize $ABC + DEF + GHI = J$.

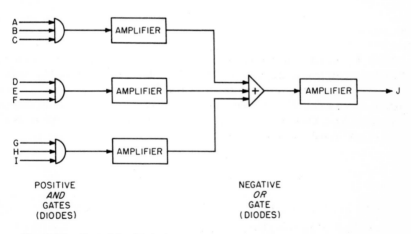

Fig. 6-13. The building block of Fig. 6-4 used to circuitize $ABC + DEF + GHI = J$.

collector "on" current of 10 ma. Since the output at T2 is the result of two logical operations, the T2 amplifier can be satisfactorily operated at a switching speed of 1.0 μsec and still have the same overall speed as in single-level gating, with a switching speed of 0.5 μsec per amplifier. Although in the end there will be a second polarity inverting amplifier after T2, very little will be lost in overall speed, as the second amplifier commences switching before the first one has fully switched.

As before, first select R_4 to give a lower limit current of 0.1 ma for V_N at ground potential:

$$\underline{I_{R4}} = \frac{[1 - .01\ t_v]\ V_1}{[1 + .01\ t_r]\ R_4} = 0.1\ \text{ma}$$

$$= \frac{(0.95)\ (30)}{(1.05)\ R_4} = 0.1\ \text{ma}$$

or

$$R_4 = 270,000\ \text{ohms}$$

Calculate $\overline{I}_{R4}$ for later use:

$$\overline{I}_{R4} = \frac{[1 + .01\ t_v]\ V_1}{[1 - .01\ t_r]\ R_4} = \frac{(1.05)\ (30)}{(0.95)\ (270)} = 0.12\ \text{ma}$$

Again, calculate R_3 to give a lower limit d-c base current of 0.4 ma to guarantee bottoming the lowest gain transistor with an adequate safety margin.

$$I_{R3} = \overline{I}_{R4} + I_B = 0.12 + 0.40 = 0.52\ \text{ma}$$

And the lower limit current through R_3 is given by

$$\underline{I_{R3}} = \frac{(V_M - V_N)}{\overline{R}_3}$$

With T1 cut off, and the junction V'_C slightly below $-V_3$, the junction V_M rests (assuming equal drops in diodes D1 and D4), at the same potential as V'_C. This can be seen from the fact that the design of R_1, R_2 and R_3 for all voltage and resistor tolerances off in the worst direction, is such as to produce at junction V_L a Thevenized voltage more positive than $-V_3$. Therefore, if D1 and D4 have equal forward drops,

$$\underline{I_{R3}} = \frac{[1 - .01\ t_v]\ V_3 + \underline{V_{D'C}} - \overline{V}_N}{[1 + .01\ t_r]\ R_3}$$

Assuming $I_{D'C} = 0.1$ ma and $I_B = 0.40$ ma, Figs. 6-6 and 4-4 give $\underline{V_{D'C}} = 0.27$ volt, and $\overline{V}_N = 0.31$ volt. Then

$$\underline{I_{R3}} = \frac{(0.95)\ (6) + 0.27 - 0.31}{1.05\ R_3} = 0.52\ \text{ma}$$

or

$$R_3 = 10,300\ \text{ohms}$$

It is now necessary to calculate $\overline{I}_{R3}$ in order to design R_2, because R_2 must be a sink (for V_M at -6 volts), for $\bar{I}_{R3}$, plus enough current to put a 6 volt charge on C_1 in a specified time. To determine the capacitor's current its magnitude must first be fixed. This is done as in the single-level method by the reverse current that must pass through it to achieve 1 μsec turn-off (sum of storage, plus active-region decay time), as this required reverse current is larger than the forward current for 1 μsec turn-on. To arrive at the required turn-off current, calculate from $\bar{I}_{R3}$, the maximum forward d-c base current just prior to turn-off, as this drives operation deepest into saturation. Thus

$$\bar{I}_{R3} = \frac{(\overline{V_M - V_N})}{R_3}$$

$$= \frac{[1 + .01\ t_v]\ V_3 + \overline{V}_{D'c} - \underline{V_N}}{[1 - .01\ t_r]\ R_3}$$

$$= \frac{(1.05)\ (6) + 0.45 - 0.21}{(0.95)\ (10.3)} = 0.67\ \text{ma}$$

and

$$\bar{I}_B = \bar{I}_{R3} - \underline{I}_{R4} = 0.67 - 0.10 = 0.57\ \text{ma}$$

Now divide the 1 μsec turn-off time into 0.5 μsec for storage time, and 0.5 μsec for active-region decay time. Then from Fig. 6-7 — by interpolation between the worst transistor curves — it can be seen that for a base current just prior to turn-off of 0.57 ma to achieve 0.5 μsec storage time, a reverse base drive of about 0.6 ma is required.

But from Fig. 4-16, to achieve 0.5 μsec active-region decay time requires 0.65 ma. So a reverse current of 0.60 ma will give a total storage plus decay time of approximately $0.50 + 0.55 = 1.05$ μsec. For safety therefore, increase the reverse base current to 0.70 ma. This should give a storage time of 0.48 μsec from Fig. 6-7, and a decay time of 0.50 μsec according to Fig. 4-16.

During the turn-off process, C_1 carries an average current that is the sum of this 0.70 ma, plus the average capacitor discharge current that circulates between C_1 and R_3. So take as before, the average circulating current as $\frac{1}{2}\ I_{R3}$. Then

$$I_{C1}\ (\text{Total}) = 0.70 + \frac{1}{2}\ I_{R3}$$

$$= 0.70 + \frac{0.67}{2} = 1.04\ \text{ma}$$

And to keep C_1 sufficiently large that on the turn-off process it does not charge up in less than the sum of the storage plus decay time, or 1 μsec:

$$C_1 = \frac{I_{C1}\ (\text{Total})\ \Delta t}{\Delta V}$$

$$= \frac{(1.04 \times 10^{-3})\ (1 \times 10^{-6})}{6} = 173\ \text{mmf}$$

which can be rounded off to 180 mmf.

When V'_C falls from its upper to its lower level during the turn-off process, V_L follows it, but V_M is slower as the capacitor C_1 prevents too fast a fall-time. Then D_4 disconnects, and it is the average current that R_2 is able to supply to C_1 that fixes the fall-time at V_M. It is possible to turn on T2 in the required 1 μsec, even though the fall-time at V_M may be much longer, because Fig. 4-10 shows that an average base current of only 0.56 ma is needed to achieve 1 μsec turn-on time. If, then, R_2 is made a sink for an average base current of 0.56 ma $+ \bar{I}_{R4} = 0.56 + 0.12 = 0.68$ ma, a lower limit current of 0.56 ma would be available for the base, and always turn-on T2 1 μsec after the start of the fall-time at V'_C. The fall-time at V_M however, would be quite long, because during the fall-time an upper limit average current through R_3 can be spoken of as one-half its maximum value, or $\frac{1}{2}(0.67) = 0.34$ ma. Thus, if R_2 were designed to be a sink for an average current of only 0.68 ma, of this, the amount available for C_1 would be $0.68 - 0.34 = 0.34$ ma, which would produce a fall-time at V_M of

$$\frac{C \Delta V}{I} = \frac{(180 \times 10^{-12})\ (6)}{(0.34) \times 10^{-3}} = 3.2 \ \mu sec$$

This may be permissible, for after all, the output at V_C would have completed its switching in 1 μsec. But at high repetition rates trouble may be encountered; the voltage swings at V_M would not be unique. They would be only a fraction of the 6 volts at either of the collectors. Then any attempt to turn off T2 before putting a full 6-volt charge on C_1 at the fall-time, would make it impossible to put enough reverse current through C_1 to completely clean out the stored charges. Therefore it is better to design R_2 to be a sink for at least the 0.68 ma needed to turn on T2 in 1 μsec, plus enough additional current to pull V_M down by 6 volts in the same time.

As just previously shown, 1.04 ma is required to charge 173 mmf — say, 180 mmf — to 6 volts in 1 μsec. Then, as above, to produce 1 μsec fall-time at V_M, choose

$$\underline{I_{R2}} \ (\text{Average during fall-time}) = 1.04 + \frac{1}{2}\ \bar{I}_{R3}$$

$$= 1.04 + \frac{1}{2}\ (0.68) = 1.38 \ \text{ma}$$

and as before, take the average current during fall-time as the current for V_M halfway in its swing:

$$\underline{I_{R2}} \ (\text{Average during fall-time}) = \frac{[1 - .01\ t_v]\ V_2 - 3}{[1 + .01\ t_r]\ R_2} = 1.38 \ \text{ma}$$

$$= \frac{(0.95)\ (30) - 3}{(1.05)\ R_2} = 1.38 \ \text{ma}$$

Or

$$R_2 = 17,500 \ \text{ohms}$$

It is now possible to fix R_1. During the rise time R_1 must be a source of average current for the maximum value of average current demanded by R_2, plus the 0.70 ma previously calculated (p. 137), that must be supplied through C_1 to achieve 1 μsec turn-off time. Thus,

$\underline{I_{R1}}$ (Average during rise-time) $= \bar{I}_{R2}$ (Average during rise-time) $+ 0.70$

$$= \frac{[1 + .01\ t_v]\ V_2 - 3}{[1 - .01\ t_r]\ R_2} + 0.70 \text{ ma}$$

$$= \frac{(1.05)\ (30) - 3}{(0.95)\ (17.5)} + 0.70 \text{ ma} = 2.41 \text{ ma}$$

And again take the average current available from R_1 during the rise-time as that available with V_L midway in its swing. Then

$$\underline{I_{R1}} \text{ (Average during rise-time)} = \frac{[1 - .01\ t_v]\ V_1 + 3}{[1 + .01\ t_r]\ R_1} = 2.41 \text{ ma}$$

$$= \frac{(0.95)\ (30) + 3}{1.05\ R_1} = 2.41 \text{ ma}$$

Or

$$R_1 = 12,500 \text{ ohms}$$

Now assume a need to verify the steady-state design of R_1 and R_2. That is, for V_L at ground potential, the lower limit current available from R_1 must be at least equal to the upper limit current demanded by R_2, plus two back-leakage currents demanded by D5 and D6. (The input at D and E may be at the lower level.) Then,

$$\underline{I_{R1}} \text{ (V_L at ground)} = \frac{[1 - .01\ t_v]\ V_1}{[1 + .01\ t_r]\ R_1}$$

$$= \frac{(0.95)\ (30)}{(1.05)\ (12.5)} = 2.16 \text{ ma}$$

and

$$\bar{I}_{R2} \text{ (V_L at ground)} = \frac{[1 + .01\ t_v]\ V_2}{[1 - .01\ t_r]\ R_2}$$

$$= \frac{(1.05)\ (30)}{(0.95)\ (17.5)} = 1.89 \text{ ma}$$

For 0.1 ma back-leakage in D5 and D6, the total upper limit current flowing out of the V_M node is 2.09 ma, which, being less than the 2.16 ma R_1 pours into the node, makes the design satisfactory in the steady-state, too.

Finally, calculate the number of gates a transistor output can drive. First, the d-c drive capability is fixed by the minimum absorption current capability of R'_L with the transistor off. This was calculated (p. 128) as 6.95 ma. The upper limit current the node V'_C must absorb to inhibit a single gate is

$$\bar{I}_{\text{INHIBIT}} = \bar{I}_{R1} + 3 \, I_{BL}$$

where $3 \, I_{BL}$ is the back-leakage from the diodes D2, D3 and D4, because the condition may exist where B, C and D or E are at the upper level. Now

$$\bar{I}_{R1} = \frac{[V_1 - V_L]}{R_1}$$

$$= \frac{[1 + .01 \, t_v] \, V_1 + [1 + .01 \, t_v] \, V_3 + V_{D'C} - V_{D1}}{[1 - .01 \, t_r] \, R_1}$$

$$= \frac{(1.05) \ (30) + (1.05) \ (6) + 0.27 - 0.35}{(0.95) \ (12.5)} = 3.12 \text{ ma}$$

For 0.1 ma diode back-leakage,

$$\bar{I}_{\text{INHIBIT}} = 3.12 + 0.3 = 3.42 \text{ ma}$$

Then the number of gates a transistor output can drive in the steady-state is $6.95/3.42 = 2.02$ ma, or two gates.

The fall-time at a transistor output is given by the average absorption current capability of R'_L during the fall-time. This has been calculated (p. 128), as 8.1 ma. The maximum value of average current a single gate pours into the node V'_C during fall-time, is calculated as on page 129:

$$\bar{I}_G \ (\text{Average during fall-time}) = \frac{[1 + .01 \, t_v] \, V_1 + 3}{[1 - .01 \, t_r] \, R_1} + \frac{1}{2} \, [3 \, I_{BL}]$$

$$= \frac{(1.05) \ (30) + 3}{(0.95) \ (12.5)} + \frac{0.3}{2} = 3.05 \text{ ma}$$

Therefore, if a transistor output drives two gates, there is available for driving capacitance on the transistor output bus, a current of 8.1 ma $- 2 \ (3.05) = 2$ ma. For 100 mmf capacity on the output bias, this will give a fall-time of

$$\Delta t = \frac{C \, \Delta V}{I} = \frac{(100 \times 10^{-12}) \ (6)}{2 \times 10^{-3}} = 0.3 \text{ μsec}$$

But the unloaded active-region decay time was calculated to be 0.5 μsec. To a first approximation the above calculated 0.3 μsec should be expected to add to this 0.5 μsec as the square root of the sum of the squares, or to give a total decay time (excluding storage) of approximately 0.58 μsec.

It was initially decided, however, to follow T2 with a phase-inverting amplifier so as to require only positive diode gates. Consider then, whether it is possible to load T2 with two gates, similar to the gate G1, and also in addition a phase-inverting amplifier. The amplifier will be the same as that in Fig. 6-11, and will consist of R_3, R_4, C_1, R_L, D_C and T2. The effect of this amplifier will be to add a d-c current of $\bar{I}_{R3}$ to be absorbed by R_L when T2 is cut off. On the fall-time at V_C, additional current will also be needed from R_L to charge up the input capacitor C_1, of the new amplifier.

As shown just previously, each gate supplies to the collector node of an off transistor a d-c current of 3.42 ma. Consequently, there is left for R_3 of the phase-inverting amplifier, a current $6.95 - 2(3.42) = 0.11$ ma. And since $\bar{I}_{R3}$ is 0.67 ma, even considering only d-c effects, this stage cannot be added and have the circuit work under the assumed tolerances. Reducing R_L by 10%, however, will provide another 0.7 ma of current. Sufficient margin has been built into the

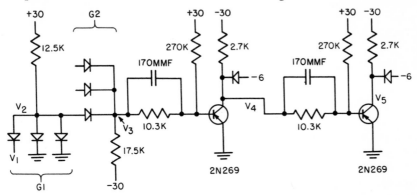

Fig. 6-14. Two-level, positive AND, positive OR gate building block on which waveforms of Fig. 6-15 were measured.

transistor input circuit, that it need not be redesigned for the lowered collector load; it is merely operated with a slightly reduced margin of safety.

The fall-time at T2 will be somewhat slowed up. It was calculated (p. 128), that the average current available from R_L during fall-time is 8.1 ma. If R_L were reduced by 10%, there would be available 8.9 ma. As it has been shown that the minimum value of the average current flowing into a collector node during fall-time is 3.05 ma, if two gates and an additional amplifier are driven, there is available for driving capacitance (stray wiring capacitance, plus C_1 of our phase inverter), a current

$$I_C = 8.9 - 2(3.05) - \tfrac{1}{2} I_{R3} = 8.9 - 6.1 - 0.34 = 2.46 \text{ ma}$$

Then, assuming 100 mmf of stray wiring capacitance, and $C_1 = 170$ mmf, our capacitive charge time should be

$$\Delta t = \frac{C \,\Delta V}{I} = \frac{(270 \times 10^{-12})\,(6)}{2.46 \times 10^{-3}} = 0.66 \text{ μsec}$$

And assuming as before, that this adds to the 0.5 μsec of active-region decay time as the square root of the sum of the squares, there should be a fall-time of about 0.83 μsec.

Measurements have been made on such a building block. The exact circuit is shown in Fig. 6-14, and waveforms are shown in Fig. 6-15. The waveforms

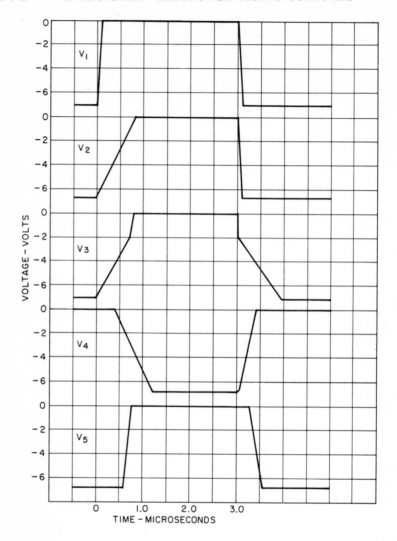

Fig. 6-15. Measured waveforms for circuit of Fig. 6-14, with V_4 and V_5 each loaded with two AND gates such as G1 and 100 mmf.

are somewhat idealized. Leading and trailing edges are not quite as linear as shown, but the beginning and end points of the transitions are exactly as illustrated. The waveforms shown, are taken with both V_4 and V_5 each loaded with two positive diode gates such as that at the input to the building block and with 100 mmf to simulate output wiring capacitance. The 10,300 ohms in the base of T1 was actually reduced to give a d-c base current with T1 on, of 0.57 ma, to simulate the condition calculated (p. 137), that would give

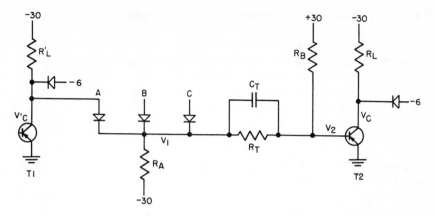

Fig. 6-16. Building block consisting of single-level negative AND gate, with transistor inverting amplifier.

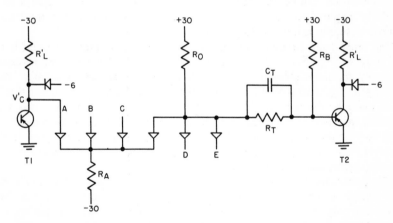

Fig. 6-17. Building block consisting of two-level, negative AND, negative OR gate, driving transistor inverting amplifier.

maximum storage effects in T1. The diodes used were again of the 1N34 type that have higher forward voltage drops, than the 1N270. The waveforms in Fig. 6-15 are seen to agree satisfactorily with the calculated values.

A circuit such as Fig. 6-14 can be used at repetition rates close to 250 kc, but care must be observed, as the progressive narrowing of a pulse in passing through a number of such chains in series (compare the width of the waveforms V_1 and V_5 in Fig. 6-15), does not eventually result in a pulse width of less than 1 μsec.

6.4. Single- and Double-Level Gating with Negative Diode AND Gates at Transistor Outputs. Sections 6-2 and 6-3 employed positive diode AND gates at transistor outputs. Negative AND gates could equally well have been used in this position. This is shown for single- and double-level gating in Figs. 6-16 and 6-17.

Design procedure here is much the same as in Secs. 6-2 and 6-3. Start at the base of the output transistor with assumed collector load currents and turn-on and turn-off speeds, and calculate backwards. The major point of difference is that R_L or R'_L now take only a small fraction of the transistor "on" current. Most of the transistor "on" current is supplied to the negative AND gate resistors to inhibit the AND gates. The current into R_L and R'_L serves only to discharge stray wiring capacity on a transistor output bus at signal fall times. The current in R_A cannot be depended upon to help achieve the required fall-time as it is designed to be a sink for current through (Fig. 6-17), R_O, R_T, C_T, and back-leakage through the diodes at D and E. And if a transistor, say T1, drives more than one gate, all but one of the gates that it drives may be inhibited by some of the inputs at say, B or C, being up at ground.

Therefore, for the one gate that is to be enabled, a sink current is needed to draw current out of the node, say V'_C, to achieve the required fall-time. Although this sink current can be obtained from R_A by making it somewhat smaller than would be required to drive its loads in the forward direction, it is more convenient to supply it through R_L or R'_L.

One other point of difference between the circuits of Figs. 6-16 and 6-17, and those of Figs. 6-4, 6-11, is that in Figs. 6-16 and 6-17 it may be necessary to supply an appreciable d-c level shift at the base of an "off" transistor. Particularly in Fig. 6-16 with T1 on, the potential at V'_C may be -0.1, but that at V_1 is lower by the forward drop of a diode that may be as much as 0.4 volt. R_B must therefore be designed to supply a current of 0.1 ma as before, for reverse current that will flow into the base, plus a current V_1/R_T to provide the d-c level shift. For R_T of approximately 10,000 ohms, as in the previous circuit, this requires an additional $0.5/10 = 50$ μa from R_B.

6.5. Conclusions. It has been shown that with a transistor of $f\alpha_{co}$ of 4 mc, such voltage-switching logical chains give a pyramiding factor of only two (one output can only drive two inputs), for a switching speed of 0.5 μsec per level of logic. This pyramiding factor of two is very awkward, and in most cases in a large-scale computer would be too expensive and cumbersome. The obvious alternatives are to use a transistor with higher $f\alpha_{co}$, or a better type of gating structure. Although in subsequent chapters more efficient structures will be examined, the detailed analysis presented here is useful as a basis to the analysis of other structures, and to computer-switching circuits in general. To calculate the switching speed and pyramiding factor obtainable with higher frequency transistors using the structures of this chapter, collector current curves such as those in Fig. 4-2, base-current curves, (Fig. 4-4), turn-on and turn-off speed curves (Figs. 4-10 and 4-16), and storage-time curves such as in Fig. 6-7, are necessary.

Chapter 7

CURRENT-SWITCHING DIODE GATE LOGIC WITH TRANSISTOR INVERTING AMPLIFIERS

In Chapter 6, diode gates were designed with relatively large output voltage swings that drove transistor amplifiers through current limiting resistors. But a transistor can be switched from full "off" to full "on" by base voltage swings of a few tenths of a volt. Between the extremes of this voltage swing, the base input impedance changes from a very high to a very low value. Therefore, it should be possible to design the usual type of constant current diode gating circuits, in which a constant d-c current is switched in or out of the base of a transistor, by permitting the gate output voltage to move only a few tenths of a volt across this region where the base input impedance changes from its very high to very low value.

This chapter shows a number of possible configurations of such current switching gates, and performs worst-case calculations on the most likely.

7.1. Evolution of Current-Switching Gates. Consider the circuit of Fig. 7-1. Here, V_1 is chosen large compared to 0.3 volt, the base-to-emitter voltage of an "on" transistor. The resistor R_1 is chosen so that the base current ($V_1 - V_B)/R_1$ is large enough to bottom the collector of the lowest gain transistor for a specified collector load current. Then if the potential V_A is slightly more negative than the most negative potential V_B may assume (according to Fig. 4-5A, approximately 0.30 volt for a collector load current of 10 ma), the diode D1 disconnects, R_1 draws all its current from the transistor base, and the transistor is switched full on.

Now assume V_A is raised to a potential positive with respect to ground by an amount equal to the forward drop of the diode D1 at a current V_1/R_1 (approximately 0.30 volt). Then the open circuit potential at V_B (with the transistor out of the circuit), is zero, and if the transistor is put back into the circuit, R_1 draws all its current from the generator at V_A, the transistor base current is zero, and the transistor is shut off. Thus, potential swings at V_A from -0.30 to $+0.30$ volt have switched the transistor from full on to full off. On the negative excursion of the input it does not matter too much how far negative V_A goes, so long as D1 disconnects. If V_A is permitted to go more negative than the disconnect point for D1, and if there is a finite rise-time at the positive excur-

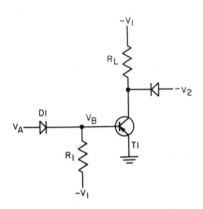

Fig. 7-1. Basic current-switching circuit. By small voltage changes at V_A, R_1 can be forced to derive its current entirely from either V_A or the base of T1.

sion, we merely suffer an additional turn-off delay equal to the rise-time from the most negative potential of V_A, to the disconnect point of D1.

Consider the nature of the driver at V_A. Needed here is a constant current generator capable of supplying a current V_1/R_1, and which can be moved in potential between the limits -0.30 to $+0.30$ volt. Note the circuit of Fig. 7-2.

V_3 is chosen large compared to the voltage excursions at V_A (-0.30 to $+0.30$ volt) so that the combination of V_3 and R_3 can be spoken of as a "constant current" generator. Select R_3 so that its lower limit current is equal to the upper limit current of R_1. Then if switching is performed with a driver at V_D, the lowermost potential at V_D must be sufficiently low to permit D1 to disconnect. If D1 does disconnect, all the current available from R_3 is switched into the driver at V_D. Consequently V_D must be permitted to go below -0.30 volt by the maximum forward drop across D3 at a current of approximately V_3/R_3.

The driver at V_D, at its lower level then, must be a sink for the upper limit current from R_3, and need only go as far negative as approximately -0.60 volt (assuming an approximate 0.30 volt drop across D3). The upper level potential at V_D must cut the transistor off, by forcing the open circuit potential at V_B to rise to ground, or to a slightly positive potential.

Consider driving V_D from the collector of a transistor. If this driving transistor when turned full on is permitted to saturate, its potential may still be as negative at -0.1 to -0.2 volt (Fig. 4-3). Then, because at the upper level most of the current from R_3 flows through D1, the voltage rise through D3 is less than the drop through D1. This presents a level shift problem. If V_D on its upper-level is made no more positive than -0.1 to -0.2 volt, in order to switch T1 off, somewhere in the chain between the cathode of D3 and that of D1, a positive level shift of approximately $+0.5$ volt must be introduced.

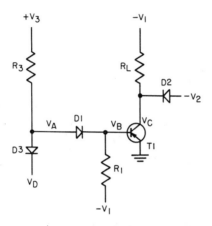

Fig. 7-2. Current switching through two levels of diodes. By small voltage changes at V_D, R_1 can be forced to derive its current entirely from R_3, or from the base of the transistor.

Before examining this level shift problem however, consider how the structure of Fig. 7-2 may be used to perform logical operations in addition to giving power gain.

The combination of R_3 and D3 comprise a single input, positive AND gate, driving D1 and R_1 as a single input positive OR gate. Thus logical operations can be performed with this structure by adding more diodes at V_A and V_B. If this is done and the input driven from a transistor such as T1, we have the structure of Fig. 7-3. This is a double-level gating structure performing the logical operations of $\overline{F} = ABC + D + E$ (for positive true signals). It is the exact logical equivalent of Fig. 6-11. In the discussion on this figure it was stated that it would be convenient in most cases to come out of a building block with the same polarity of input signal as obtained on entering, to avoid the problem of mixing positive and negative gates. Therefore, if the structure of Fig. 7-3, is used, a polarity-reversing amplifier must be added after T2 as was done in Chapter 6.

Then, aside from the problem of level shift mentioned above, if speed were not a factor, the structure of Fig. 7-3 would make a very efficient gating scheme. The collector-clamping voltage $-V_2$, would only have to be approximately 0.60

volt to allow the OR diode D4 to disconnect. The problem of d-c level shift could easily be taken care of by using silicon diodes for the AND gate, and germanium diodes for the OR gates. From Figs. 5-2 and 5-4 it can be seen that the silicon AND diode will always have a larger voltage rise than the drop in the germanium OR diode; a positive, open-circuit base voltage can always be depended on for the driving transistor at its upper level. The d-c supply voltage at five, or even ten times the collector-voltage swings, would still be very low,

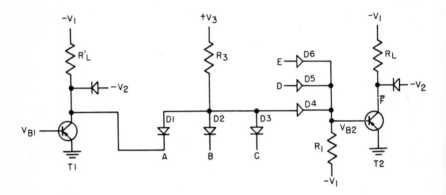

Fig. 7-3. A three-input positive AND gate driving a three-input positive OR gate in a current-switching mode of operation similar to Fig. 7-2.

and the d-c current and power drain would also be low. This would result in a considerably lessened cooling problem. The d-c level of a logical one signal would be approximately $-$ 0.1 volt; that of a zero signal, approximately $-$ 0.6 volt.

The matter of speed complicates this, however, and makes d-c level shift more expensive to solve, as shown below.

If I_{R1} is chosen (Fig. 7-3), just large enough to turn on the lowest gain transistor in the steady-state (unity overdrive), then as shown in Chapter 4 (p. 59), the turn-on time will be three common-emitter time constants. For a transistor such as the RCA 2N269 with $f\alpha_{co}$ of 4 mc, this would be 6 μsec. And if the current available from R_3 were chosen equal to that demanded by R_1, there would be no reverse base drive, and the active-region decay time would also be 6 μsec (Chapter 4, p. 74). Furthermore, if there were a high gain transistor at T2, the base current provided to bottom the lowest gain transistor would drive the higher gain transistor into saturation, and there would also be a storage problem.

If the transistors have a high enough value of $f\alpha_{co}$ so that these turn on, and storage and decay times can be tolerated, this is a satisfactory method. But transistors with higher $f\alpha_{co}$ are more expensive, and in general have a lower maximum current rating. With some complication in circuitry and therefore added expense, Fig. 7-3 can be made to work at relatively high speed with transistors of $f\alpha_{co}$ of only 4 mc. The additional expense of this procedure how-ever, must be weighed against the cost of the relatively simple circuit of Fig. 7-3 with expensive higher frequency transistors.

To compare these two approaches it is necessary to consider just what is in-volved to achieve fast response from the method of Fig. 7-3, with relatively low-frequency transistors. If I_{R1} is just enough to bottom the lowest gain transistor (with some allowances for deterioration of β), I_{R3} can still be chosen larger than I_{R1} (for $V_{B2} = 0$). Consequently, for the lowest gain transistor there will still be a turn-on time of 3 common-emitter time constants, but the excess of current, $I_{R3} - I_{R1}$, is then available as reverse base drive. There would be no storage time for the lowest gain transistor, and this reverse drive would decrease the active-region decay time. For the higher gain transistors (which would be driven into saturation by I_{R1}), this reverse drive would decrease both storage and decay time, but there would still be a fairly large storage time because of the worst-case design requirements. A lower limit current would have to be provided through R_1 for an aged, initially low gain transistor, sufficient to bot-tom it. Then for new, higher gain transistors, with R_1 and V_1 tolerances off in that direction that will increase the base current, operation would be very heavily in saturation just prior to turn-off.

Similar trouble in the circuits of the last chapter showed that the reverse drive through the input capacitors had to be very large (a factor of 4 or so), compared to the d-c turn-on current. But the circuits discussed in Chapter 6 had the advantage that the input capacitor provided a low-impedance path for reverse base current to speed up turn-off time, and also provided a path for an initially larger base turn-on current than was permitted by the limiting resistor at the input. The turn-on time was therefore decreased, as well as the turn-off time. In the circuits of the previous chapter, however, the turn-off current only had to overcome storage effects due to the upper limit d-c base drive current. The a-c overdrive current that decreased turn-on time had decayed to zero by the time it was desired to turn off the transistor.

An attempt can be made to speed up turn-on time in the circuit of Fig. 7-3 by increasing the current demanded by R_1. The same reverse drive can be main-tained at turn-off by increasing the current in R_3 so that $I_{R3} - I_{R1}$ gives the same reverse drive as before. Now however, this is not enough, for the in-creased base drive that gave fast turn-on is still present just prior to turn-off, whereas considerably more reverse base drive is actually needed to eliminate the worsened storage effects.

Neglecting for the moment, resistance and voltage tolerances, make a rough estimate of the current required. Assume a need to switch 10 ma on and off in 0.5 μsec (circuit of Fig. 7-3). Figure 4-10 shows that to turn on 10 ma in 0.5 μsec requires a forward base current of 0.92 ma. So V_1 and R_1 are selected to give this current (V_{B2} will be approximately $-$ 0.34 volts from a curve such as

Fig. 4-4). Then at turn-off, R_3 must be a source of current for this 0.92 ma to be supplied to R_1, plus additional current to be supplied to the base to eliminate the storage effects of 0.92 ma of forward current just before turn-off. For 0.5 μsec turn-off, allow 0.25 μsec for storage, and 0.25 μsec for active-region decay time.

From Fig. 6-7, by interpolation between the worst transistor curves, to achieve 0.25 μsec storage for 0.92 ma of forward current just before turn-off, requires a reverse base drive of roughly 2.8 ma. And from Fig. 4-16 for an active-region decay time of 0.25 μsec, a reverse base drive of 1.27 ma is required. Thus, a reverse drive of 2.8 ma would give total storage plus turn-off time of somewhat under 0.5 μsec. The reverse base drive could probably be reduced to approximately 2.3 ma and attain storage time of about 0.35 μsec, and active-region decay time of 0.15 μsec. This would be a better sharing of the 0.5 μsec available between storage and decay time.

R_3 would therefore have to be a source of current for 0.92 ma to R_1, and 2.3 ma to the base, or a total of 3.2 ma. To inhibit the AND gate, the resistor R'_L would have to be a sink at the $-V_2$ level of approximately 40% more than this, or 4.5 ma, taking resistance and voltage tolerances into account (from -5% to $+5\%$ on each of R_1, V_1, R_3 and V_3).

If R'_L draws a nominal current of 10 ma with T1 on, then 5% voltage tolerance on it — and on V_1 — and even assuming only a 10% voltage change at the collector from the on to the off case ($V_2 \cong -2.0$, $V_1 \cong -20$ volt), will reduce this by 20%, or to 8 ma. The result of all this is that a single output can only drive 8/4.5, or less than 2 inputs, which is an intolerable situation.

The basic cause of this inefficiency is that to speed up turn-on, the base was overdriven in the forward direction. And since all this overdrive was still present at turn-off, it was necessary to go to extremely large reverse base drives to obtain low storage times.

The remedy then, is to obtain fast turn-on with a large initial forward overdrive, and somehow reduce this overdrive to less than the saturation point just before turn-off.

The antisaturation feedback method of Fig. 4-24 gives this effect. It need be only slightly modified to permit a reverse base drive to decrease the active-region decay time (see Fig. 7-4).

In this Figure (7-4), D7, and D'7 are silicon diodes; all others are germanium diodes. Recall how the circuit works. The current in R_1 is chosen to turn on the required collector current in the specified time. Thus, from Fig. 4-10 it requires 0.92 ma of base current to turn on 10 ma of collector current in 0.5 μsec. So the current through R_1 is chosen to be 0.92 ma. At turn-on, as V_A falls sufficiently for D4 to disconnect, all the 0.92 ma that R_1 demands comes from the base of T2. This provides the required 0.5 μsec turn-on speed. During this time, the potential V_R is below ground by the drop voltage across the silicon diode D7 (approximately 0.5 volt), plus the base-to-emitter voltage of T2 (about 0.3 volt). Therefore, V_R is approximately at -0.8 volt.

Until the collector current rises to $(V_1-V_2)/R_L$, the potential at V_C remains below V_2 by the forward drop across diode D9. V_2, as will be shown, will be in the vicinity of -1 to -2 volts. Consequently, until almost all the required 10 ma has been turned on there is a reverse voltage across diode D8 (cathode at -0.8 volt, anode below -1.0), and it is effectively out of the circuit. While it is out of the circuit, all the 0.92 ma demanded by R_1 flows through the base

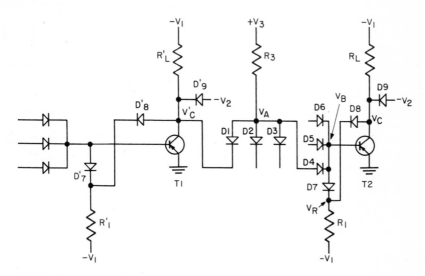

Fig. 7-4. Negative feedback antisaturation scheme applied to basic current-switching circuit of Fig. 7-2.

giving the fast turn-on. When V_C has risen far enough for forward voltage to appear across D8 (this occurs at V_C approximately at -0.8 volt with respect to ground), some of the current required by R_1 comes through D8. In the equilibrium state, the 0.92 ma is partly supplied by the base through D7, and mainly from the collector via D8. The conditions that obtain are

$$\frac{V_C - V_1}{R_L} + I_{D8} = \beta I_{BASE\ T2}$$

and

$$I_{D8} + I_{BASE\ T2} = 0.92 \text{ ma}$$

V_C however, is known to be somewhere between zero and -0.8 volt (say -0.4), and the total collector current must be in the vicinity of 10 ma. At this point, from Fig. 4-5B, β is 50. The above relations for $R_L = 2000$ ohms; $V_1 = -20$ volts, gives $I_{BASE} = 0.20$ ma, and $I_{D8} = 0.72$ ma.

Now $V_C = V_B + V_{D7} - V_{D8}$. Since D7 is a silicon and D8 is a germanium diode, the voltages across these diodes are about 0.5 and 0.3 volt, respectively (the exact voltages are considered in the next section). And from Fig. 4-5A at $I_C = 10$ ma, $V_B = -0.26$ volt. Thus V_C is at -0.46 volt with respect to

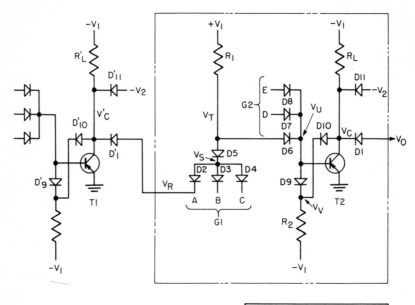

NOTE:
D'I, DI, D2, D3, D4, D5, D9 —
SILICON DIODE; ALL OTHERS
GERMANIUM

Fig. 7-5. Basic building block: A three-input positive AND gate driving a three-input positive OR gate in the current-switching mode of operation; antisaturation negative feedback applied to the transistor inverting amplifier; silicon diode level shifting to permit a building block output to drive a similar block input.

ground, and with V_B at -0.26 volt relative to ground, the collector junction always has a reverse bias and there can be no storage effects. The circuit sits balanced at the edge of saturation with enough of the 0.92 ma flowing into the base to force a small positive voltage across D8.

Then referring back to Fig. 7-4, the reverse current that must be delivered to the base of T2 from R_3 ($= I_{R3} - I_{R1}$), need only be sufficient to give an active-region decay time of 0.5 μsec. From Fig. 4-16, this is 0.65 ma. Since I_{R1} will be set at 0.92 ma, this gives 1.57 ma for I_{R3}. This compares to 3.2 ma before voltage and resistance tolerances were considered (p. 150), without the antisaturation feedback diodes.

This scheme therefore, is efficient, but has introduced a new problem. The upper level voltage at a collector is not now so unique. Since it is fixed by $V_C = V_B + V_{D7} - V_{D8}$, production spread, temperature variation, and general aging of these diode and base forward voltage drops, will vary the d-c level of the collector of an "on" transistor. This d-c level is now in the vicinity of -0.46 volt rather than -0.1 volt, as before. If this upper level voltage at V'_C is to turn off the base of transistor T2, then a large d-c level rise must be provided to make the open-circuit voltage at V_B equal to zero, or somewhat positive. However this rise is produced, it must be adequate for worst-case drops of all the diodes in the chain from the collector of T1 through the AND and OR gates, to the base of T2. Consequently, it is necessary to have fairly good data, or make conservative assumptions about the forward characteristics of these diodes.

Here again, the large forward drops of silicon diodes at low currents can be made use of to provide the required upward d-c level shift. A preliminary calculation shows that it requires the equivalent drop of somewhat more than two silicon diodes to take care of worst-case conditions. The final circuit upon which worse-case calculations are to be performed is shown in the next section.

7.2. Double-Level, Current-Switching, Positive AND-OR Gates with Transistor Inverting Amplifiers. Figure 7-5 shows a configuration that performs two levels of logic, avoids saturation, and solves the difficulty of d-c shift. It is capable of relatively high-frequency operation with low-frequency transistors, and is more efficient than the voltage-switching circuits of the previous chapter. (It was first proposed by the writer.)

This circuit performs the logical operation $ABC + D + E = \overline{F}$ (for positive true signals). The terms F and E are in general the outputs of diode AND gates exactly similar to that which feeds the OR diode D6. Assume that the three AND gates and one OR gate are located close to one another, and to the amplifier input, so that the only place where capacities have to be reckoned with is at the amplifier output. As discussed on p. 147, T2 must be followed with a polarity-reversing amplifier so as to come out with the same polarity as obtained on entry. Both the first- and second-stage amplifiers after the OR gate are designed to switch 10 ma on and off. The input to the second amplifier is much like the input to the AND gate G1. Therefore, when calculating drive capability at each amplifier output, estimate the loading effect of the input to the second amplifier stage as equal that of a single AND gate such as G1.

Calculate the circuit for a total delay of 1.0 μsec from V_R to the output of the second amplifier. This 1.0 μsec may be assumed to be entirely in the turn-on and turn-off times of the two-stage amplifier, because capacitive charging delays are small. The voltage excursions at V_R, V_T, and V_U are approximately 1 to 2 volts, and capacities at V_T and V_U are small because the diode clusters are close together, and close to the amplifier input. For a total of 1 μsec delay, design each stage of the two-stage amplifier to have a turn-on and an active-region decay time (no storage time because of the antisaturation feedback), of 0.5 μsec.

As before, these worst-case design calculations are performed assuming $\pm 5\%$

tolerance on all voltages and resistors. The same symbols are used as heretofore: a line above a term indicates its maximum value due to it, or to the terms on which it depends being off tolerance in such a direction as to maximize it.

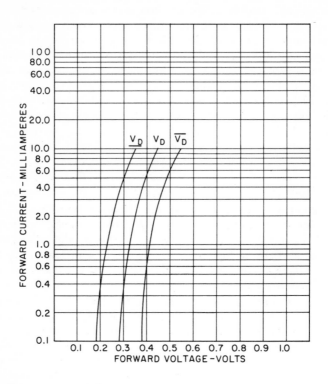

Fig. 7-6. Forward voltage v. forward current: Transitron 1N270, with assumed extreme limits.

Similarly, a line below a term indicates lower limit values due to all tolerances being off in such a direction as to minimize it.

The diodes D1, D2, D3, D4, D5, D9, and D'1 (which occupies a position corresponding to D1), are silicon diodes. All others are germanium. Diode D1 or D'1, and D5, provide the upward d-c level shift mentioned above. Diodes D2, D3, and D4 form the usual positive AND gate, and contribute to the d-c level shift. Diodes D6, D7, and D8 make a positive OR gate. Silicon diode D9, and germanium diode D10, form the antisaturated feedback circuit. The diodes D1 or D'1 will be common to all AND gates driven by a transistor. Consequently, the output of an amplifier will not be the collector itself, but the collector shifted upward in voltage level by the forward drop of a silicon diode.

Since the type of circuit is critical with respect to diode forward voltage drops, care must be taken to design for the worst-case condition of these voltage drops. In the circuit of the previous chapter where voltage swings were approximately 6 volts, the nominal forward voltage drops at specified currents at 25°C as given in the manufacturers data sheets were used. Although some allowance should have been made for production spread, aging and temperature variation, these effects were small compared to 6 volts, and it was safe to ignore them because

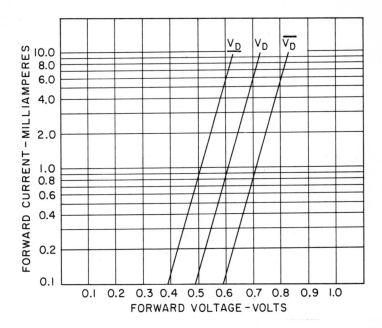

Fig. 7-7. Forward voltage v. forward current: Transitron silicon diode 1N482, with assumed extreme limits.

consideration was given to the worst-case variation of all voltages and resistors. The germanium and silicon diodes used in the circuit of Fig. 7-5 are the IN270 and IN482 (Transitron). The curve marked V_D in Fig. 7-6, is given by the manufacturer as the nominal characteristic at 25°C of the IN270. The curve marked V_D for the IN482 in Fig. 7-7 represents measurements on the average diode of a randomly selected sample. The curves marked $\underline{V_D}$ and $\overline{V_D}$, drawn parallel to the nominal curve and shifted 0.1 volt either side of it, will be taken as the best and worst characteristic at any temperature between 25°C and 55°C. Assume these variations account for production spread, aging and temperature.

These assumed best and worst characteristics are based on the writer's experience with diodes of this type. They are quite conservative, especially in the lower current region where the best and worst curves are usually a good deal closer to the nominal curve than the 0.1 volt postulated. Nevertheless, to ensure adequate safety margin, overdesign and assume the $\pm$ 0.1 volt variation holds throughout the entire current range. In the calculation that follows, forward voltage drops at specified currents will be taken either from $\underline{V_D}$ or $\overline{V}_D$, whichever is the worst-case for the design point in question.

Before starting the calculation, fix $-V_1$ and $+V_1$ at -20, and $+20$ volts, respectively. A preliminary calculation shows that a collector must move about 2 volts for OR diodes such as D6 to disconnect. For good efficiency, take the supply voltage as ten times the collector voltage swing. A factor of 10 can be afforded as the voltage swing is so small. This leaves in Fig. 7-5 only R_1, R_2, R_L, and V_2 and the pyramiding factor, to be calculated.

The first step is to calculate R2. According to Fig. 4-10, to turn on 10 ma in 0.5 μsec requires a base drive of 0.92 ma. Therefore

$$\underline{I_{R2}} = \frac{[V_1 - V_V]}{\overline{R}_2} = \frac{V_1 - \overline{V}_U - \overline{V}_{D9}}{\overline{R}_2} \tag{7-1}$$

Take the worst-case base-to-emitter voltage as the curve of Fig. 4-4 shifted $\pm$ 0.05 volt parallel to itself. Hence at $I_B = 0.92$ ma, $\overline{V}_U = -0.42$ volt. And from the $\overline{V}_D$ curve of Fig. 7-7, $\overline{V}_{D9} = 0.70$ volt. Then

$$0.92 = \frac{[1 - .01\ t_v]\ 20 - 0.42 - 0.70}{[1 + .01\ t_r]\ R_2}$$

$$= \frac{(0.95)\ (20) - 0.42 - 0.70}{(1.05)\ R_2} = \frac{17.88}{1.05\ R_2}$$

or

$$R_2 = 18{,}500 \text{ ohms}$$

It is now necessary to calculate the maximum negative potential at the collector of an "on" transistor, to verify that if a transistor, say T1, is on, and its collector is — because of tolerances in the diode D'9 and D'10 — at this maximum negative potential, the open circuit potential at V_U is still zero, or somewhat positive for worst-case diode drops in the chain from V'_C to V_U. Then, calculating the "on" potential at V_C (which is the same as that at V'_C when T1 is on), gives, when V_T falls far enough for D6 to disconnect, $\overline{V}_C$ (maximum negative at upper level)

$$= \overline{V}_U + \overline{V}_{D9} - \underline{V}_{D10}$$

Here, however, interest is in these forward drops in the equilibrium state, when the 0.92 ma demanded by R_1 has already reapportioned itself as estimated above to approximately 0.20 ma of base current, and 0.72 ma of current through D10, as it is during the equilibrium state that the upper level collector potential is fixed by the diode drops. Thus, $\overline{V}_U$ is read from Fig. 4-4 as -0.31 volt at a base current of 0.20 ma, $\overline{V}_{D9}$ from Fig. 7-7 at a current of 0.20 ma, as $-$ 0.63 volt, and V_{D10} from Fig. 7-6 at a current of 0.72 ma, as 0.22 volt. Then

$\overline{V}_C$ (maximum negative at upper level)

$$= -\ 0.31\ -\ 0.63\ +\ 0.22\ =\ -\ 0.72\ \text{volt}$$

This also, is equal to the maximum negative potential at the upper level at V'_C when T1 is on. When the currents in D2, D5 and D6 are calculated and their forward drops are known it will be seen whether a potential of $-$ 0.72 volt at V'_C is level-shifted upwards sufficiently to force V_U to zero or above, so as to cut off T2.

Fix R_1 so that on turn-off it can supply the upper limit current demanded by R_2, plus two back-leakage currents to D7 and D8, plus enough reverse base current for the base of T2 to achieve an active-region decay time of 0.5 μsec. From Fig. 4-16, this last current is 0.65 ma. Therefore

$$I_{R1} = \overline{I}_{R2} + 2I_{BL} + 0.65 \tag{7-2}$$

and

$$\overline{I}_{R2} = \frac{[\overline{V_1 - V_V}]}{\underline{R_2}} = \frac{[1 + .01\ t_v]\ V_1 - \overline{V}_V}{[1 - .01\ t_r]\ R_2} \tag{7-3}$$

Assume V_U is at ground (it will be shown later that this is nearly so), so that $\overline{V}_V$ is simply the maximum drop across D_9 at 0.92 ma. From Fig. 7-7 this is 0.70 volt. Then

$$\overline{I}_{R2} = \frac{(1.05)\ (20)\ -\ 0.70}{(0.95)\ (18.5)} = 1.17\ \text{ma}$$

Then from Eq. 7-2

$$I_{R1} = 1.17 + 2\ (0.1) + 0.65 = 2.02\ \text{ma}$$

and

$$I_{R1} = \frac{[\overline{V_1 - V_T}]}{\overline{R_1}} = \frac{[1 - .01\ t_v]\ V_1 - \overline{V}_T}{\overline{R_1}} \tag{7-4}$$

where

$$\overline{V}_T = V_U + \overline{V}_{D6}$$

As the turn-off transient is now being considered, take V_U to be midway between ground and the value it has with T2 on, or ½ $(-.31) = -$ 0.16 volt. During the turn-off transient, all the 2.02 ma made available from R_1 flows through D6. According to Fig. 7-6, the value of $\overline{V}_{D6}$ at 2.02 ma is 0.44 volt. Therefore $\overline{V}_T = -$ 0.16 + 0.44 = 0.28 volt. Equation 7-4 then gives

$$I_{R1} = \frac{(0.95)\ (20)\ -\ 0.28}{1.05\ R_1} = 2.02\ \text{ma}$$

or

$$R_1 = \frac{18.7}{(1.05)\ (2.02)} = 8800\ \text{ohms}$$

Now check to see whether an upper level potential at V'_C of $-\ 0.72$ volt has been level shifted by D'1 and D5 sufficiently to keep T2 turned off. The lower limit open circuit potential at V_U is given by

$$V_U = -\ 0.72\ +\ V_{D'1}\ +\ V_{D2}\ +\ V_{D5}\ -\ \overline{V}_{D6} \qquad (7\text{-}5)$$

Equation 7-5 refers to the equilibrium state — after the turn-off transient. In this state, of the 2.02 ma from R_1 there may be as little as 0.65 ma flowing into D5, because of the 2.02 ma required by Eq. 7-2, R_2 may be taking its full upper limit current of 1.17 ma, and the diodes D7 and D8 may be leaking their full 0.1 ma each. Consequently, V_{D5} in Eq. 7-5 must be taken as the value at 0.65 ma, which from Fig. 7-7 is 0.49 volt. Furthermore, this 0.65 ma will be shared almost equally between the three gate diodes D2, D3, and D4. Therefore, in Eq. 7-5 V_{D2} and $V_{D'1}$ must be taken as the values at 0.22 ma which, according to Fig. 7-7 is 0.43 volt. And since D6 may be carrying the full upper limit current to R_2 plus two back-leakage currents to D7 and D8, take $\overline{V}_{D6}$ as the value at 1.37 ma. From Fig. 7-6 this is $-\ 0.42$ volt. Thus Eq. 7-5 gives

$$V_U = -\ 0.72\ +\ 0.43\ +\ 0.43\ +\ 0.49\ -\ 0.42\ =\ +\ 0.21\ \text{volt}$$

Thus sufficient level shift has been built in with the silicon diodes to keep T2 off, even if V'_C at its maximum-negative upper level is at $-\ 0.72$ volt. This could almost have been achieved with the AND gate diodes D2, D3, D4 being germanium rather than silicon diodes, which would have been cheaper. But the increased operating margin provided by the silicon diodes is desirable.

Recall that a reverse current bias of I_{CO} must be supplied to keep the collector leakage current down to I_{CO} (Chapter 3, p. 53). In Chapter 6 (p. 121), a value of I_{CO} of 0.1 ma was assumed. Since in the steady-state I_{R1} exceeds I_{R2} by 0.65 ma in the worst-case, operation is safe in this respect. If the base of T2 starts demanding current at higher temperatures, some of the 0.65 ma normally flowing into D5 commences flowing through D6 into the base of T2, and the potential at V_U changes very little. Another way of looking at this, is that the impedance looking back from V_U is effectively the sum of the nonlinear diode impedances R_{D6}, R_{D5}, R_{D2}, $R_{D'1}$, which are very small. Current can therefore be drawn out of the V_U node without any appreciable voltage change.

It is now necessary to calculate how far the collector of an "off" transistor must be allowed to fall. Recall that it need fall only far enough to allow D6 to disconnect, so that R_2 draws all its current from the base of transistor T2, rather than from R_1. Then starting from the most negative potential at V_U, the potential at V'_C is fixed by the worst-case diode drops in D5, D2 and D'1. From Fig. 4-5A at 10 ma of collector current, V_U is -0.26. As ± 0.05 volt tolerance was assumed on the base voltage curve, V_U (maximum negative) $= -0.31$ volt. This is also the potential at V_T for D6 to disconnect. Then

$$\underline{V'_C} \text{ (minimum negative)} = -0.31 - \overline{V}_{D5} - \overline{V}_{D2} - \overline{V}_{D'1}$$

$$(7\text{-}6)$$

. In Eq. 7-6, take V_{D5} at the upper limit current through R_1, because D6 has been assumed disconnected, which means that all the current drawn by R1 must pass through D5. Therefore

$$\overline{I}_{R1} = \frac{[1 + .01 \; t_v] \; V_1 + V_T}{[1 - .01 \; t_r] \; R_1} \tag{7-7}$$

$$= \frac{(1.05) \; (20) \; + \; 0.3}{(0.95) \; (8.8)} = 2.56 \text{ ma}$$

In Eq. 7-7, V_T has been taken as -0.3 volt as this is the disconnect point for D6. And from Fig. 7-7 $\overline{V}_{D5}$ at 2.56 ma is 0.76 volt. Here, however, it cannot be assumed as it was in the upper level case, that all the current through D5 is shared equally by D2, D3, and D4, because the situation may arise where the drivers at D3 and D4 are at their upper level, and T1 is to inhibit the gate by itself. Then the voltage drop across D2 must be taken at a current of 2.56 ma. And since the diode D1 will be common to all gates such as G1 that T1 drives, $\overline{V}_{D'1}$ must be taken as the drop at the maximum current. As will be seen, it is possible to drive a maximum of three gates such as G1. Then it is necessary to take $\overline{V}_{D'1}$ at 3 (2.56) $= 7.7$ ma. According to Fig. 7-7 $\overline{V}_{D'1} = 0.82$ volt, and therefore Eq. 7-6 gives:

$\underline{V_C}$ (minimum negative)

$$= -0.31 - 0.76 - 0.76 - 0.82 = -2.65 \text{ volts}$$

For D6 to disconnect, fix V_2 so that if it is 5% less than nominal in absolute value, the potential at V'_C with T1 cut off, and D'1 barely conducting (say, 0.1 ma), is -2.65. D'1 barely conducting is the condition for a transistor driving the maximum number of gates so that all the current demanded by R'_L comes mainly from the resistors R_1, rather than from V_2 via the clamp diode D'1. Then

$$0.95 \; V_2 + \underline{V_{D'11}} = 2.65 \text{ volts}$$

From Fig. 7-6 $\underline{V_{D'11}}$ at 0.1 ma is 0.18 volt. Then V_2 is given by

$$V_2 = \frac{2.65 - 0.18}{0.95} = 2.6 \text{ volts}$$

Now fix R_L to draw 10 ma when it and V_1 are at their nominal values, and V_C is at its nominal value with T2 on. The nominal value of V_C for T2 on is given by

$$V_C = - [V_U + V_{D9} - V_{D10}]$$

Here, V_U from Fig. 4-5A is 0.26 volt, at $I_B = 0.2$ ma; V_{D9} from Fig. 7-7 is 0.52 volt at 0.2 ma, and V_{D10} from Fig. 7-6 is 0.32 volt at 0.72 ma. Therefore

$$V_C = - [0.26 + 0.52 - 0.32] = - 0.46 \text{ volt}$$

Then R_L is given by

$$R_L = \frac{20 - 0.46}{0.01} = 1950 \text{ ohms}$$

Finally, calculate the number of gates such as G1 that can be driven. This is given by the lower limit current drawn by $\overline{R}'_L$ (or R_L), with T1 cut off. Thus

$$
\begin{aligned}
\underline{I_{RL}} &= \frac{[V_1 - V'_C]}{R'_L} \\[2mm]
&= \frac{[1 - .01\, t_v]\, V_1 - [1 + .01\, t_v]\, V_2 - \overline{V}_{D'11}}{[1 + .01\, t_r]\, R_L} \qquad (7\text{-}8) \\[2mm]
&= \frac{(0.95)\,(20) - (1.05)\,(2.6) - 0.38}{(1.05)\,(1.95)} = 7.8 \text{ ma}
\end{aligned}
$$

Here, $V_{D'11}$ has been taken at the current of 0.1 ma, (from Fig. 7-6), so that V'_C is thus still barely clamped to V_2. Since the upper limit current from a gate calculated from Eq. 7-7 is 2.56 ma (the AND gate diodes D3 and D4 being silicon, their back-leakage current is negligible, and only current through R_1 need be considered), 7.8/2.56 = 3.05, or, three gates can be driven from a transistor output.

This ends the calculation. For purposes of illustration measurements on a circuit such as Fig. 7-5 have been taken, and the results are shown in Figs. 7-9 and 7-10. The actual circuit on which measurements were made is shown in Fig. 7-8.

Figure 7-8 is seen to have a two-stage amplifier preceded by a three-input diode AND gate feeding one terminal of a three-input OR gate. The only germanium diodes are those in the OR gate, the collector clamp diode to -2.0 volts, and the feedback diode from the collector to the top of the 18,000-ohm resistors. All others are silicon diodes. The circuit on which the indicated measurements were made was set up with all voltages and resistors at their nominal values, and with a random choice of transistors. Delays and transition times better than those calculated could actually be expected, because operation is far from the worst-case condition of components and voltages.

Figure 7-9 shows the effect of three gates such as G1 plus 100 mmf, at V_3, and two gates such as G1 plus 100 mmf, at V_2. Figure 7-10 shows the waveforms with no external loads at the output terminals.

7.3. Single-Level Current-Switching Diode Logic with Transistor Inverting Amplifier. The desirability of single-level gating was discussed in Chapter 6 (p. 117), where it was shown that if the chains are alternating AND

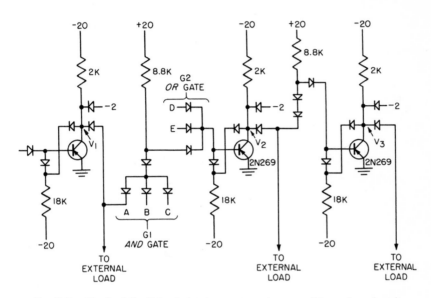

Fig. 7-8. Circuit of Fig. 7-5 calculated to meet worst-case conditions of supply voltages, resistance tolerances, diode forward drops, and diode reverse leakages.

and OR gates, there may be an advantage in single-level gating because of the possibility of performing operations at each logical level. Also, because the basic building block is smaller in single-level gating, in any attempt to package a universal building block the single-level gating scheme will have less unused components. Consider then, how to build single-level current switching diode gates (see Fig. 7-11).

Here, a three-input negative AND gate is driving a transistor inverting amplifier. A negative AND gate (positive OR gate), is used, because then the input current to the driver transistor is independent of the number of input signals at the lower level. A positive AND gate could possibly be used, but this would have the objectionable feature that the input current to the amplifier would depend upon the number of inputs to the gate at the lower level. This will be seen more clearly in the next section when double-level negative diode gates are considered.

In Fig. 7-11, the antisaturation circuit has been slightly modified. Because of the direction of current flow in the diodes D4, D5, and D6, the reverse base drive I_{R1} must be provided for fast active-region decay time, directly at the base of the transistor. R_1 is therefore chosen so that its lower limit current is sufficient to give the required active-region decay time as read from Fig. 4-16.

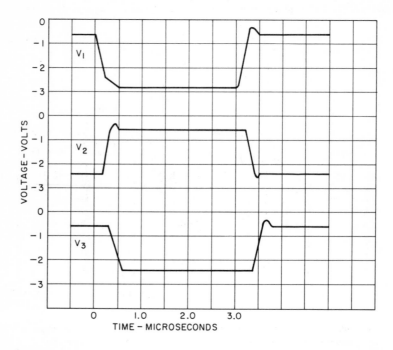

Fig. 7-9. Measured waveforms for circuit of Fig. 7-8: V_2 loaded with two gates such as G1 plus 100 mmf, and V_3 loaded with three gates such as G1 plus 100 mmf.

Diodes D4, D5, and also D6 (although the primary purpose of D6 is to prevent saturation), provide an upward d-c level shift so that the most negative upper level potential at V'_C still produces a zero, or slightly positive open circuit potential at V_P to keep T2 shut off. The current through R_2 is chosen so that at its lower limit it is a sink for the upper limit current from R_1, plus sufficient base current from T2 to give the required turn-on speed as read from Fig. 4-10. When T1 turns off, its collector must fall only far enough for diode D1 to disconnect, so that all the current demanded by R_2 comes from R_1, and the base of T2.

The collector load resistors R_L are, for such negative gates, chosen to be only relatively small current sinks. In the case where a collector was used to drive positive AND gates, R_L had to be a sink for sufficient current to inhibit all the gates being driven. The transistor served to supply enough current to this sink to force the collector potential to a sufficiently high upper level to enable the positive AND gates. Where negative gates are concerned, the transistor "on" current is mostly delivered to the negative AND gate resistors such as R_2, to inhibit these gates. The current allocated to R_L or R'_L need be only enough

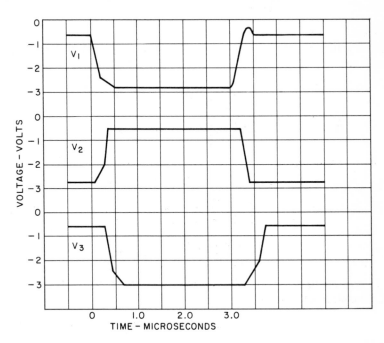

Fig. 7-10. Measured waveforms for circuit of Fig. 7-8: no external loads at output terminals.

to discharge stray capacitance at collector output buses when the transistors turn off.

It will be seen that the required collector voltage swings for a diode such as D1 to disconnect, are approximately 2.5 volts, as for the double-level gating structures. For good gating efficiency it is desirable to keep the ratio of d-c supply voltages to collector voltage swing as large as in the double-level circuit, so again choose V_1 to be -20 volts. V_3 and R_1 form a constant current generator to provide the reverse base drive needed for the desired turn-off speed. As the transistor base potential moves only approximately 0.3 volt, V_3 does not have to be very large to achieve a good constant current source. Nevertheless, for uniformity, choose V_3 as far above ground as V_1 is below ground.

Design the structure of Fig. 7-11 to give 0.5 µsec turn-on and turn-off times (for $I_C = 10$ ma). This corresponds to the same total delay as the circuit of Fig. 7-8 which had a delay of 1 µsec through two levels of logic, and two amplifiers.

The first component value to be calculated is R_1. From Fig. 4-16, to turn off 10 ma in 0.5 μsec requires a reverse base drive of 0.65 ma. At this point there is of course, no storage time because diodes D6 and D7 prevent saturation. Then

$$\underline{I_{R1}} = \frac{[V_3 - V_P]}{\overline{R_1}} = 0.65 \text{ ma} \qquad (7\text{-}9)$$

is chosen.

During turn-off, the base is sufficiently close to ground to take $V_P = 0$. Therefore

$$\frac{[1 - .01 \ t_v] \ V_3}{[1 + .01 \ t_r] \ R_1} = 0.65 \text{ ma}$$

$$\frac{(0.95) \ (20)}{1.05 \ R_1} = 0.65 \text{ ma}$$

or, $R_1 = 27,800$ ohms.

Later, the upper limit current through R_1 is required:

$$\overline{I}_{R1} = \frac{[1 + .01 \ t_v] \ V_3}{[1 - .01 \ t_r] \ R_1} \qquad (7\text{-}10)$$

$$= \frac{(1.05) \ (20)}{(0.95) \ (27.8)} = 0.80 \text{ ma}$$

To turn on 10 ma in 0.5 μsec requires, from Fig. 4-10, a base drive of 0.92 ma. Therefore select R_2 so

$$\underline{I_{R2}} = \overline{I}_{R1} + 0.92 = 0.80 + 0.92 = 1.72 \text{ ma} \qquad (7\text{-}11)$$

Then

$$\underline{I_{R2}} = \frac{[V_1 - V_L]}{\overline{R_2}} = 1.72 \text{ ma}$$

$$\underline{I_{R2}} = \frac{[1 - .01 \ t_v] \ V_1 - \overline{V}_P - \overline{V}_{D6} - \overline{V}_{D5} - \overline{V}_{D4}}{[1 + .01 \ t_r] \ R_2} \qquad (7\text{-}12)$$

Since Eq. 7-12 must hold during the turn-on transient, take $\overline{V}_P$ as the base drop at 0.92 ma, and drops on other diodes at 1.72 ma. The base potential from Fig. 4-4 is 0.39 volt, and the silicon diode drop from Fig. 7-7 is 0.74 volt. Then

$$I_{R2} = \frac{(0.95) \ (20) - 0.39 - 0.74 - 0.74 - 0.74}{(1.05) \ (R_2)}$$

$$= 1.72 \text{ ma}$$

$$R_2 = \frac{16.7}{(1.05) \ (1.72)} = 9200 \text{ ohms}$$

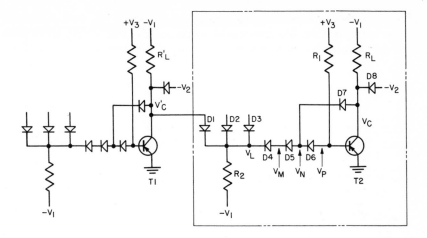

Fig. 7-11. Basic building block: Single-level gating in the current-switching mode. A three-input negative AND gate driving a transistor inverter with negative feedback for antisaturation; silicon diode level shifting to permit a building block output to drive a similar building block input.

Now check that the maximum negative upper level potential at V'_C will shut off T2.

V_C (maximum negative upper level value)

$$= \overline{V}_P + \overline{V}_{D6} - \underline{V}_{D7} \qquad (7\text{-}13)$$

Equation 7-13 considers the steady-state potential at a collector. As already shown, in the steady-state, the current required by R_2 reapportions itself so that only enough flows to the base to supply that demanded by the collector load. If the collector load is about 10 ma, then the base current is 0.2 ma (Fig. 4-5B). The worst-case base drop at this current from Fig. 4-5A is 0.31 volt. The current through D6 is this 0.2 ma plus $\overline{I}_{R1}$, which is 0.80 ma. According to Fig. 7-7, at 1 ma $\overline{V}_{D6}$ is 0.71 volt.

$$I_{D7} = I_{R2} - (I_{BASE} + I_{R1})$$

$$= 1.72 - (0.20 + 0.80) = 0.72 \text{ ma}$$

From Fig. 7-6, $\underline{V}_{D7}$ at 0.72 ma is 0.22 volt. Therefore

V_C (maximum negative upper level value)

$$= -\ 0.31 - 0.71 + 0.22 = -\ 0.80 \text{ volt}$$

This is also the maximum negative upper level voltage at V'_C when T1 is on.

Now calculate from V'_C towards T2 to check that -0.80 volt at V'_C will result in a zero, or somewhat positive open circuit potential at V_P:

V_P (lowermost upper level value)

$$= -0.80 - \overline{V}_{D1} + \underline{V}_{D4} + \underline{V}_{D5} + \underline{V}_{D6} \qquad (7\text{-}14)$$

Then in the steady-state, if T2 has been successfully shut off, of the 1.72 ma required by R_2 (Eq. 7-11), 0.80 ma is being supplied by R_1, so take $\overline{V}_{D1}$ in Eq. 7-14 at 0.92 ma. From Fig. 7-6 this is 0.41 volt. And $\underline{V}_{D4}$, $\underline{V}_{D5}$, $\underline{V}_{D6}$, are all to be taken at 0.80 ma of forward current. From Fig. 7-7 this is 0.50 volt. Thus, Eq. 7-14 gives

V_P (lowermost upper level value)

$$= -0.80 - 0.41 + 0.50 + 0.50 + 0.50$$

$$= +0.29 \text{ volt}$$

Therefore operation is safe, and T2 will be cut off even at an upper level potential of -0.80 volt at V'_C, and with all diodes in the chain from V'_C to V_B being off tolerance in the worst direction. Now calculate how far V'_C must be allowed to fall (when T1 is cut off), in the negative direction for D1 to disconnect. For D1 to disconnect, its anode must go at least as far as the most negative potential at V_L. Therefore

V_L (maximum negative)

$$= \overline{V}_P + \overline{V}_{D6} + \overline{V}_{D5} + \overline{V}_{D4}$$

It is important that D1 disconnect during the transient turn-on period when V_P is at its maximum negative value, because a full 0.92 ma is flowing in the base at that time. From Fig. 4-4 at 0.92 ma, V_P is -0.39 volt (recalling 0.05 volt is allowed for aging). The diode drops are all to be taken at 1.72 ma because the diodes are carrying the base current, plus the current through R_1. From Fig. 7-7 these drops are 0.74 volt. Then

V_L (maximum negative)

$$= -0.39 - 0.74 - 0.74 - 0.74 = -2.31 \text{ volt}$$

And if V_2 is chosen as -2.5 volts operation is safe even when it is 5% low, This compares with the 2.6 volts calculated for the double-level circuit on page 159.

Finally, calculate the pyramiding factor. When a gate is inhibited, the transistor driver T1 must supply the upper limit current for R_2 plus two diode back-leakage currents to D2 and D3. Therefore for each gate a transistor drives it must supply a current:

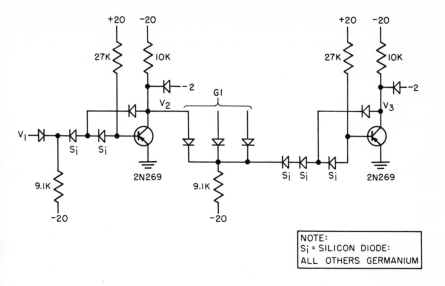

Fig. 7-12. The circuit of Fig. 7-11 calculated to meet worst-case conditions of all supply voltages, resistor tolerances, diode forward drops, and diode back-leakages.

$$\overline{I}_G = \overline{I}_{R2} + 2I_{BL}$$

$$\cong \frac{[1 + .01\ t_v]\ V_1}{[1 - .01\ t_r]\ R_2} + 2I_{BL}$$

$$= \frac{(1.05)\ (20)}{(0.95)\ 9.2} + 2\ (0.1) = 2.6\ \text{ma}$$

As 10-ma of collector current is assumed, if R_L or R'_L drew no current, $10/2.6 = 3.8$, or three gates could be driven. As it is not possible to drive four gates, all the current in excess of that required to drive three gates, can be allocated to R_L. This permits the driving of large capacitive loads with fast fall times. Then R_L is chosen to draw $10 - 3\ (2.6) = 2.2$, or, say, 2 ma. Fix R_L to draw 2 ma for V_1 at its nominal value, and V'_C at its most negative upper level value. This gives

$$R_L = \frac{20 - 0.8}{.002} = 9600\ \text{ohms}$$

This completes the design of the single-level structure. In actual use it would be treated in the same way as the single-level gating structure in Fig. 6-5. The circuit would be the same whether the logic called for an AND or OR gate. If an AND gate were required, negative true signals (voltage level of -2.5 volts), would have to be supplied. In cases where the correct polarity of signal was not available, a phase-inverter building block would be necessary. This could be of the same structure as in Fig. 7-11, but used as a single input gate by omitting perhaps, diodes D2 and D3. To check the calculations, measurements were taken on such a single-level gating structure. The exact circuit is shown in Fig. 7-12. All resistors and voltages were set at their nominal values. The transistors were selected at ran-

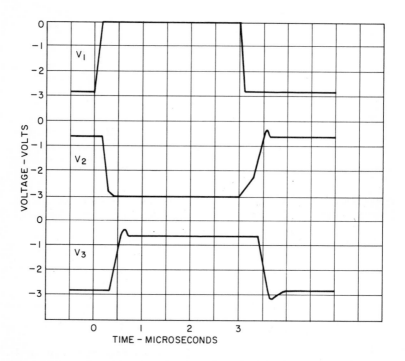

Fig. 7-13. Measured waveforms for Fig. 7-12: V_2 loaded with two gates such as G1 plus 100 mmf, and V_3 loaded with three gates such as G1 plus 100 mmf.

dom. A load corresponding to two gates (4300-ohm resistor to − 20 volt), and 100 mmf of capacity was driven from V_2. At V_3, a load corresponding to three gates (3000 ohms to − 20 volts), and 100 mmf of capacity, was applied. The measured waveforms are shown in Fig. 7-13. The delays are seen to be less than calculated, which was to be expected, as voltages, resistors and transistors were not at their worst-case value.

7.4. Double-Level, Current-Switching Negative AND—OR Gates with Transistor Inverting Amplifiers. The structure of Fig. 7-11 can be used to perform double-level, negative true signal gating by merely adding more OR silicon diodes at V_M. Thus, in Fig. 7-14 is shown a three-input negative AND gate driving a three-input negative OR gate, that feeds an amplifier. As for double-level voltage-switching logic, a two-stage amplifier, would probably be used, so that the polarities of the input and output signals are the same.

The circuit of Fig. 7-14 performs the logical operation $ABC + D + E = \overline{F}$ (for negative true signals). The inputs D and E may be negative diode gates like the ABC gate. This circuit has one less silicon diode than the equivalent

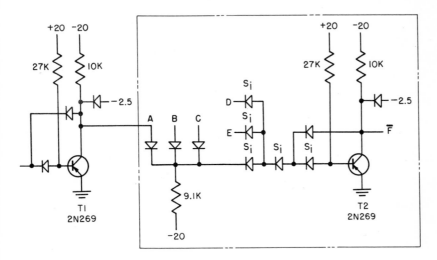

Fig. 7-14. A three-input negative AND gate driving a three-input negative OR gate in the current-switching mode. Transistor inverting amplifier with negative feedback for antisaturation; silicon diode level shifting to permit a building block output to drive a similar building block input.

positive gate, double-level circuit of Fig. 7-5. It has however, the somewhat undesirable feature that if the OR gate is enabled on more than one of its inputs, the additional current required by the three inputs must come out of the collector of T2. This may add an additional 1 to 2 ma of collector current, which is easily available from the collector. But it may also change the turn-off delay somewhat, if all the OR inputs go from the lower to the upper level, simultaneously, because there is still only the same 0.65 ma of reverse current that now has to switch off approximately 12, instead of 10 ma. The effect however, will be no greater than approximately 0.1 μsec.

The calculations for Fig. 7-14 would result in the same component values and pyramiding factor as for the single-level circuit of Fig. 7-11. The only difference is that the 9100-ohm AND gate resistor must now be a sink for the additional two back-leakages of the OR gate diodes. As these are silicon, this is negligible.

**7.5. Current-Switching Diode Logic with High-Frequency Transistors —
Double-Level Gating.** It has been shown that current-switching circuits have a pyramiding factor of three as compared to two for voltage-switching circuits

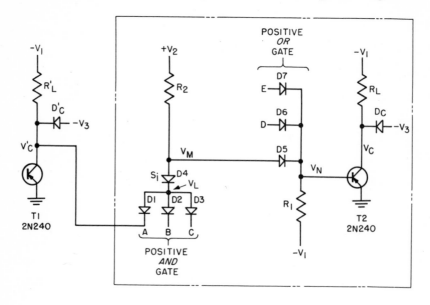

Fig. 7-15. The current-switching technique using high-frequency transistors and permitting transistor to saturate. Basic building block is a transistor inverting amplifier driven by a cascade of a three-input positive AND gate, and a three-input positive OR gate.

of the same speed, using the same transistor. But this has necessitated a cumbersome diode structure designed primarily to avoid saturation effects. The antisaturation feedback circuit has resulted in an ambiguity as to the upper level output voltage, and increased the level shift problem.

Now calculate the capabilities of the simplest current-switching circuit using high-frequency transistors that will be permitted to saturate in the "on" state. Since they are high-frequency transistors it may be possible to tolerate the worst saturation effects, and eliminate the antisaturation feedback diodes responsible for most of the level shift problems. Though the higher frequency transistor is in general more expensive, eliminating a level shifting diode and the two antisaturation diodes, may result in equal cost for the two schemes.

The first circuit to consider is one such as that in Fig. 7-15 — a two-level three-input positive true signal, AND-OR cascade, driving a transistor inverting amplifier.

Diode D4 is a silicon diode; take its characteristics to be as in Fig. 7-7. All other diodes are germanium, with characteristics as in Fig. 7-6. The transistors

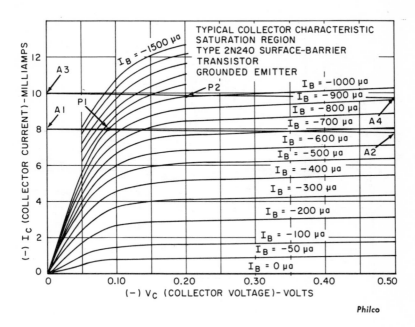

Fig. 7-16A. Saturation region collector characteristics of the type 2N240 surface-barrier transistor.

T1 and T2 will be Philco type 2N240. This transistor type has an $f\alpha_{co}$ of 45 mc, and a d-c beta of 10, at 10 ma. It has a power dissipation rating of 30 mw at 25°C, and a maximum collector voltage rating of 6 volts. Design will be from the output curves of Figs. 7-16A and B and the base curves of Fig. 7-17.

To calculate switching speeds, curves showing turn-on time versus forward base drive, and turn-off and storage time versus reverse base drive are required. For the RCA 2N269, turn-on time and active-region decay time was calculated from the static collector current curves, and a knowledge of $f\alpha_{co}$ (Eqs. 4-13 and 4-23). It was safe to do this, because the static collector current curve used (Fig. 4-3), represented the manufacturer's worst transistor, and the value of 4 mc for $f\alpha_{co}$ is a guaranteed lower limit value in the production spread. As similar worst-case data for the 2N240 was not available, measurements were made on a random sample of 24 transistors. Although the sample was not large enough to encompass the worst transistors in a large production spread, the measurements showed good agreement with known characteristics of this transistor type. For methods of calculation here, this small sample was sufficient.

Data on the 2N240 are shown in Figs. 7-18A to 7-21. Measured turn-on times show fairly good agreement with values calculated from Eq. 4-13. Storage times are seen to be negligible even for large forward overdrive factors. Active-

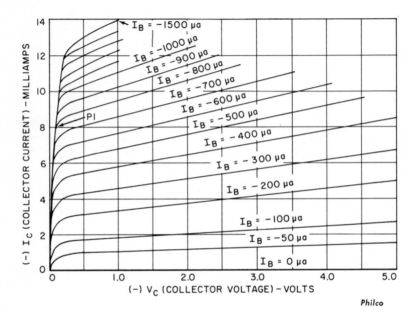

Philco

Fig. 7-16B.   Typical collector characteristics of type 2N240 transistor.

region decay times are seen to be dependent on the forward base current just before turn-off. This is not in agreement with the theory discussed in Chapter 4. The method used in gathering data is discussed in the Appendix.

A preliminary calculation of the circuit of Fig. 7-15 shows that something of a level shift problem still exists. This forces the use of the single-level shifting silicon diode D4.

The first choice to be made in the design is the nominal collector current of an "on" transistor. The manufacturer rates the transistor at a maximum of 15 ma. For safety it is desirable to derate this (even though in the "on" state at the maximum collector-to-emitter voltage operation will still be far from the rated maximum power dissipation of 30 mw). If too low a current is chosen, operation will be in a region where diode back-leakage currents are an appreciable fraction of the currents being switched. In the higher current region current gains are small. As a compromise, derate the maximum collector current value by a factor of approximately two, and choose 8 ma.

Then choose the lower limit current in R_1 to adequately bottom an aged transistor, but not so large as to result in large storage and turn-off times. From Fig. 7-16B it is seen that at 0.8 ma of base current, and with a load resistor drawing 8 ma with the transistor fully turned on, the collector potential bottoms to approximately $-$ 0.1 volt (point P1). Deration of the d-c beta of this tran-

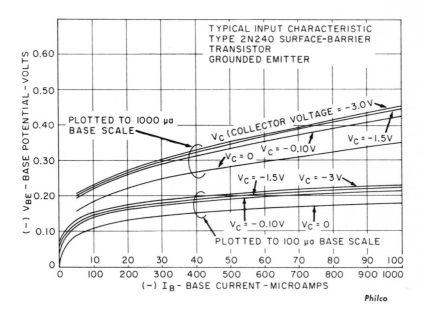

Fig. 7-17. Typical input characteristics of type 2N240 transistor.

sistor as heavily as the 2N269 (for which a factor of 50% was used), cannot be afforded. General industry experience with this transistor type, and data available from the manufacturer[1] indicate that derating the d-c beta to 80% of that shown by Fig. 7-16B is safe. Therefore select 1.0 ma as the lower limit current through R_1. It will soon be seen that high efficiency gating with a large collector supply voltage is required. Arbitrarily choose -20 volts; later calculations will show that this cannot be appreciably decreased. For a nominal collector current of 8 ma this fixes R_L (and R'_L) at 2500 ohms.

The bottomed collector potential for a new transistor is obtained from a 2500-ohm load line $(A1 - A2)$, to $-$ 20 volts drawn on Fig. 7-16A. This load line intersects the 1.0 ma point at $V_{CE} = -$ 0.09 volt (point P1). To estimate the collector potential for a transistor aged to 80% of a new one, renumber the current ordinates in Fig. 7-16A to 80% of the values shown thereon. If a

---

[1] *Report on Reliability Tests Conducted on Transistor Type 2N240:* Philco Corp., Lansdale Tube Company Division, Lansdale, Pa.

2500-ohm load line ($A3 - A4$) is now drawn to $- 20$ volts from the 8 ma point on this renumbered curve, it will be seen that the load line intersects the 1.0 base curve at a collector potential of $- 0.2$ volt (point P2). It will then be necessary to guarantee that in the worst-case, the forward drops in diodes D1, D4, D5, and a collector potential of $- 0.2$ volt at V'_C, results in an open circuit

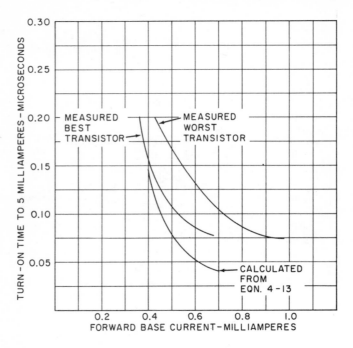

Fig. 7-18A. Turn-on time to 5 ma v. amplitude of forward base current step for 2N240 transistor.

potential at V_N slightly more positive than ground. It is this requirement that compels the use of the level-shifting silicon diode D4.

As in all other circuits discussed, to ensure good d-c turn-off there must be available a reverse base current (for V_N at ground), equal to I_{CO} at the highest operating temperature. The manufacturer rates the maximum value of I_{CO} at $25°C$ at 3 μa. This roughly doubles every $10°C$, and will be 48 μa at $65°C$, which can be taken as the highest temperature. Double this for safety, and guarantee a minimum reverse base current of 100 μa. In Fig. 7-15, this means that when V'_C is at its upper level, the lower limit current available from R_2 must supply the upper limit current demanded by R_1, plus two back-leakage currents demanded by diodes D6 and D7 (as before, assume a diode back-leakage current of 0.1 ma), plus at least 100 μa of reverse base current for good d-c shut-off. For good turn off speed, as will be shown, it is necessary to supply

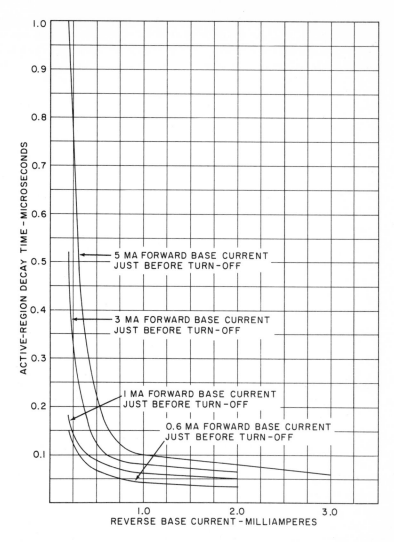

Fig. 7-18B. Active-region decay time from I_C (max.) of 5 ma v. reverse base current for the 2N240 transistor. Curves show measured data on worst transistor of a random sample.

a reverse base current of more than this, so that in satisfying the turn-off speed requirement the d-c shut-off requirement, will also be met.

A tentative calculation of worst-case diode drops shows that when V'_C is at its lower level, for V_M to fall far enough for D5 to disconnect, requires V'_C to be no more positive than about -1.6 volts. Thus for safety, fix the collector-clamp supply voltage, V_3 at -2 volts. A further tentative calculation shows that to achieve good gating efficiency, R_L (or R'_L), must be made a good constant current source — constant to at least 10%. Since the collector voltage swing is 2 volts, this fixes the collector supply voltage at − 20 volts. Similarly, the AND gate supply voltage is fixed at + 20 volts. At the end of this design

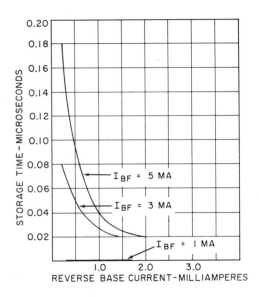

Fig. 7-18C. Storage time v. reverse base current for various forward base currents just before turn-off (I_{BF}), for the 2N240 transistor; 5-ma collector current at edge of saturation. Curves show measured data on worst transistor of a random sample.

when the pyramiding factor is calculated, it will be seen that this choice was reasonable.

First calculate R_1 to give a lower limit base current of 1 ma as discussed above. Figure 7-17 shows that at 1 ma of base current, at a collector-to-emitter potential of 0.1 volt, the base-to-emitter potential is − 0.42 volt. As for the 2N269, assume tolerances of ± 0.05 volt on all base drops. Thus in Fig. 7-15, for 1 ma of base current, V_N is − 0.47 volt in the worst-case.

Hence

$$I_{R1} = \frac{[V_1 - V_N]}{R_1} = .001 \tag{7-15}$$

$$= \frac{[(1 - .01\ t_v)\ V_1 - 0.47]}{[1 + .01\ t_r]\ R_1} \tag{7-16}$$

$$R_1 = \frac{(0.95)\ (20)\ -\ 0.47}{(1.05)\ (.001)} = 17{,}600\ \text{ohms}$$

Now calculate for later use, the upper limit current drawn by R_1. It is given by

$$\overline{I}_{R1} = \frac{\overline{[V_1 - V_N]}}{R_1}$$

$$= \frac{[1 + .01 \ t_v] \ V_1 - 0.37}{[1 - .01 \ t_r] \ 17.6}$$

$$= \frac{(1.05) \ (20) - 0.37}{(0.95) \ (17.6)} = 1.23 \ \text{ma}$$

Now select from Figs. 7-20 and 7-21, the reverse base current to give a pre-selected storage plus active-region decay time. The lower limit forward base current (1 ma), was chosen primarily for considerations of d-c. That is, it was

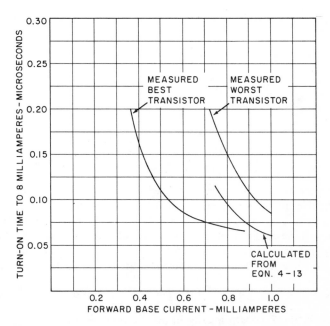

Fig. 7-19. Turn-on time to 8 ma v. amplitude of forward base current step for the 2N240 transistor.

chosen to give a collector potential for an aged "on" transistor of $-$ 0.2 volt at worst. Figure 7-19 shows that this base current would turn on 8 ma in 0.085 μsec for the worst transistor. Round this up to 0.1 μsec, and select the reverse base current to give an equal storage plus active-region decay time, so as to make optimum use of the fast turn-on time.

From Fig. 7-20 it will be seen that for a forward base current of 1.2 ma just prior to the turn-off pulse, the storage time for zero reverse base drive is under 0.01 μsec which can be considered negligible. Figure 7-21 shows that for a forward base current just before turn-off, of 1.2 ma, to achieve 0.1 μsec decay time, requires a reverse base current of approximately 0.3 ma. Therefore, select the lower limit current available from R_2 (Fig. 7-15), to equal the upper limit current demanded by R_1, plus the two diode back-leakage currents demanded by D6 and D7, plus the 0.3 ma reverse base current. Thus

$$\underline{I_{R2}} = \frac{[V_2 - V_M]}{\overline{R_2}} \tag{7-17}$$

$$= \overline{I}_{R1} + 2I_{BL} + I_{BR}$$

$$= 1.23 + 2\,(0.1) + 0.3 = 1.73 \text{ ma}$$

In the above Equation, transistor T2 is assumed shut off, V_N is at ground potential, and V_M is above ground by the worst-case forward drop in diode D5. Take the current through D5 as all the current in Eq. 7-17, or 1.73 ma. From Fig. 7-6, the worst-case forward drop at this current is 0.43 volt. Equation 7-17 then gives

$$\frac{[1 - .01\ t_v]\ V_2 - \overline{V}_{D5}}{[1 + .01\ t_r]\ R_2} = 1.73 \text{ ma}$$

or

$$R_2 = \frac{(0.95)\ (20) - 0.43}{(1.05)\ (1.73)} = 10,200 \text{ ohms}$$

All the components are now calculated. Assume a need to verify that the most negative upper level potential at V'_C still turns off T2, and that for T1 in the off state, V_M has been permitted to fall far enough for D5 to disconnect.

It has been shown that 1 ma of forward base current will produce in the worst-case an upper level potential at V'_C of -0.2 volt. This must result in a zero or positive worst-case open circuit potential at V_N for T2 to turn off. Thus

$$\underline{V_N} = \overline{V}'_C + \underline{V}_{D1} + \underline{V}_{D4} - \overline{V}_{D5} \tag{7-18}$$

Interest in Eq. 7-18 is primarily in the d-c case — after V'_C has risen to its upper level. In this case the 0.3 ma of reverse base current to T2 will have dropped to 0.1 ma, just the amount required by the base for good d-c turn-off at the highest temperature. Consequently, of the 1.73 ma delivered by R_2, D5 will be carrying only the upper limit current of R_1 (1.23 ma), the back-leakage currents of D6 and D7 (0.2 ma), and the 0.1 ma of reverse base current to T2, or a total of 1.53 ma. And from Fig. 7-6 $\overline{V}_{D5}$ at 1.53 ma is 0.42 volt.

Take the drop $\underline{V}_{D4}$ in Eq. 7-18, at 0.2 ma, because this current goes to the base of T2 during the turn-off transient but flows into the AND gate sinks in the steady-state. From Fig. 7-7 V_{D4} is -0.43 volt at 0.2 ma. V_{D1} will be taken at

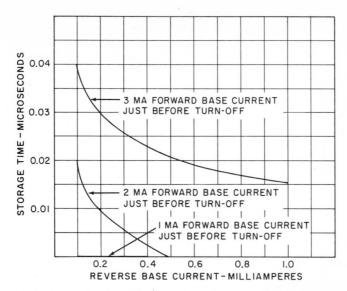

Fig. 7-20. Storage time v. reverse base current for various forward base currents just prior to turn-off pulse. For the 2N240 transistor: 8-ma collector current at edge of saturation. Curves show measured data on worst transistor of a random sample.

$0.2/3 \cong 0.1$ ma, as the 0.2 ma divides about equally through D1, D2, D3. From Fig. 7-6 $\underline{V_{D1}}$ is 0.18 volt. Thus Eq. 7-18 gives

$$\underline{V_N} = -\ 0.2\ +\ 0.18\ +\ 0.43\ -\ 0.42$$

$$=\ -\ 0.01 \text{ volt}$$

This is close enough to ground to be satisfactory because all worst-case effects have been taken into account. It can be made positive with respect to ground by increasing the current through R_2 by about 0.1 to 0.2 ma, without changing the drive capability of the circuit.

Now verify that D5 will disconnect with V'_C at its lower level. Figure 7-17 shows that at 1 ma of base current, the base potential is $-\ 0.42$ volt. This increases to $-\ 0.47$ for our assumed $\pm\ 0.05$ volt tolerance in base potential voltage drops. Thus, for D5 to disconnect V_M must fall to $-\ 0.47$ volt. If D5 does disconnect, diodes D4 and D1 will have to carry the upper limit current delivered by R_2 (since the inputs at diodes D2 and D3 may be at their upper level). This upper limit current through R_2 is

$$\frac{(1.05)\ (20)\ +\ 0.47}{(0.95)\ (10.2)} = 2.2 \text{ ma}$$

From Fig. 7-6, $\overline{V_{D1}}$ is 0.44 volt, and from Fig. 7-7, $\overline{V_{D4}}$ is 0.75 volt at this current. Therefore, the potential at V'_C must be below $-(0.47\ +\ 0.44\ +$

0.75 volt), or −1.66 volts. Since the collector clamp supply voltage, V_3 was chosen as −2.0 volts, even when it is 5% closer to ground operation would still be safe, and D5 would still disconnect. V_3 could have been chosen as −1.75

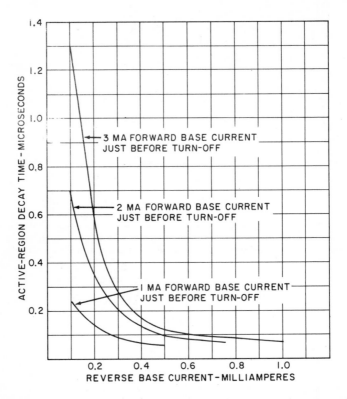

Fig. 7-21. Active-region decay time from I_C (max.) of 8 ma v. reverse base current for the 2N240 transistor. Curves show measured data on worst transistor of random sample.

volt, and the collector supply voltage ten times this value, or −17.5 volt, and attained the same gating efficiency with somewhat less d-c dissipation.

Finally, calculate the pyramiding factor of this circuit. With T2 off, the minimum current absorption capability of R'_L is

$$I_{R'_L} \text{ (T1 off)} = \frac{(0.95)\ (20) - 2}{(1.05)\ (2.5)}$$

$$= 6.5 \text{ ma}$$

It has just been calculated that with T1 off, the upper limit current through R_2 is 2.2 ma. To inhibit a single gate in the worst-case, a transistor output node must be a sink for the 2.2 ma, plus two back-leakage currents through D2 and D3, or a total of 2.4 ma. Thus the pyramiding factor is 6.5/2.4 = 2.7.

Operation consequently falls a bit short of being able to drive three inputs from one output. By tightening tolerances slightly, or increasing the nominal

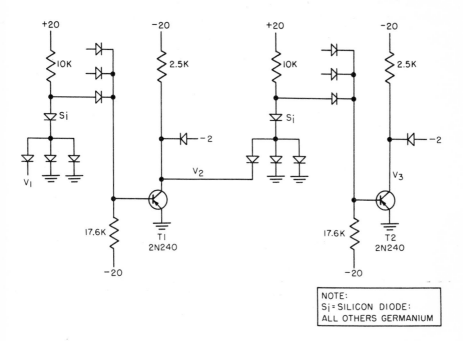

Fig. 7-22. The circuit of Fig. 7-15 calculated to meet worst-case conditions of all supply voltages, resistor tolerances, diode forward drops, and diode back-leakages.

collector current to 9 or 10 ma, a pyramiding factor of three can be easily achieved.

A circuit such as calculated above has been assembled, and its output waveforms measured. The exact circuit is shown in Fig. 7-22, and its waveforms in Figs. 7-23 and 7-24. All voltage and resistors were set at their nominal values and the transistors were selected at random. The germanium diodes were Transitron 1N270, and the silicon diodes were Transitron 1N482.

The waveforms in Fig. 7-23 were taken with no external loads at either collector. Figure 7-24 shows the waveforms obtained with maximum load at each collector. The loads were a 5000-ohm resistor from V_2 to the +20 volt supply, simulating two external gate loads, and a 3300-ohm resistor from V_3 to the +20 volt supply, simulating three external gate loads.

The waveforms in Figs. 7-23 and 7-24 are seen to agree satisfactorily with calculated values. The maximum operating frequency of a circuit such as in

Fig. 7-22 is approximately 3 to 4 mc. As in previous double-level circuits, there will usually be two inverting amplifiers after each positive OR gate, so that all AND and OR gates operate on positive true signals.

7.6. Current-Switching Diode Logic with High-Frequency Transistors — Single-Level Gating. The single-level, negative AND gate structure corresponding to Fig. 7-11 can be built with high-frequency transistors, thus avoiding

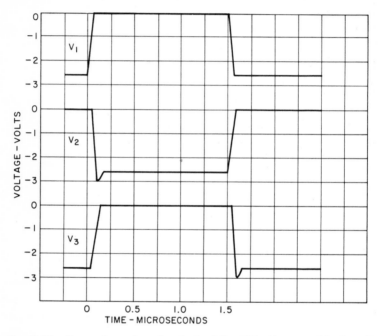

Fig. 7-23. Measured waveforms for circuit of Fig. 7-22. No external loads at V_2 or V_3.

the antisaturation feedback circuit and its attendant problems. The exact circuit analyzed is shown in Fig. 7-25.

A trial calculation shows that there is still something of a level shift problem, and two silicon diodes, D4 and D5, will be needed, to cause the most negative upper level potential at V'_C to result in a zero or positive open circuit potential at V_M.

The collector clamp voltage is not too important. It must be sufficiently low that when T1 is off, its collector is permitted to fall far enough for D1 to disconnect. A tentative calculation shows this to be approximately -2.0 volts. As for the double-level gating method, choose the collector and negative AND gate supply voltage at -20, for good gating efficiency. The supply voltage for R_2 is not firmly fixed. It and R_2 form a constant current source to supply reverse base current to the transistor for fast transient turn-off, and steady-state keep-off.

Since the base voltage moves only about -0.5 volt, V_2 need only be large compared to this. Choose it arbitrarily as $+10$ volts.

As in the single-level gating method, choose a nominal "on" collector current of 8 ma, and a lower limit forward base current of 1.0 ma to give a worst-case bottomed collector potential of -0.2 volt (see page 174). With this forward base current it was seen from Fig. 7-19 that there would be somewhat under

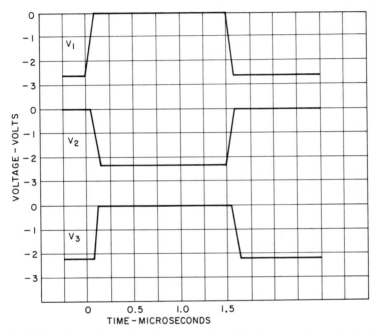

Fig. 7-24. Measured waveforms for circuit of Fig. 7-22. Two external gate loads at V_2; three external gate loads at V_3.

0.1 μsec of turn-on time. And Fig. 7-21 showed that for 1.2 ma of forward base current just before turn-off, to attain 0.1 μsec of active-region decay time requires a reverse base current of 0.3 ma. Therefore, choose R_2 so that when V'_C is at its upper level, and all the current demanded by R_1 is being supplied from the collector of T1, the lower limit current from R_2 (all of which is available for the base of T2), is 0.3 ma. For the case when T1 is off and its collector has fallen to somewhat below $-V_3$, disconnecting diode D_1, choose the lower limit current demanded by R_1 to equal the desired 1 ma of minimum forward base drive, plus the upper limit current supplied by R_2.

The first step is then to choose R_2. It is given by

$$I_{R2} = \frac{[V_2 - V_M]}{\overline{R_2}} = 0.3 \text{ ma} \tag{7-19}$$

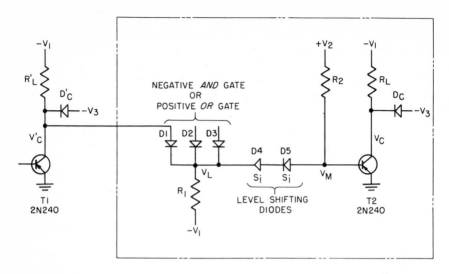

Fig. 7-25. Single-level current-switching logic with high-frequency transistors. A three-input negative AND gate driving a transistor inverting amplifier that is permitted to saturate.

In Eq. 7-20, assume V_M is at ground potential. It will actually be moving from about -0.5 volt to ground during the turn-off transient, but this is negligible. Then

$$\frac{[1 - .01\ t_v]\ V_2}{[1 + .01\ t_r]\ R_2} = 0.3\ ma$$

or

$$R_2 = \frac{(0.95)\ (10)}{(1.05)\ (0.3)} = 30{,}000\ ohms$$

and

$$\bar{I}_{R2}\ (T2\ on) = \frac{[V_2 - V_M]}{R_2} \tag{7-20}$$

$$= \frac{[1 + .01\ t_v]\ V_2 + V_{BE}}{[1 - .01\ t_r]\ R_2}$$

Here V_{BE} is taken as the maximum base-to-emitter voltage at a base current of 1 ma. From Fig. 7-17, this is 0.47 volt. Thus

$$\bar{I}_{R2}\ (T2\ on) = \frac{(1.05)\ (10) + 0.47}{(0.95)\ (30)} = 0.39\ ma$$

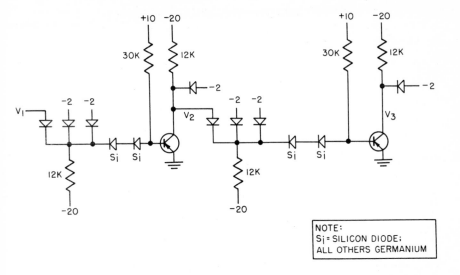

Fig. 7-26. The circuit of Fig. 7-25 calculated to operate under worst-case condition of supply voltages, resistor tolerances, diode forward drops, and diode back-leakages.

Now select R_1 so that its lower limit current is equal to the upper limit current from R_2, plus the required minimum base drive:

$$\underline{I_{R1}} \text{ (T2 on)} = \frac{[V_1 - V_L]}{\overline{R_1}}$$

$$= \overline{I}_{R2} + 1.0 = 1.39 \text{ ma}$$

or

$$\frac{[1 - .01 \text{ } t_v] \text{ } V_1 - [\overline{V}_M + \overline{V}_{D5} + \overline{V}_{D4}]}{[1 + .01 \text{ } t_r] \text{ } R_1}$$

$$= 1.39 \text{ ma} \qquad (7\text{-}21)$$

Since in this case diode D1 is disconnected, all the 1.39 ma comes through D4 and D5. At this current the worst-case diode drop from Fig. 7-7 is -0.73 volt. Then

$$R_1 = \frac{(0.95) \text{ } (20) - (0.47 + 0.73 + 0.73)}{(1.05) \text{ } (1.39)}$$

$$= 11,700 \text{ ohms}$$

To inhibit the negative AND gate consisting of R_1 and diodes D1, D2, D3, the transistor must supply the upper limit current demanded by R_1, plus back-leakage currents to diodes D2 and D3. The upper limit current drawn by R_1 for T1 in the "on" state, is:

$$\bar{I}_{R1} \; (T1 \; on) \; = \; \frac{[V_1 - V_L]}{R_1}$$

$$= \; \frac{[1 + .01 \; t_v] \; V_1 - (V'_C + V_{D1})}{[1 - .01 \; t_r] \; R_1} \qquad (7\text{-}22)$$

In Eq. 7-22, take V'_C as 0.1 volt, and V_{D1} (at approximately 1.5 ma), from Fig. 7-6, as 0.22 volt. Then

$$\bar{I}_{R1} \; (T1 \; on) \; = \; \frac{(1.05) \; (20) - (0.1 + 0.22)}{(0.95) \; (11.7)}$$

$$= \; 1.86 \; ma$$

Therefore, to inhibit a single gate, T1 must supply $(1.86) + 2 \; (0.1) = 2.06$ ma.

But a base drive adequate to turn on 8 ma has been provided. If no current at all is allocated (or say, 0.1 ma), to R_L or R'_L a single output could drive $8/2.06 = 3.9$, inputs. With slight tightening of tolerances, this could be increased to four full inputs. Then however, when T1 turns off, any stray capacitance at a collector output node would have only the 0.1 ma allocated to R'_L to discharge it. This would result in a slow fall-time. Therefore, attempt to drive only three gates from one output node, and allocate to R'_L the difference between the full 8 ma available from T1, and the current required to inhibit three gates. Thus, for R'_L there is a current of $8 - (3) \; (2.06) = 1.8$ ma. Since the 2.06 ma had been calculated at the upper limit potential of V_1 (21 volts), then

$$R'_L \; = \; \frac{V_1 - V'_C}{0018} \; = \; \frac{21 - 0.1}{0018}$$

$$= \; 11,600 \; ohms$$

This 1.8 ma of current allotted to R'_L should produce on a 100-mmf capacitive load at a collector output node, a fall-time

$$\Delta t \; = \; \frac{C \, \Delta V}{I} \; = \; \frac{(100 \times 10^{-12}) \; (2)}{1.8 \times 10^{-3}} \; = \; 0.11 \; \mu sec$$

But the reverse base current of 0.3 ma will produce (from Fig. 7-21), an unloaded active-region decay time of 0.1 µsec. Therefore, the actual fall-time with the 100 mmf capacitive load will never be more than $0.10 + 0.11 = 0.21$ µsec.

Now verify that for V'_C at its most negative upper level potential, the open circuit voltage at V_M is zero or positive.

$$\underline{V_M} = \underline{V'_C} + \overline{V}_{D1} + \underline{V}_{D4} + \underline{V}_{D5} \qquad (7\text{-}23)$$

Here, of the 0.3 ma supplied by R_2, assume 0.2 ma flows through D4 and D5 into the current sink R_1; the remaining 0.1 ma (maximum value of I_{CO}), may be drained away to supply reverse base current to the transistor T2. Therefore, take $\overline{V}_{D1}$ at a current of 2.06 −0.2, or 1.86 ma. In Fig. 7-6, the worst-case drop at this current is 0.44 volt. And since D4 and D5 both carry 0.2 ma, the minimum forward drop at the current from Fig. 7-7 is 0.43 volt. Then Eq. 7-23 gives

$$\underline{V_M} = - \; 0.2 \; - \; 0.44 \; + \; 0.43 \; + \; 0.43$$

$$= + \; 0.22 \;\; \text{volt}$$

Consequently, T2 is sure to be cut off for the most negative upper level potential at V'_C.

Finally, verify that when T1 is off its collector has been permitted to fall far enough for D1 to disconnect. For D1 to disconnect V'_C must fall at least to the most negative potential of V_L:

$$\underline{V_L} = \underline{V_M} + \overline{V}_{D4} + \overline{V}_{D5} \qquad (7\text{-}24)$$

Here, take $\overline{V}_{D4}$ and $\overline{V}_{D5}$ at $\overline{I}_{R1}$ (T2 on). This will be approximately 20% greater than I_{R1} (T2 on), as operation goes from V_1 and R_1 both 5% off tolerance in one direction, to 5% off tolerance in the opposite direction. Therefore, take these drops at a current $(1.2)\,(1.39) = 1.68$ ma. From Fig. 7-7 the drop at this current is 0.74 volt. Thus Eq. 7-24 gives

$$\underline{V_L} = - \; (0.47 \; + \; 0.74 \; + \; 0.74) \; = \; - \; 1.95 \;\; \text{volts}$$

And with a clamp supply voltage of −2, the least negative lower level potential at V'_C is

$$V'_C = - \; [(0.95)\,(2) \; + \; V_{D'C}]$$

$$= - \; [1.90 \; + \; 0.18] \; = \; - \; 2.08 \;\; \text{volts}$$

Thus, V'_C always falls far enough for D1 to disconnect.

This completes the calculation. A circuit such as Fig. 7-25 has been assembled, and its output waveforms measured. The exact circuit is shown in Fig. 7-26, and its measured waveforms in Figs. 7-27 and 7-28. The waveforms of Fig. 7-27 are for the basic circuit of Fig. 7-26, but with the equivalent of two gate loads (a 6000-ohm resistor from V_2 to the −20-volt supply), at V_2, and three gate loads (a 4000-ohm resistor from V_3 to the −20-volt supply), at V_3.

In Fig. 7-28, no resistive gate loads were driven, but V_2 and V_3 were each loaded with 100-mmf capacitors.

The waveforms in Figs. 7-26, and 7-27, are again seen to agree well with calculated values. The maximum operating frequency of such a structure would

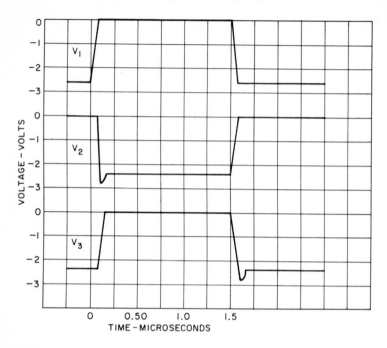

Fig. 7-27. Measured waveforms for Fig. 7-26. Two external gate loads at V_2; three external gate loads at V_3.

(as do all other structures), depend on capacitive loads to be driven, but it can be made to operate at 3 mc to 4 mc, with a pyramiding factor of three.

Summary and Conclusion. Summarized, the advantages of current-switching circuits over voltage-switching circuits, are as follows. Both in the single- and double-level versions with the 2N269 transistor, an output point can drive three input points, rather than the two it was possible to drive with the voltage-switching technique. In the double-level structure in the two-stage amplifier that follows the positive OR gate, drive capability can be traded between the collectors of the first and second stages. Thus, in Fig. 7-8, if there were no loads to drive at V_2, approximately 30 ma could be switched in the second amplifier (and still be within the maximum dissipation rating of 35 mw at 55°C). It would then be possible to have a drive capability at the output of V_3, of up to nine inputs. It is possible, of course, to trade in a similar way with voltage-switching circuits.

Although the 50% gain in drive capability is not spectacular, a drive capability of only two is inadequate in very many situations, and a drive capability of more than three is not too frequent. Also, the larger pyramiding factor has been achieved with smaller supply voltages, which means a smaller heat dissi-

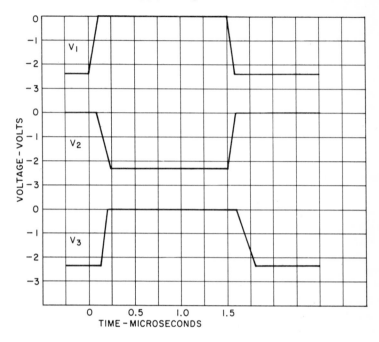

Fig. 7-28. Measured waveforms for Fig. 7-26. 100-mmf capacitive loads at both V_2 and V_3. No external resistive loads at either V_2 or V_3.

pation problem. A further advantage is that an off transistor operates at 2 volts (for the 2N269 circuits), rather than 6 volts, which should contribute to greater transistor lifetime. The current-switching circuits with the 2N269 should be usable up to about 1 mc.

Current-switching circuits using the 2N240 have a pyramiding factor equal that of those using the 2N269, but can operate up to about 3 mc. They also use less diodes but a more expensive transistor.

There are a great many applications where an operating frequency of 1 to 2 mc is required. It is likely that circuits such as have been calculated for the 2N240, used with a higher-gain but lower-frequency transistor, such as the Raytheon 762, or General Transistor type 316, would yield a pyramiding factor greater than three, but with the required operating speed.

Chapter 8

RESISTANCE LOGIC WITH TRANSISTOR INVERTING AMPLIFIERS

The low impedance at the base of an "on" transistor and its unique collector voltage in the saturation region, make possible a simple and inexpensive method of logic using resistors for AND and OR gating, and transistors for power amplification. It is very attractive for low-frequency circuits, but becomes less economical, more complicated, and less efficient at higher frequencies. Nevertheless, with a good high-frequency transistor it still retains many of its useful features even at high frequencies.

This chapter discusses and performs worst-case design calculations on such resistance logic schemes.

8.1. The Fundamentals of Resistance Gating. Resistance AND and OR gating followed by transistor inverting amplifiers has been widely used.[1]. Basically, the circuit is shown in Fig. 8-1.

For illustration, the output of one three-input gate after amplification and polarity inversion by T1, driving one input of an exactly similar structure, has been shown.

The clamp at the collector is not essential to the circuit. It standardizes output voltages, and for high-frequency operation makes the worst-case design simpler to achieve. Circuits designed here, have such a collector clamp.

The circuit works as follows. The input signals $A, B, C,$ are themselves the outputs at a collector, such as signal D. Thus the signal voltages swing between the potential at the collector of a saturated transistor — about -0.1 to -0.2 volt — and a lower level potential below $-V_2$, by the forward drop in diode D1.

---

[1] Beaulieu, D. E. Burkhart, D. P., and Propster, Ch., "The Bizmac Transcoder," Part IV, pp. 294-299, *I. R. E. Wescon Convention Record*, 1957.
Rowe, W. D., and Royer, G. H., "Transistor NOR Circuit Design," Paper No. 196, *AIEE Transactions*, Vol. 76 (1957), pp. 263-267.

The combination of R_3 and V_3 is not essential to the circuit, either. It is the familiar constant current source of I_{CO} discussed in Chapter 3 (p. 53). It supplies a reverse base current of I_{CO} at the highest operating temperature to ensure that the collector leakage current does not increase above I_{CO}.

The input gating resistors R_A, R_B, R_C (all equal), are so chosen that if any one of them is at the lower level voltage, the base current it draws is sufficient to bottom the transistor with a collector load resistor of R_L, and a supply voltage of $-V_1$. If more than one input is at the lower level, the base current is that

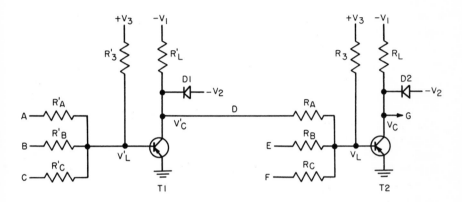

Fig. 8-1. Basic resistance gating building blocks.

much greater, and the collector current is driven more heavily into saturation. Only if all inputs are at the upper level of approximately -0.1 to -0.2 volt, is the base current zero, and the transistor shut off. Its collector then falls towards $-V_1$, but is caught by the clamp diode at $-V_2$.

A current-summing network has thus been built. The sum of all the currents demanded by the input resistors is supplied almost entirely from the transistor base. Also, because the impedance looking into the base is usually low compared to the input resistors, the input signal generators are well isolated from one another.

As can be seen the circuit is an OR gate for negative signals (d-c level of $-V_2$), and an AND gate for positive signals (d-c level of -0.1 to -0.2 volt). The integral building block consisting of the gate resistors and the transistor, performs (for positive true signals), the logical operation of $ABC + \overline{E} + \overline{F} = G$. Thus, basically, the structure is a single-level structure, the exact logical equivalent of Fig. 6-4. The circuit would be used exactly as other single-level phase-inverting circuits previously discussed. Consequently, if AND gating were required, positive or upper level true signals would have to be supplied. OR gating would require negative or lower-level true signals.

In those cases where the correct polarity signal is not available, a phase-inverting building block would have to be interposed. But as discussed in Chapter 6 (p. 118), as the cascades are usually alternating AND and OR gates, the correct polarity of signal is always available without adding a phase inverter. The phase inverter if needed, would be of exactly the same structure as that shown in Fig. 8-1, but using only one gating resistor at the input. Two such single-input structures with the output of the first feeding the input of the second, and vice versa, would form a flip-flop. Thus, there is the useful feature that a single basic building block can be used to fabricate nearly all the required elements for a computer — AND gates, OR gates, phase inverters, and flip-flops.

8.2. Resistance Gating at Low Frequencies. Ignoring for the moment, turn-on, turn-off and storage time problems, perform a worst-case design of the structure in Fig. 8-1. Here, consider only d-c effects — that when a single input turns a transistor on, it is adequately bottomed, and if all inputs are at their worst-case upper level value the driven transistor is shut off. Calculate all component values, and finally the pyramiding factor. Do this as before, assuming that outputs are driving only average type computer gates — three-input gates. Although the pyramiding factor and the magnitude of the input-gating resistors do change with the number of inputs of driven gates, this change is relatively small. In any event, the design calculation will show how to take this into account in special cases where the number of inputs is more than three.

Assume ± 5% tolerance on all resistors and voltages, and use the same symbols — lines above and below terms to designate upper and lower limit values, as in previous chapters. Use as a first example, the RCA 2N269, and as before, assume a need to switch it on to a nominal current of 10 ma. The value of reverse base current (current through R_3, Fig. 8-1), to ensure good d-c cut-off at the highest operating temperature, shall be taken as 0.1 ma (see Chapter 6, p. 121). The d-c base current to turn on a transistor should be so chosen that if a transistor ages by a factor of two above its characteristics as indicated in Fig. 4-3, the potential at an "on" collector shall still be no more negative than approximately −0.2 volt. If imperfectly bottomed collectors are permitted to assume potentials appreciably more negative than this, level shift problems will be encountered again. Then the current from R_3 will have to be increased to supply 0.1 ma of reverse base drive to the base of T2, and enough additional current to R_A, R_B, and R_C in parallel; to provide a level shift equal to the most negative potential of points V'_C at their upper level. This is discussed in more detail on p. 193.

The design of this structure is somewhat similar to that of the voltage-switching diode gate circuits of Chapter 6. Selection of the magnitude of V_1 and V_2 was discussed on p. 121, where the need to make R_L a fairly good constant current source was shown. Then the current it is capable of absorbing (from the resistors it drives, such as R_A), when it is at its lower level, is not much less than the nominal 10 ma it takes from the collector when the transistor is on. It was decided that a ratio of $-V_1$ to V_2 of 5 to 1, giving a current absorption capability of only 20% less than the 10 ma demanded when the transistor is on, was adequate. To make it somewhat more efficient — say 10%, to have an absorption capability of 9 rather than 8 ma, is desirable. But as shown in Chapter 6, a good choice of the absolute value of V_2 would be about 6 volts, so that tolerances in the base drops and V_{D1} would only amount to approximately 5% of the nominal voltage across the base input resistor.

Since a relatively constant d-c base current will be important later, when dealing with speed of response, fix V_2 at −6 volts. Then, to take only a 10% loss in current absorption capability of R_2 with the transistor off, requires a supply voltage of 60 volts. As this would be expensive in d-c power dissipation and its attendant problems, settle for a supply voltage of −30 volts, giving a nominal current absorption capability in R'_L with the transistor off, of 8 ma.

The choice of V_3 is not firmly dictated. With R_3 it must form a relatively constant current source to supply I_{CO} to the base, and some additional current to the input gating resistors for a d-c level shift. Since the bottom end of R_3 moves approximately 0.30 volt between the transistor on and off condition, a relatively low voltage will give a good constant current source. In the absence of other compelling reasons (in the voltage-switching diode circuits of Chapter 6 there was already a source of +30 volts available), take V_3 as far above ground as −V_2 is below ground, or as +6 volts.

The first component to be fixed is R_3. For V_L at ground, R_3 must supply a lower limit current of 0.1 ma to the base of T2 (see p. 121), plus additional current to R_A, R_B and R_C to bring V_L up to ground for the most negative upper level potential at points such as V'_C. Later, conditions will be such that this most negative upper-level potential at the collector of an "on" transistor is never more negative than −0.2 volt. Tentatively, estimate the value of the gating resistors R_A, R_B, R_C as about 6000 ohms. It will be seen that this is close enough for the purpose of the present calculation. Thus, for V_L to be at ground, R_3 must in addition supply a level shifting current to each of R_A, R_B, R_C of $0.2/6000 = 33$ μa, or a total of 100 μa. This is sufficiently small that it can be increased by say, 25% to 125 μa to account for an optimistic estimate of 6000 ohms for the value of the gating resistors. Then the lower limit current to be supplied by R_3 must be $0.1 + 0.125 = 0.225$ ma. Thus,

$$\underline{I_{R3}} = \frac{[1 - .01 \; t_v] \; V_3}{[1 + .01 \; t_r] \; R_3} = 0.225 \text{ ma} \qquad (8\text{-}1)$$

$$R_3 = \frac{(0.95) \; (6)}{(1.05) \; (.225)} = 24{,}000 \text{ ohms}$$

For later use, calculate here the upper limit current supplied by R_3 when the transistor is on. When the transistor is on, the potential at V_L is approximately −0.3 volt (Fig. 4-5A). Therefore

$$\bar{I}_{R3} = \frac{[1 + .01 \; t_v] \; V_3 + 0.3}{[1 - .01 \; t_r] \; R_3} \qquad (8\text{-}2)$$

$$= \frac{(1.05) \; (6) + 0.3}{(0.95) \; (24)} = 0.29 \; ma$$

Now choose the gating resistor R_A, R_B, R_C, exactly. To do this, first decide on the minimum base current to be provided when two of the inputs are at their upper level, and only one input is at the lower level. Recall, it was decided never to permit a bottomed collector potential to be more negative than -0.2 volt. As the collector supply voltage is -30, and a nominal "on" current of 10 ma was assumed, the value of R_L is 3000 ohms.

If a 3000-ohm load line is drawn on Fig. 4-3 from the 10-ma current point (it is virtually a horizontal line on this scale), it will be seen that it intersects the -0.2 collector voltage point at a base current of approximately 0.3 ma. But aging must be allowed for. This can be done in the following manner (a carry over from common computer circuit design practice with vacuum tubes).

Assume the aging deteriorates the curves of Fig. 4-3 by a factor of two. That is, at any specified collector voltage and base current, the collector current is half that shown on the curve. Thus, the shape of the aged transistor curves is obtained by simply halving the current ordinates in Fig. 4-3. To find the collector potential for an aged transistor therefore, draw the 3000-ohm load line from the 20-ma point in Fig. 4-3. Then this curve intersects the -0.2 volt collector potential at a base current of 0.6 ma. If the transistor were a new one, the bottomed collector potential at the intersection of a 3000-ohm load level from the 10-ma collector current point with the 0.6 ma base current curve, would be approximately -0.08 volt. This satisfies the bottomed collector requirement and the gating resistors can consequently be chosen so that in the worst-case, for two inputs at the upper level and one input at the lower level, 0.6 ma of base current is provided.

Assume that in Fig. 8-1 the signals E and F are at their upper level and D is at the lower level. Then, R_A must be a sink in the worst-case for the upper limit current through R_3, plus the upper limit currents through R_B and R_C (small, but not negligible), plus 0.6 ma for the base. Thus,

$$\frac{[V'_C - V_L]}{\bar{R}_A} = \bar{I}_{R3} + \bar{I}_{RB} + \bar{I}_{RC} + 0.6 \qquad (8\text{-}3)$$

Where

$$\bar{I}_{RB} = \bar{I}_{RC} = \frac{\bar{V}_L}{R_B}$$

Assume here, that in the current contribution of R_B and R_C, their respective input points are at ground, although it was shown above that for a new transistor from Fig. 4-3, it would only go as far positive as -0.08 volt. Although the difference is small, better than nominal transistors may be closer to ground than -0.08 volt, and for simplicity it can be taken at ground potential. The value of V_L shall be taken from Fig. 4-4 at 0.6 ma of base current. As previously, assume worst-case variations of ± 0.05 volt around this last base curve. Thus, at 0.6 ma the maximum negative value of V_L from Fig. 4-4 is -0.36 volt. Then

$$\frac{[1 - .01\ t_v]\ V_2 + \underline{V_{D1}} - 0.36}{[1 + .01\ t_r]\ R_A}$$

$$= 0.29 + \frac{2\ (0.36)}{[1 - .01\ t_r]\ R_A} + 0.6 \qquad (8\text{-}3a)$$

Take $\underline{V_{D1}}$ from Fig. 7-6 at a current of 0.1 ma on the assumption that R'_L is driving its maximum load, and all but 0.1 ma of the current it demands comes from these loads leaving the clamp diode D1 barely conducting. Thus $\underline{V_{D1}}$ from Fig. 7-6 is -0.18 volt. Then Eq. 8-3a gives

$$\frac{(0.95)\ (6) + 0.18 - 0.36}{1.05\ R_A}$$

$$= 0.29 + \frac{0.76}{R_A} + 0.6$$

or
$$R_A = 5100\ \text{ohms}.$$

This fixes all the component values. Now calculate the pyramiding factor. Assume that of all the N resistors such as R_A, driven by a collector, one is at the upper limit of its resistance tolerance, and is driven just hard enough to turn on its transistor. Then from Eq. 8-3a, it pours into the V'_C node, a current

$$I_{RA} = \frac{[1 - .01\ t_v]\ V_2 + \underline{V_{D1}} - 0.36}{[1 + .01\ t_r]\ R_A}$$

$$= \frac{(0.95)\ (6) + 0.18 - 0.36}{(1.05)\ (5.1)} = 1.05\ \text{ma} \qquad (8\text{-}4)$$

Assume the other N-1 resistors are at the lower limit of their resistance tolerance so that they supply more than their nominal share of current to the sink resistor R'_L. Thus each of these N-1 resistors supplies a current

$$I = \frac{[1 - .01\ t_v]\ V_2 + \underline{V_{D1}} - 0.36}{[1 - .01\ t_r]\ 5.1}$$

$$= \frac{(0.95)\ (6) + 0.18 - 0.36}{(0.95)\ (5.1)} = 1.13\ \text{ma} \qquad (8\text{-}5)$$

And by Eq. 8-4, a voltage of

$$[1 - .01\ t_v]\ V_2 + \underline{V_{D1}} = -5.88\ \text{volts}$$

has been assumed at the upper end of R'_L. Thus the minimum absorption current capability of R'_L is given by

$I_{R'_L}$ (Minimum sink capability)

$$= \frac{[1 - .01 \; t_v] \; V_1 - 5.88}{[1 + .01 \; t_r] \; R'_L}$$

$$= \frac{(0.95) \; (30) \; - \; 5.88}{(1.05) \; (3)} = 7.2 \; \text{ma} \qquad (8\text{-}6)$$

And since of the N units being driven, one contributes 1.03 ma to R'_L, and N-1 contribute 1.13 ma each, the pyramiding factor is given by

$$7.2 = 1.03 + (N - 1) \; (1.13) \qquad (8\text{-}7)$$

or $N = 5.5$. Therefore, even taking into account d-c effects alone, only five inputs may be driven from one output.

It can be seen then, that resistance and voltage tolerances, and the need to derate the d-c beta of the transistor, have resulted in a low pyramiding factor. Recall that a minimum base drive of 0.6 ma for 10 ma of collector current, was decided upon. Therefore, a d-c beta of $10/0.6 = 16.7$ is being specified. Figure 4-3 shows that the d-c beta for a new worst-case transistor at 10 ma, is $10/0.2 = 50$. Operation has thus been derated considerably for aging, primarily to ensure good turn-off of a supposedly off transistor. It may not be necessary to derate so heavily if the familiar level-shifting properties of a silicon diode are used. Consider the circuit of Fig. 8-2. The silicon diode would provide an

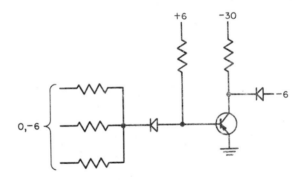

Fig. 8-2.   Resistance gating with silicon diode for level shifting.

upward level shift of about $+0.5$ volt, and imperfect bottoming of an "on" transistor could be tolerated. The d-c beta would therefore not have to be derated so heavily.

It would probably be possible to safely specify a minimum d-c base drive of about 0.4 ma rather than 0.6 ma and achieve an increase in pyramiding factor, and provide a greater margin of safety in turning off a transistor. But the junction of the gating resistors (in the case of two-input resistors at their upper level, and one input at its lower level), will be below ground not by the base drop of an "on" transistor alone, but by this drop plus the forward drop of a silicon diode. The one resistor that is turning the transistor on will then have to carry away a larger current from the remaining resistors (I_{RB} and I_{RC} in Eq. 8-3 will be greater). This effect will tend to reduce the gain in pyramiding

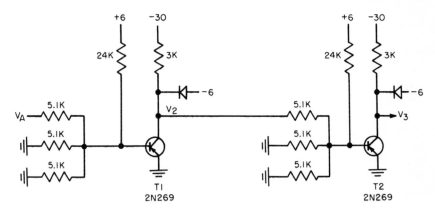

Fig. 8-3. Resistance gating building block calculated to operate under worst-case conditions of supply voltages, resistor and transistor tolerances.

factor, but the greater margin of safety in cutting a transistor off will still remain.

Although the structure of Fig. 8-1 has not been designed for fast switching applications, it is of interest to see how a signal propagates through the circuit. Waveforms have been taken on such a circuit transmitting a 5 μsec pulse at a repetition rate of 100 kc. The exact circuit is shown in Fig. 8-3 and the measured waveforms in Fig. 8-4.

The solid line waveforms in Fig. 8-4 were taken with no external loads connected at V_2 and V_3. The dashed line waveforms were taken with an 820-ohm load to ground at V_3, and a 1000-ohm load at V_2. These simulated driving, in the worst-case, five gate inputs at V_3, and four inputs at V_2. In all measurements the two unused gate resistors at each stage were grounded, simulating the condition of logical enabling signals at these points. Although permitting the ends of these resistors to remain open-circuited would also have provided an enabling signal, short-circuiting them to ground simulates actual circuit operation. In actual circuit operation this condition shortens storage and decay time, somewhat. During most of the storage and active-region decay time, while charges are still stored in the base region, the potential at the base remains close to the value it had when the transistor was on — approximately −0.3 volt. Thus, each enabling signal at ground contributes through its input resistor a reverse base current of $0.3/5.1 = 59$ μa. Though not very large, this current does contribute to the shortening of the storage and decay time.

The measured waveforms of Fig. 8-4 were taken with all voltages and resistors at their nominal values, and with transistors selected at random. Consequently, the waveforms should be expected to show better response time than would be obtained with worst-case components and voltages. If desired, turn-on, storage and active-region decay times could be calculated from Figs. 4-10, 4-16, and 6-7, respectively. In subsequent sections a number of ways of speeding up this basic resistance gating circuit will be considered.

8.3. Resistive and Inductive Speed-up of Resistance Gating Circuit. Consider the most direct means of speeding up the response time of the basic resistance gating circuit. On page 193, the current available through R_3 was fixed to equal I_{CO} (to be supplied to the base for good d-c turn-off), plus an additional component to be supplied to the gate resistors for level shifting purposes. This can be increased to include a component for decreasing storage and decay times. Select the added component of current by reference to Figs. 4-16 and 6-7. The current drawn by R_A when V'_C is at its lower level (Fig. 8-1) would then have to be increased so that the base current available for turning on the transistor, $I_{RA} - I_{R3} - (I_{RB} + I_{RC})$, is sufficiently large. This net base current would be chosen from Fig. 4-10 to give the required turn-on speed.

The procedure would work to some extent, but it would not be capable of very large reduction in the transition times when the worst-case design is attempted, because quite large reverse base drives for say, 0.5 μsec of storage plus decay time would be needed. This would make I_{R3} large, and I_{RA} larger. The net base current would then be the difference between two large currents, and small percentage changes in either would result in large percentage changes in this difference. Since this base turn-on current would then be ambiguous, it would be necessary to design a lower limit reverse base current adequate, in the case of the upper limit forward base current, to switch the transistor off with the required speed. The end result of this would be quite small pyramiding factors. Nevertheless, moderate decrease in transition times are obtainable in this manner without too much inefficiency.

As another means of speeding up the basic circuit, consider using inductances to generate speed-up current spikes (Fig. 8-5).[1]

Here, the source of reverse base current for fast turn-off is the inductance L_1. How ever it is decided to supply the reverse base current, whether entirely through R_3 as discussed above, or through L_1, its average value as determined from Figs. 4-16 and 6-7, will have to be the same for a given switching speed.

Consider how to choose L_1 and R_1. A rigorous worst-case calculation will not be performed; it is only desired to get an idea of the order of magnitude of these components. During the transistor "on" time, a current is stored in L_1. When

[1] Younker, E. Leroy, "A Transistor Driven Magnetic Core Memory," *I.R.E. Transactions on Electronic Computers*, March 1957.

the input signals move up to ground, the base potential remains almost constant at the value it had during the "on" time, until all excess base charges have been swept out. Since the base potential remains stationary it can be said that the

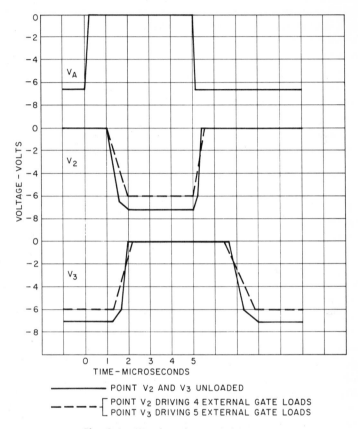

POINT V₂ AND V₃ UNLOADED
⎾ POINT V₂ DRIVING 4 EXTERNAL GATE LOADS
⎿ POINT V₃ DRIVING 5 EXTERNAL GATE LOADS

Fig. 8-4. Waveforms for circuit of Fig. 8-3.

upper end of L_1 looks into a short circuit to ground. The current in L_1 then decays through the base as $I_{MAX}e^{-t/T}$ where $T = L_1/R_1$.

The average value of this current, initially stored in the inductance during the transistor "on" time, supplies the reverse base drive for decreased storage and decay time. The average value of this over a time interval T_{AV} is given by

$$I_{AV} = I_{MAX} \left(\frac{T}{T_{AV}} \right) [1 - e^{-T_{AV}/T}] \qquad (8\text{-}8)$$

Permit a maximum storage time of 0.5 μsec. The required reverse base drive will depend on the forward base current just prior to turn-off. Assume that in the worst-case it will be no greater than 1 ma. Figure 4-10 indicates that 0.92 ma of forward base current would be needed for 0.5 μsec turn-on time; thus, a 10% variation from lower to upper limit forward base drive is being permitted. From Fig. 6-7, for 1 ma of forward current just prior to shut-off, to achieve a storage time of only 0.5 μsec requires a reverse base current of 1.70 ma. R_3 and V_3 would be permitted to remain unchanged giving a nominal reverse base

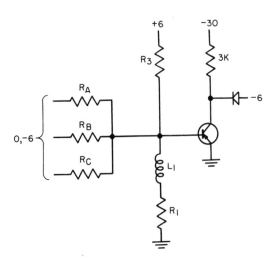

Fig. 8-5.   Resistance gating with inductance at transistor base for fast turn-off.

current of $6/24 = 0.25$ ma. Therefore, the combination of L_1 and R_1 will have to supply the balance of $1.70 - 0.25 = 1.45$ ma. Choose the average current given by Eq. 8-8 equal to this. Since interest is in the average current over the desired 0.5 μsec storage time, take $T_{AV} = 0.5$ μsec. It is undesirable to make the time constant T too long as operation would then be sensitive to repetition rate. If T is made too small, the average current is then a small fraction of the maximum current. As a compromise, choose $T = 0.5$ μsec, giving from Eq. 8-8 an average current $I_{AV} = 0.63\ I_{MAX}$. And for $I_{AV} = 1.45$ ma, $I_{MAX} = 2.3$ ma.

Now in the steady-state, when the transistor is on, design will be for a nominal forward base current of 0.92 ma, in order to achieve 0.5 μsec turn-on time. From Fig. 4-4, the base potential at this current is -0.33 volt. This fixes R_1, as a maximum current through the L_1, R_1 combination of 2.3 ma was calculated. Thus

$$R_1 = \frac{0.33}{.0023} = 140 \text{ ohms}$$

And since the time constant $T = L_1/R_1$ has been set equal to 0.5 μsec, then

$$L_1 = (0.5 \times 10^{-6})\ (140) = 70 \text{ microhenries}$$

At this point, fix the value of the input resistors R_A, R_B, R_C. They must now be sinks for the 2.3 ma supplied by R_1, for the nominal 0.25 ma supplied by R_3, and for the nominal 0.92 ma of base current for 0.5 µsec turn-on time, or a

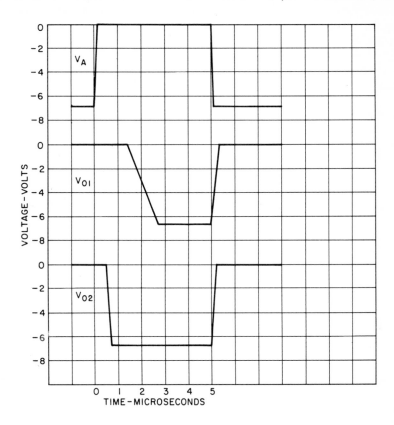

Fig. 8-6. Measured waveforms for circuits of Fig. 8-7.

total of 3.47 ma. Since the nominal voltage across R_A will be $6 - 0.33$, or 5.67 volts, then

$$R_A = \frac{5.67}{3.47} = 1640 \text{ ohms}$$

The active-region decay time will be small, because at the end of the storage time there will still be a current available from the inductance of

$$I_{MAX} \ e^{-t/T} = 2.3 \ e^{-1} = 0.85 \text{ ma}$$

As the resistor R_1 will still be supplying its nominal 0.25 ma, a total of 1.1 ma of reverse base drive remains available at the end of the storage time. By Fig. 4-16, this should give an active-region decay time of 0.30 μsec. Since the inductive current is decaying, the actual time will be slightly larger than this.

Waveforms have been taken on such a circuit and the results are shown in Fig. 8-6. The exact circuits from which the waveforms were taken are shown in Fig. 8-7. The output waveform for the original circuit without inductive speed-up is shown for comparison, and the inductance is seen to be effective.

In actual practice however, it would be difficult to perform a safe worst-case design. The circuit would be very sensitive to changes in base-to-emitter voltages. A transistor with a high base voltage drop may not turn on fully, because of the current demanded by the input gating resistor, a disproportionate share may be contributed by the inductance-resistance combination, resulting in insufficient current to the base. Also, the pyramiding factor is seen to be quite low, because the current drawn through the gating resistors had to be increased by a large amount.

8.4. Capacitive Speed-up of Resistance Logic Circuits. By shunting the gating resistors with capacitors, current spikes can be provided at the leading and trailing edge of the signals to speed up response times.

Calculate the magnitude of the capacitance required for the basic circuit of Fig. 8-3. The capacitance is fixed by the turn-off operation. It must be made

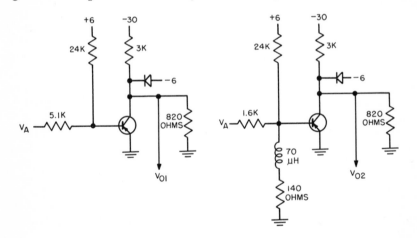

Fig. 8-7. Circuits on which the waveforms of Fig. 8-6 were measured.

sufficiently large that (referring to Fig. 8-3), when V_A goes positive, the capacitor does not charge up fully before all excess charges stored in the base are completely swept out. If the capacitor is too small, the characteristic waveform at a collector that has been in saturation, is shown in Fig. 8-8.

Here it will be seen that for too small a shunting capacitor, the capacitive current into the base has been maintained long enough to come out of the saturation region. But before all the charges corresponding to the edge of active-region operation have been swept out, the capacitive current has ceased as the capacitor has been fully charged. Although the collector waveform eventually comes down to its lower level — and sooner than if there had been no reverse current at all — such a waveform cannot as a rule be tolerated in computer circuits of this nature. There are many occurrences such as the setting of flip-flops, that operate on voltage slopes rather than on d-c voltage levels. Thus, on

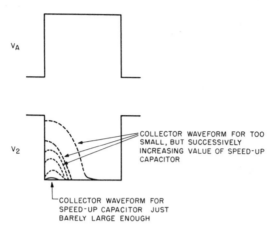

Fig. 8-8. Collector output waveforms for various shunting capacitors across input resistors in Fig. 8-3.

the single command of V_A to turn off, the collector has produced two negative-going voltage slopes separated in time. A flip-flop receiving such a signal may interpret this as two separate impulses, and count them as such.

Assume a desired sum of storage plus active-region decay time of 0.5 μsec. If some fraction of this is allocated to storage and some to decay time, the required capacitive current can be read from Figs. 4-16 and 6-7. With this current and its time duration fixed, and the magnitude of the voltage change across the capacitor fixed, the capacitance of the capacitor is determined. The first step, then, is to determine the required capacitive current. This is given by the upper limit forward base current just before turn-off. Referring to Fig. 8-1, this current is

$$\overline{I_B} = \overline{I_{RA}} - \underline{I_{R3}} - (\underline{I_{RB}} + \underline{I_{RC}}) \qquad (8\text{-}9)$$

where

$$\overline{I_{RA}} = \frac{\overline{[V'_C - V_L]}}{\underline{R_A}} = \frac{[1 + .01\ t_v]\ V_2 + \overline{V_{D1}} - \underline{V_L}}{[1 - .01\ t_r]\ R_A} \qquad (8\text{-}10)$$

In Eq. 8-10, take V_{D1} as the value at the maximum current possibly being

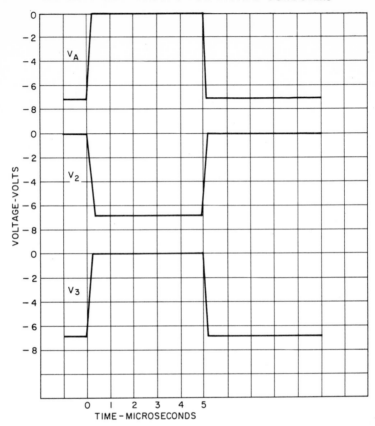

Fig. 8-9.   Measured waveforms for Fig. 8-12. No external loads at V_2 or V_3.

drawn from D1, or about 7 ma. From Fig. 7-6, this is 0.51 volt. It is not yet known at what current to take V_L but if it is taken at the nominal base current operation is surely safe, and the difference is not significant. Thus Fig. 4-4 gives V_L at 0.6 ma as 0.31 volt. Then Eq. 8-10 gives

$$\overline{I}_{RA} = \frac{(1.05)\ (6)\ +\ 0.51\ -\ 0.31}{(0.95)\ (5.1)} = 1.33\ \text{ma}$$

And since in Fig. 8-1 I_{R3} has been fixed at 0.23 ma, Eq. 8-9 gives

$$\overline{I}_B = 1.33\ -\ 0.23\ -\ \frac{(2)\ (0.3)}{(1.05)\ (5.1)}$$

$$= 0.98\ \cong\ 1\ \text{ma}$$

Of the 0.5 μsec for complete turn-off, allocate 0.3 μsec for storage. Then

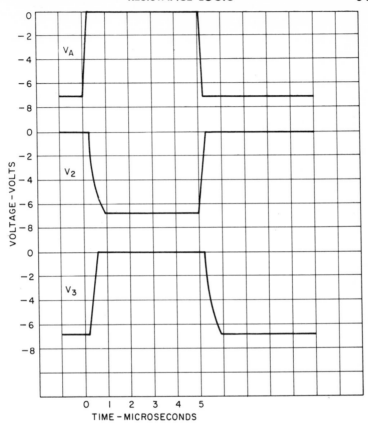

Fig. 8-10. Measured waveforms for Fig. 8-12. Two gate loads at V_2; three gate loads at V_3.

Fig. 6-7 shows that for a base current just prior to turn-off of 1.0 ma, to achieve 0.3 μsec storage time requires 2.6 ma of reverse base current for a worst-case transistor. If this 2.6 ma is maintained, the active-region decay time can be read from Fig. 4-16. The last point on this curve shows 0.21 μsec for 1.4 ma of base current. The slope is too great to extrapolate the curve out to the 2.6-ma point with any degree of accuracy, but it looks as if it will certainly be less than 0.1 μsec. For safety, take it as this value. Thus a 2.6-ma reverse base current should result in a total turn-off time of 0.4 μsec, or somewhat better than that strived for. Now on turn-off, as V_A (Fig. 8-1), goes positive, the capacitor across R_A will have to carry this 2.6 ma, plus the average value of the d-c current R_A conducted during the "on" time. Since the last current component was 1 ma, the total capacitor current on turn-off will be $2.6 + \frac{1}{2} = 3.1$ ma. The capacitor

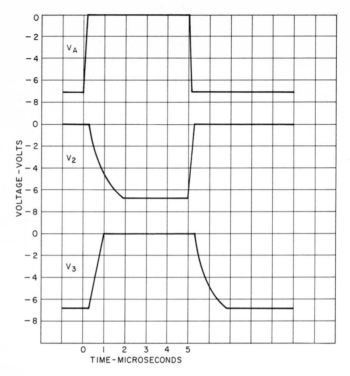

Fig. 8-11.   Measured waveforms for Fig. 8-12.   Four gate loads at V_2; five gate loads at V_3.

must then be large enough that 3.1 ma through it does not remove the 6-volt charge it accumulated during the "on" time in sooner than 0.4 µsec. Thus C is given by

$$C = \frac{I \Delta T}{\Delta V} = \frac{(003)\ (0.4 \times 10^{-6})}{6} = 206 \text{ mmf}$$

The gating resistors, bias resistor and collector load resistor for such an increased speed-resistance logic circuit, remain as calculated in Sec. 8-2.

Waveforms of this circuit (Fig. 8-12), have been taken, and are shown in Figs. 8-9, 8-10, 8-11, for various loading conditions at each collector. In Fig. 8-9, no external loads were driven at either V_2 or V_3. In Fig. 8-10, the equivalent of two gates (2400 ohms and 400 mmf in parallel to ground), was fed from V_2, and the equivalent of three gates (1800 ohms and 600 mmf in parallel to ground), was driven from V_3. Figure 8-11 is an attempt to drive the full load permitted by d-c considerations — four inputs at V_2, and five inputs at V_3 (p. 196). This amounted to 1200 ohms and 800 mmf in parallel to ground at V_2, and 1000 ohms and 1000 mmf in parallel to ground at V_3.

The waveforms in Fig. 8-11 show longer rise and fall times than 0.5 μsec, but these times are now primarily determined by the loading effect of the 200 mmf at each gate input. Thus an active-region decay time of less than 0.1 μsec had been estimated (p. 205). As this is small compared to the actual fall-time in Fig. 8-11, it can be said that a negative-going, infinitely steep current step was effectively applied at the collector of T2 in Fig. 8-12. Consider what the fall-time should then be. V_3, in Fig. 8-12 has been loaded with 1000 ohms and 1000

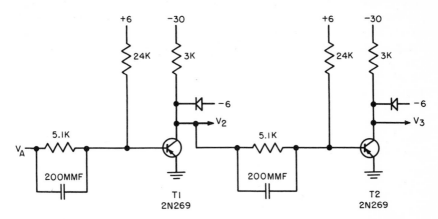

Fig. 8-12. Circuits on which waveforms of Figs. 8-9, 8-10 and 8-11 were measured.

mmf to ground. Thus the equivalent circuit during turn-off is as in Fig. 8-13 A.

In the equivalent circuit of Fig. 8-13 A, the switch has been effectively opened in 0.1 μsec. Figure 8-13 B shows the equivalent circuit for Fig. 8-13 A. Here, V_{TH} is the Thevenized voltage looking back from the capacitor, and is

$$\frac{1}{1 + 3} \ (-30) = - \ 7.5 \ \text{volt}$$

The resistor R_{TH}, is the Thevenized impedance looking back from the capacitor, and is the 1000-ohm and 3000-ohm resistors in parallel, or 750 ohms. The output voltage then falls as

$$V_O = 7.5 \ (1 - e^{-t/R_1 \ C_1})$$

where

$$R_1 \ C_1 = (750) \ (1000 \times 10^{-12}) = 0.75 \ \text{μsec}$$

The output voltage from this relation should then reach the 6-volt level in a time given by

$$6 = 7.5 \ (1 - e^{-t/0.75})$$

This gives $t = 1.2$ μsec, which is quite close to the value shown in Fig. 8-11.

The rise-time in the waveforms of Figs. 8-9 to 8-11 is not independent of the transistor, as was the fall-time. Consider how rise times may be calculated. When T1 (Fig. 8-12), switches off, all the current demanded by its 3000-ohm load resistor is available to turn on bases fed from T1. Because of the low impedance of the 200-mmf capacitors shunting the gating resistors, the base current is large. During the fall-time at V_2, the average current demanded by the 3000-ohm load resistor is the current calculated for V_2 midway between 0 and -6 volts. Thus the collector load is a sink for a nominal current of $27/3 = 9$ ma. If there are five gate resistors, and their 200-mmf shunting capacitors are fed from V_2 (as is the case for waveform V_3, Fig. 8-11), each base receives a turn-on current of $9/5 = 1.8$ ma. From the transistor characteristics, Fig. 4-5B, at 1-8 ma of base current, the d-c collector current would be 48 ma. But the collector current rises to 48 ma as given by Eq. 4-13. The collector current then is

$$I_C = \beta \, I_B \, [1 - e^{-t/T_{CE}}] \qquad (8\text{-}11)$$

when T_{CE} is $\beta/2\pi \, f\alpha_{co}$ and β is to be evaluated at a base current of 1.8 ma. Thus β is $48/1.8 \cong 27$, and

$$T_{CE} = \frac{27}{2 \, \pi \, 4 \times 10^{+6}} = 1.07 \; \mu\text{sec}$$

The collector current rises as

$$I_C = 48 \, [1 - e^{-t/1.07 \times 10^{-6}}]$$

The equivalent circuit at the rising collector is then as shown in Fig. 8-14. Here, R_{TH} is the Thevenized resistance seen looking out from the collector, and for Fig. 8-11 is 1000 ohms and 3000 ohms in parallel, or 750 ohms. In Fig. 8-11 C_L was 1000 mmf.

The output voltage is then given by the differential equation:

$$I_{MAX} \; [1 - e^{-t/T1}] = \frac{V}{R_{TH}} + C_L \frac{dV}{dt} \qquad (8\text{-}12)$$

The solution of this differential equation is

$$V = I_{MAX} \, R_{TH} \left[1 - \left(\frac{1}{1 - \dfrac{T1}{R_{TH} \, C_L}} \right) e^{\frac{-t}{R_{TH} \, C_L}} + \left(\frac{\dfrac{T1}{R_{TH} \, C_L}}{1 - \dfrac{T1}{R_{TH} \, C_L}} \right) e^{-t/T1} \right]$$

$$(8\text{-}13)$$

For $R_{TH} = 750$ ohms, $C_1 = 1000$ mmf, and $I_{MAX} = 48$ ma,

$$V = 36 \, [1 + 2.32 \, e^{-t/0.75} - 3.32 \, e^{-t/1.07}] \qquad (8\text{-}14)$$

And relation 8-14 rises 7 volts in 0.65 μsec. This compares with a measured value in Fig. 8-11 of 0.70 μsec (waveform V_3). Thus, calculated rise and fall times for maximum loads at each collector are seen to agree satisfactorily with measured values.

In circuits of this nature the actual rise and fall time may not be too important, because an output waveform can fully switch a transistor more quickly than the time required to reach its equilibrium value. Because of capacitive inputs to transistors, base currents are given by the rate of change of the driving signal

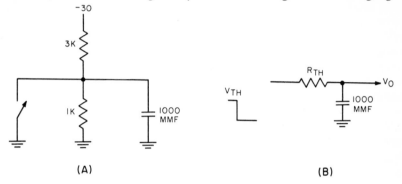

(A)   (B)

Fig. 8-13. Equivalent circuits at collector of T1 in Fig. 8-12, during turn-off.

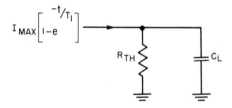

Fig. 8-14. Equivalent circuit at collector of T1 in Fig. 8-12, during turn-on.

rather than its d-c voltage level. Thus in Fig. 8-11, V_3 has been fully turned on in the time V_2 has taken to move slightly more than half way to its lower voltage level. Similarly, the rising slope at V_3 would be able to shut off a transistor at a point about half way up its slope. Such a transistor driven from V_3, would commence turning off halfway up the rising slope of V_3, and if it were driving a full five-gate input would require the above calculated 1.2 μsec to move down to its lower level. This characteristic ambiguity as to whether a signal is in its "one" or "zero" state, depending on its rate of change of voltage, can give rise to logical difficulties, and should be considered in actual applications.

Even though waveforms such as V_2, Fig. 8-11, can produce enabling signals on their slopes, in most applications it would not be a safe thing on which to depend. Thus, if such a waveform were being used to gate narrow pulses through pulse amplifiers, it would be desirable for the waveform to spend at least 50%

of its time at the lower voltage level, because of the ambiguity as to the exact duration of the slope. This would (for V_2, Fig. 8-11), limit the highest square-wave repetition rate so that the half-period is 4 μsec, which would give a maximum repetition rate of 125 kc. If a limit is fixed so that one output drives a maximum of three inputs as in Fig. 8-10, operation can be as high as 250 kc (again assuming the half-period is twice the sum of the storage plus fall-time).

There is one further fairly serious restriction on such resistance logic circuits using speed-up capacitors. It was seen that because of the high impedance of the gating resistors relative to the base input impedance, the signal generators are well isolated from each other, and from the base of the driven transistor. Thus, the input resistors (Fig. 8-1), are so designed that if any input signal is at its lower level, whether one or more of the other signals move to the upper level makes little difference to the driven transistor. It only moves from a very heavily, to a less heavily saturated condition, and the collector potential varies little.

With speed-up capacitors across the input resistor, however a very different situation exists. Consider the circuit of Fig. 8-1 with the gate resistors shunted by 200-mmf capacitors. If all three inputs are at their lower level, and two move up to ground simultaneously, there is a large capacitive current

$$I_C = 2C \left(\frac{\Delta V}{\Delta t} \right)$$

delivered to the summing point of the gating resistors. This may be enough to momentarily turn the transistor off and produce a negative-going spike at the output, even though one input is at the lower level supposedly inhibiting the gate. Consider Fig. 8-11. There, for waveform V_3, the capacitive current at the rise-time would be given by

$$I_C = 2C \frac{\Delta V}{\Delta t} = 2 \frac{(200 \times 10^{-12}) \ 6.8}{(0.7 \times 10^{-6})} = 3.9 \ \text{ma}$$

The one input at the lower level has forced the base to be at approximately −0.30 volt (Fig. 4-4). Thus, the equivalent circuit is given by Fig. 8-15.

The 200-mmf capacitor of the supposedly inhibiting input will absorb (in being driven from −0.30 volt to ground), a current of only

$$C \frac{\Delta V}{\Delta t} = \frac{(200 \times 10^{-12}) \ (0.3)}{0.7 \times 10^{-6}} = 86 \ \mu\text{a}$$

The 5100 ohms will absorb a current of

$$\frac{\Delta V}{R} = \frac{0.3}{5.1} = 59 \ \mu\text{a}$$

Thus, of the 3.9 ma flowing into the summing point, $3.9 - (0.086 + 0.059) = 3.8$ ma flows into the base as reverse current drive. Now just prior to the two inputs having gone positive, operation was heavily in saturation. There was a d-c forward base current of three times the minimum drive of a single input (0.6 ma from p. 194, or 1.8 ma). From Fig. 6-7, interpolation shows that for a reverse base drive of 3.8 ma, for a forward base current just before turn-off of 1.8 ma, storage time will be about 0.45 µsec. If this 3.8 ma is maintained beyond 0.45 µsec, it will be seen from Fig. 4-16 that at this reverse base drive, the active-region decay time is negligible.

Thus, in the case of one input remaining at the lower level, and two simultaneously going to the upper level, it is quite certain that the reverse capacitive

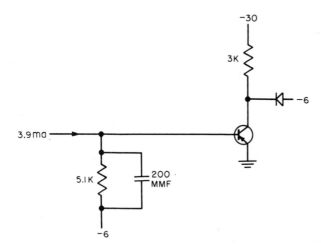

Fig. 8-15. Equivalent circuit at the base of transistor in Fig. 8-1 with 200 mmf speed-up capacitors across input resistors, and two input points simultaneously moving up while one input remains down.

current (since it lasts for 0.70 µsec in V_3), is sufficient to bring the transistor out of saturation and produce a negative spike at the collector. The duration and amplitude of the spike will depend on the actual rise-time of the signal, and the loading at the transistor output. Also, if the gate has more than three inputs and all but one move upwards simultaneously, the capacitive current will naturally be greater, and the output spike will be larger.

All the gate inputs have a low impedance for such spikes because of these speed-up capacitors. Consequently, these spikes will be propagated through a chain of such stages, increasing in amplitude at each stage. Obviously, this trouble does not occur when all but one gate input remain at the lower level, while the one input moves from its lower level to ground. In such a condition the capacitive current delivered to the summing point is lower, operation is more heavily in saturation, and the multiple inputs at the lower level absorb more of this capacitive current, leaving considerably less for the base.

This difficulty offers two alternatives. First, the logic could be restricted so that not more than one input would ever be permitted to simultaneously move from the lower to the upper level. This is not too severe a restriction, and in most cases (one important exception being a set of gates that decode the state of a binary counter), is possible. The other alternative is expensive in transistors, but is always usable. It consists of simply restricting the number of inputs to a summing point, to two. If more than two inputs are to be gated,

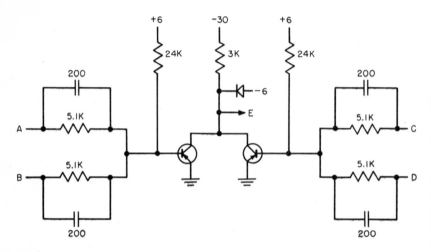

Fig. 8-16. Capacitance speed-up resistance gating using two transistors to avoid false output spikes when one input point remains down, while two or more input points simultaneously move up.

group them, two per transistor, and parallel the collectors of such transistors. This is shown in Fig. 8-16 where the logical operation $ABCD = \bar{E}$ is being performed. Any number of input signals may now be permitted to move from the lower to the upper level, without a noise spike appearing at the output.

Since the most frequent type of computer gate has a three-input signal, if forced to use the latter solution the circuit loses its most attractive feature — economy of components.

8.5. Resistance Logic with High-Frequency Transistors. It has been shown that to achieve higher frequency operation with the 2N269 transistor it was necessary to use speed-up capacitors across the input gating resistors. This gave rise to the problem of simultaneous transition of more than one input from the lower to the upper level producing "fictitious" spike output signals, even when one input remained at the lower level supposedly to inhibit the gate. This forced the use of only two inputs per transistor, and the paralleling of transistors for more than two-input gates, and lost the most desirable feature of the method — its economy.

Consider whether it may not be better to use a more expensive, high-frequency transistor that would not require speed-up capacitors shunting the gate resistors, thus still permitting one transistor per gate. The result may very likely be a faster circuit with no loss in output-drive capability.

Attempt a design employing the Philco 2N240 used in the high-frequency current-switching circuits of the previous chapter. The circuit will be as in Fig. 8-17.

Choose a nominal collector "on" current of 8 ma for the reasons discussed on p. 172. To ensure a most negative upper-level collector potential of −0.2

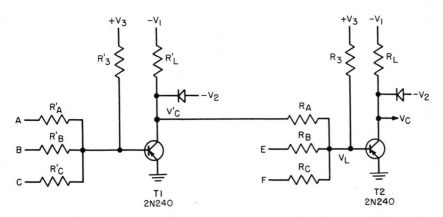

Fig. 8-17. Resistance gating building block with high-frequency transistors.

volt for an aged transistor, guarantee a worst-case forward base drive of 1.0 ma as discussed on p. 173. Now select V_1, V_2 and V_3. Since this transistor type has a maximum collector voltage rating of 6 volts, choose V_2 as far below this as possible to ensure long transistor lifetime. Calculate the voltages and components to satisfy d-c conditions, and from these voltage and component values, calculate switching speed.

The first condition imposed, is that an "on" transistor has a worst-case forward base current of 1 ma when one input is at the lower level, and two inputs are at their upper level. Thus, in Fig. 8-17, the lower limit base current is the difference between the lower limit current drawn by R_A, and the sum of the upper limit currents supplied by R_B, R_C and R_3. (Note that $R_A = R_B = R_C$). In calculating currents supplied by R_B and R_C assume that the input ends of these resistors (points such as V'_C), are at ground. It was shown on p. 174, that 1 ma of forward base current guarantees a most negative upper-level collector potential of −0.2 volt. Nevertheless, for a new high β transistor at upper limit forward base drives, collectors may bottom to within 0.04 volt from ground. But the worst-case condition for turning a transistor on is that disproportionately more of the current demanded by R_A is supplied by R_B and R_C, leaving less for the base. Therefore, specify the most positive upper-level potential at E and F for the case when it is desired to turn on T2. To be conservative, take this most positive upper-level potential as ground. Then

$$I_B = 0.001 = \frac{[V'_{CO} - V_L]}{\overline{R}_A} - (\overline{I}_{RB} + \overline{I}_{RC} + \overline{I}_{R3})$$

where V'_{CO} is the potential at the collector of T1, when it is off.

Take V_L as the maximum base potential for a base current of 1 ma from Fig. 7-17. Adhering to the practice of assuming $\pm$ 0.05 volt tolerance on base potential curves, gives $V_L = -0.47$ volt at $V_C = -0.10$ volt from Fig. 7-17. Then

$$0.001 = \frac{[1 - .01\ t_v]\ V'_{CO} - \overline{V}_L}{[1 + .01\ t_r]\ R_A} - \frac{2\ \overline{V}_L}{[1 - .01\ t_r]\ R_A}$$
$$- \frac{[1 + .01\ t_v]\ V_3}{[1 - .01\ t_r]\ R_3} \qquad (8\text{-}15)$$

$$0.001 = \frac{(0.95)\ V'_{CO} - 0.47}{(1.05)\ R_A} - \frac{2\ (0.47)}{(0.95)\ R_A}$$
$$- \frac{1.05\ V_3}{0.95\ R_3} \qquad (8\text{-}16)$$

Now the condition is expressed that for all three inputs at their most negative upper-level potential, transistor T2 is cut off. For this to be true, the lower limit current available from R_3 must supply a level shifting component so that potentials of -0.2 volt at the input ends of each of the three gating resistors, result in a potential of ground at V_L. In addition R_3 must supply a reverse current of I_{CO} to the base of T2 for good d-c shut-off. As on p. 174, take I_{CO} for the transistor as 0.1 ma at 65°C. The T2 shut-off condition is then

$$I_{R3} = \frac{[1 - .01\ t_v]\ V_3}{[1 + .01\ t_r]\ R_3}$$
$$= 3\left[\frac{(0.2)}{(1 - .01\ t_r)\ R_A}\right] + 0.0001 \qquad (8\text{-}17)$$

$$\frac{0.95\ V_3}{1.05\ R_3} = \frac{0.6}{0.95\ R_A} + 0.0001$$

$$\frac{V_3}{R_3} = \frac{0.7}{R_A} + 0.00011$$

Substituting this value of V_3/R_3 in Eq. 8-16 gives

$$1.12 = \frac{0.95\ V'_{CO} - 0.47}{1.05\ R_A} - \frac{1.76}{R_A} \qquad (8\text{-}18)$$

where R_A is in kilohms.

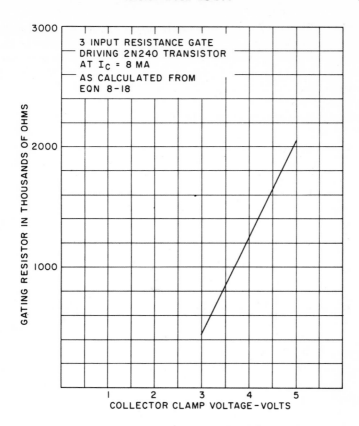

Fig. 8-18. Gating resistor v. collector output voltage swing.

Equation 8-18 gives R_A for any preselected value of V'_{CO}. It is plotted in Fig. 8-18. A value of 2 volts for the collector clamp potential results in a negative value for R_A, indicating that the prescribed turn-on and turn-off conditions cannot be met for such low collector-voltage swings.

With Eq. 8-18 it is possible to design a resistance gating structure such as Fig. 8-17. Any value of V'_{CO} can be chosen, and the corresponding value of R_A used. There is however, another condition to be met, that narrows the choice, i.e., the desire to drive from a transistor output point as many input points (resistors such as R_A), as possible.

Originally, a nominal transistor "on" current of 8 ma was chosen. This fixes $V_1/R_L = 8$ ma. The condition for maximum drive capability at an output node occurs when, say T1 cut-off, the worst-case maximum current flowing into the V'_C node from the resistors such as R_A is equal to the worst-case minimum current drawn from the node by R'_L. Assume that of the n resistors such as R_A, that can be fed from an output node, $(n-1)$ of them are at their lower tolerance limit, thus contributing a disproportionately large share of the current demanded by R'_L. Also, that the last resistor such as R_A, is at its upper tolerance limit, so that its base receives the least current. Further assume that the potential V'_{CO} (which will be fixed by the collector clamp supply V_2), is at its least negative lower level value, tending to further decrease the base current of the last of the n driven transistors.

These conditions are expressed by Eq. 8-19:

$$I_{R'_L} \ (\text{T1 off}) = \frac{[1 - .01 \ t_v] \ V_1 - [1 - .01 \ t_v] \ V'_{CO}}{[1 + .01 \ t_r] \ R_L}$$

$$= (n - 1) \left[\frac{(1 - .01 \ t_v) \ V'_{CO} - \overline{V}_L}{(1 - .01 \ t_r) \ R_A} \right] + \left[\frac{(1 - .01 \ t_v) \ V'_{CO} - \overline{V}_L}{(1 + .01 \ t_r) \ R_A} \right]$$

$$(8\text{-}19)$$

or

$$\frac{(0.95) \ (V_1 - V'_{CO})}{1.05 \ (V_1/8)}$$

$$= (n - 1) \left[\frac{(0.95) \ V'_{CO} - 0.47}{(0.95) \ (R_A)} \right] + \frac{0.95 \ V'_{CO} - 0.47}{1.05 \ R_A}$$

$$(8\text{-}20)$$

Equation 8-20 provides the drive capability, or pyramiding factor. The collector supply voltage (V_1), has been taken successively as 5, 6, and 7 times the output voltage swing (V'_{CO}). For each of these factors, V'_{CO} and R_8 have been taken as corresponding to one another, as given in Eq. 8-18, and the pyramiding factor n has been calculated from Eq. 8-20. The results are plotted in Fig. 8-19.

This Figure (8-19), indicates that to achieve a pyramiding factor of three, operation must be close to the maximum collector voltage rating of 6 volts. Only life tests can determine whether this is safe. In actual practice it would probably be better to tighten the voltage and resistor tolerances, rather than operate close to the maximum collector voltage. It would not be too uneconomical to keep voltage and resistor tolerances to $\pm 3\%$ rather than $\pm 5\%$.

Although a pyramiding factor of three is not quite achieved for a 5-volt collector swing, such a circuit has been assembled to show the waveform rise and fall times. The exact circuit is shown in Fig. 8-20. The collector clamp voltage was selected as 5 volts, with a ratio of supply-voltage to output-voltage swing, of 6. This gives a pyramiding factor from Eq. 8-20 of 2.83. The value of R_A was selected from Eq. 8-18 as 2040 ohms. The value of R_3 was calculated from Eq. 8-17 after an arbitrary choice of +10 volts for V_3, as this voltage is relatively unimportant.

Figure 8-21 shows the waveforms obtained from the circuit of Fig. 8-20, for various conditions of input driving and output loading. Waveform V_{O1} shows the unloaded output waveform with inputs B and C grounded, and V_1 applied to input A. At V_{O2}, the same input conditions can be seen, with the

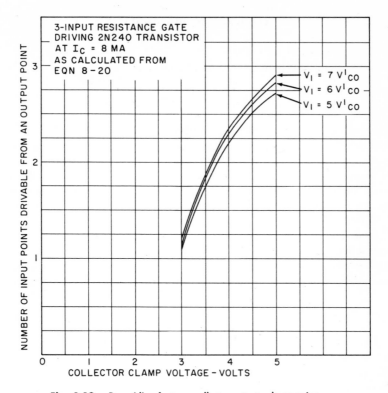

Fig. 8-19. Pyramiding factor v. collector output voltage swing.

output loaded with a 680-ohm resistor to ground simulating an output driving three inputs (approximately three 2000-ohm resistors in parallel). Waveform V_{O3} shows unloaded output waveforms with the driving signal simultaneously feeding inputs A, B, and C. At V_{O4}, all three inputs are being fed from V_1, and again, there is a 680-ohm load at the output to ground.

Response times agree satisfactorily with what would be expected from the switching characteristics of Figs. 7-19 and 7-20. Calculate for example, what should be expected for waveform V_{O4}.

The nominal forward base current just prior to turn-off is the difference between what the three 2000-ohm resistors demand, and the 24,000-ohm resistor supplies. A tentative calculation shows this base current to be approximately 6 ma. At 6 ma of base current this transistor has a base potential of approximately -0.6 volt. Therefore, the forward base current more exactly, is

$$3 \left[\frac{5 - 0.6}{2} \right] - \frac{10}{24} = 6.2 \text{ ma}$$

The reverse base current is the current available from the 24,000-ohm resistor ($10/24 \cong 0.4$ ma), plus that from the three-gate resistor whose input ends are at ground. During the turn-off process, the base moves linearly from its "on" potential of -0.6 volt towards ground. Therefore, the average current available from these gate resistors can be taken as

$$3 \left[\frac{0.6/2}{2000} \right] = 0.45 \text{ ma}$$

The total reverse base current is then 0.85 ma.

Figure 7-21 gives the active-region decay time, but only up to 3 ma of forward base current just before turn-off. Thus, at 0.85 ma of reverse current after 3 ma of forward current before turn-off, a decay time of 0.08 μsec can be read. It would be reasonable to expect twice this time, or 0.16 μsec for 6 ma of forward current just before 0.85 ma of reverse current. The measured decay time is 0.14 μsec.

From Fig. 7-20, a storage time of 0.017 μsec can be read for 0.85 ma of reverse base drive just after 3 ma of forward base current. Again, assume it will be twice this value, i.e., 0.034 for 6 ma of forward base current. The measurement of storage time is ambiguous, because the input signal rise-time

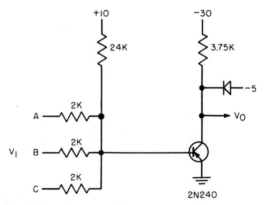

Fig. 8-20.   Circuit on which waveforms of Fig. 8-21 were measured.

is itself 0.06 μsec. If the start of the storage interval is taken as the moment the input signal reaches ground, the measured storage time is 0.04 μsec. This compares to a calculated value of 0.034 μsec.

The expected turn-on time for the forward base drive of 6 ma would be read from Fig. 7-19. The curve gives data up to 1 ma of forward base drive only. If the worst transistor curve is extrapolated out to 6 ma, a turn-on time of well under 0.05 μsec should be expected. The measured turn-on time in Fig. 8-20 is 0.04 μsec. But the measurement is limited by the oscilloscope rise-time, which is 0.035 μsec. (Tektronix 531, with model 53B preamplifier.)

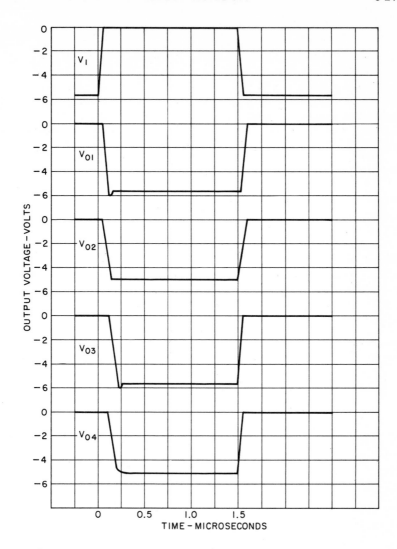

Fig. 8-21. Waveforms for circuit of Fig. 8-20 under various load conditions.

A structure such as Fig. 8-19, can operate up to frequencies as high as 2 mc (a period equal to approximately twice the sum of the storage and decay time). Since it uses no speed-up capacitors across the input gating resistors, there is no difficulty in permitting two inputs to move up to ground simultaneously.

Where expense is not an important factor, it is possible to operate at a much higher frequency, using speed-up capacitors with this high-frequency transistor. Then as already mentioned, it would be necessary to use two gate inputs per transistor, and parallel transistors as in Fig. 8-16. With only two inputs per transistor, the gating resistors could be larger, as one input resistor at the lower level would be drawing current from the base, and only one input resistor, rather than possibly two resistors at the upper level (Eq. 8-15). In addition, the level shift problem would require less current from R_3 (Fig. 8-16), as the impedance in parallel with the base is a maximum of two rather than three gate resistors in parallel. A pyramiding factor of three could probably be achieved with less than 5-volt swings at collectors; also, probably, an operating speed equal to that of the single-level diode logic method of Sec. 7.6.

Chapter 9

DIRECT-COUPLED TRANSISTOR LOGIC

An important set of computer circuits can be fabricated using the transistor as both the logical gating, and power amplifying element[1]. The practice is very uneconomical in its use of transistors, as it requires one for each input to an AND or OR gate. It has however, many advantages in that it uses only transistors and resistors, and no interstage coupling element between gates or between gates and amplifiers. The same building block is usable as an AND gate, OR gate, inverter or flip-flop. Only one supply voltage is required, and it may be as low as approximately 3 volts. Power dissipation, both in the transistors and resistors, is extremely low.

Voltage swings in this system are about 0.4 volt, and consequently there is very little loss of power in charging and discharging stray capacitances. Because of the small voltage changes, and the high-frequency transistor normally used in this method, operating speed can be very high. More of the transistor parameters must be tightly controlled, and must remain within close limits during operating lifetime, than in other schemes. This last feature restricts the operating temperature range more than most methods.

This chapter will show the usual gating structures employed, and perform worst-case designs with them.

9.1. Elements of Direct-Coupled Transistor Logic. The principles of this method (generally referred to as DCTL), can be seen from Fig. 9-1. This Figure shows a chain of three of the basic elements. The transistor normally employed is the surface-barrier transistor such as the Philco 2N240 (Figs. 9-2 to 9-4), and discussion is based on this. The resistors R_1, R_2, R_3 (usually all equal), serve as constant-current sinks, drawing current either from the collectors at the output points V_1, V_2, V_3 — when the corresponding transistors are "on" — or

[1] Beter, R. H., Bradley, W. E., Brown, R. B., and Rubinoff, M., "Directly-Coupled Transistor Circuits," *Electronics*, June 1955.

from the base at these points if the transistor whose collector is in parallel with a base, is "off".

If a transistor is on, its base current is so chosen that the collector potential has bottomed well into the saturation region to a potential no more negative than −0.1 volt (Fig. 9-2). Thus, any base connected to an "on" collector has a potential no more negative than −0.1 volt. Figure 9-4 shows that at a base potential of −0.1 volt, and a collector potential of −0.3 to −0.5 volt (it will

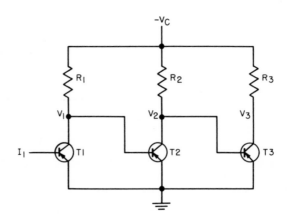

Fig. 9-1.   Chain of direct-coupled transistors.

be seen that if a transistor is off, its collector potential can go no more negative that −0.3 to −0.5 volt), the base current is 3 μa.

From Fig. 9-2 at V_{CE} of −0.3 volt, the d-c beta at a base current of 50 μa is $900/50 = 18$. Then, assuming this beta holds down to the region of very low base currents (in general, d-c beta is lower at such low base currents), the 3 μa of base current results in $3(18) = 54$ μa of collector current, a small fraction of the current demanded by the collector load resistors. The collector then starts falling towards $-V_C$ but is caught by the base-to-emitter circuit acting as a diode. The current demanded by the collector load resistor is supplied by the base (except for the above 54 μa). The actual potential at an "on" base is obtained from the intersection of the load line R_L from $-V_C$, with the base current curves of Fig. 9-4. If R_L is a 1-ma load — say, a 5000-ohm resistor returned to $V_C = −5$ volts — this base potential is the point 0 on the load line AA′ in Fig. 9-4, and is seen to be −0.41 volt.

The collector of a transistor whose base current is 1 ma, bottoms to a potential given by the intersection of a 1-ma load line (5000 ohms to −5 volts), with the 1-ma base-current curve in Fig. 9-2. This potential (P3), is seen to be well below −0.1 volt — it is actually in the vicinity of −0.01 volt. A collector potential so close to ground cannot turn on the base following it.

Thus, in the chain of Fig. 9-1, if 1 ma is drawn through the base of T1, it turns hard on, and its collector bottoms to close to −0.01 volt. This turns T2 off, its collector starts falling towards −V_C but is caught by the base-to-emitter circuit of T3, and V_2 is held at −0.41 volt. The, approximately, 1 ma demanded

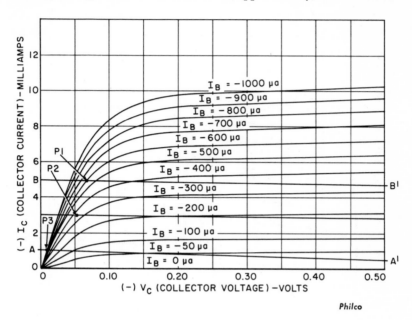

Philco

Fig. 9-2. Saturation region collector characteristics of type 2N240 transistor; with grounded emitter.

by R_2 is supplied by the base of T3, and consequently T3 is turned hard on with V_3 bottoming to about −0.01 volt.

If the base of T1 is forced to a potential no more negative than −0.1 volt, T1 is cut off. Then V_1 starts falling towards −V_C, and is caught by the base-to-emitter circuit of T2 acting as a diode. Approximately 1 ma of current demanded by R_1 is supplied from the base of T2, which is thereby turned hard on. The collector of T2 bottoms to −0.01 volt and cuts T3 off. Thus, alternate transistors in such a chain are always in the opposite state. "On" transistors force the base of transistors they drive to a potential so close to ground as to effectively cut them off. The load resistors of such cut-off transistors seek their current from bases of transistors, and thereby turn them on.

The potential −V_C is not important, it must merely be large compared to the voltage variations at a collector (approximately −0.4 volt), so that the load resistors can be considered as fairly good constant current sources. These constant load currents are being switched between collectors and bases, and the circuit is therefore often described as operating in the current mode.

If, in Fig. 9-1, the collector resistors are 1-ma loads, any collector may feed a number of bases. Recall that to ensure cutting a transistor off, it was decided not to permit its base to go more negative than -0.1 volt. This prevents a collector current from turning on to any more than 54 μa (p. 222). Then

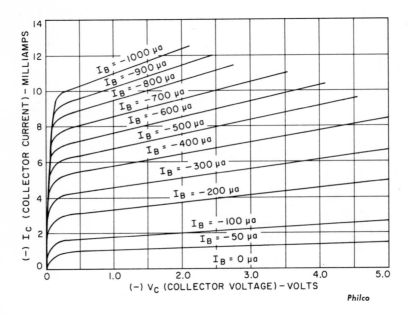

Philco

Fig. 9-3. Typical collector characteristics of type 2N240 transistor; grounded emitter.

if a 1-ma load line (5000 ohms to -5 volts), is drawn on Fig. 9-2, it will be seen that it intersects a collector potential of -0.1 volt at a base current of about 60 μa. Thus, in Fig. 9-1, if T1 is off, the 1-ma current sink R_1, is sufficient to drive $1000/60 \cong 16$ bases. Each of these bases receiving 60 μa would bottom to a collector potential no greater than -0.1 volt. This would ensure that transistors driven from the collectors of any of the 16 transistors mentioned, would turn on to no more than 54 μa (p. 222). Therefore, the 1-ma load current demanded by the resistors of each of the latter transistors is almost entirely available for turning on 16 other bases.

In a worst-case design, however, the number of inputs it is possible to drive from an output is considerably less than 16. In the first place, the curves of Figs. 9-2 to 9-4 represent the average transistor*, and here, design is for the worst transistor. Secondly, it has been assumed that if a collector is off, all the bases driven in parallel by a single resistor supply equal currents to that sink

---

* See also the table of surface-barrier transistor characteristics, p. 237.

resistor. This is by no means true, because there is a production spread of the volt-ampere base curve. Since all driven bases are in parallel, they operate at the same potential. If that potential is such as to guarantee a minimum current to the highest impedance base, then all the lower impedance bases supply more

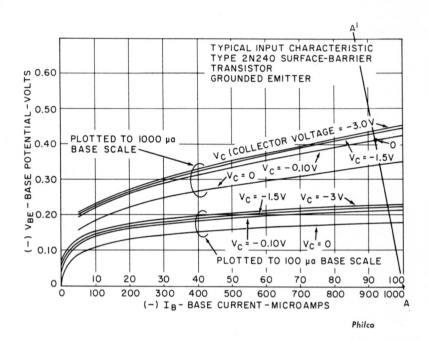

Fig. 9-4. Typical input characteristics of type 2N240 transistor; grounded emitter.

current to the sink resistor than they require to bottom their collectors to −0.1 volt. The base volt-ampere curve being quite steep, if the best and worst base characteristics are displaced along the voltage axis by only a small amount, there may still be a very large difference in currents between these two characteristics at this same base potential. This will be seen more clearly in the worst-case design.

Additional reasons for a pyramiding factor of less than the 16 estimated above, are that voltage and resistance tolerances, and temperature effects were not taken into account. These effects will be considered later.

9.2. Parallel Gating with Direct-Coupled Transistors. If each of the three inverting amplifiers in the chain of Fig. 9-1 were a group of transistors whose collectors were in parallel as in Fig. 9-5, a logical gate would result. Each transistor in Fig. 9-5 may be looked upon as a single-pole, single-throw switch. The switch is open for low base currents, and closed for sufficiently high base current. Either of the switches being closed, shorts the output, V_0, to within

0.1 volt of ground potential. If all the switches were open, V_O would fall to $-V_C$, if not caught closer to ground by a load. In the worst-case analysis of such switches they will be regarded as current controlled. From the point of view of logic, they will be considered closed by a lower level, conducting base potential of about -0.4 volt, and opened by an upper level conducting collector potential of -0.1 volt. These voltages are the logical "ones" and "zeros", and hereafter they will be spoken of as negative and positive voltages, even though

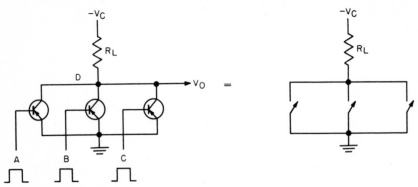

Fig. 9-5.   Transistor AND gate for positive inputs, and OR gate for negative inputs.

they are negative and positive relative only to one another, and not to ground.

Thus, the circuit of Fig. 9-5 performs an AND operation with polarity reversal for positive, "true" signals, and an OR operation with polarity reversal for negative "true" signals. Algebraically, this is described by $ABC = \overline{D}$ for positive signals, and $A + B + C = \overline{D}$ for negative signals. In a computing system, such a configuration as Fig. 9-5 can be universally used as both the AND and OR gate if the correct signal polarity is available. In those cases where it is not, a single inverter such as one of the units of Fig. 9-1, would have to be interposed.

The output of such a parallel gate can drive one of the inputs to a similar structure, in the same way as the output of the single inverting amplifier of Fig. 9-1 drives an inverter input. Thus, in the event of a need to circuitize the logical equation $ABC + DEF + GHI = J$, Fig. 9-6 would be followed if all the input signals were positive. As will be shown, a number of other bases may be driven at each of the AND and OR gate outputs, these bases representing AND or OR gate terms, or inverters. The simplicity and high-transistor count of such a method shows up strikingly in Fig. 9-6.

9.3. Series Gating with Direct-Coupled Transistors.   Single-pole, single-throw transistor switches may be connected in series, as in Fig. 9-7, to make a logical gate. Here, the output is shorted to a potential close to ground only if all the switches are closed by turning on base current. If any one of the switches is open, the output falls to $-V_C$ if not caught closer to ground by a load. The

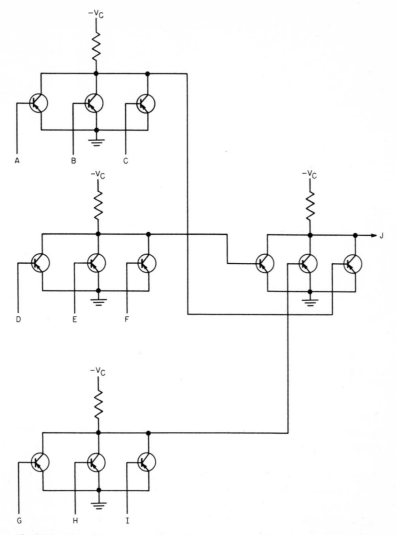

Fig. 9-6. Three three-input positive AND gates driving a three-input negative OR gate.

base input signals may come from the outputs of parallel gates, such as shown in Fig. 9-5, or from the output points V_O, of similar series gates. Since it requires negative base potentials to turn on collector current, the series gate is an AND gate for negative signals, and an OR gate for positive signals. Stated algebraically, it performs the operation $ABC = \overline{D}$ for negative true inputs, and $A + B + C = \overline{D}$ for positive true inputs.

If a series gate output is to switch a base, whether it be that at the bottom of a series stack, or one of the bases in a parallel gate, each collector-to-emitter voltage must be bottomed considerably harder than was done in the case of parallel gates. For with all the transistors in Fig. 9-7 on, the potential at V_O is the sum of three collector-to-emitter potentials that must each be no greater than -0.033, if the upper-level potential at V_O is to be no more negative than -0.1 volt.

From Fig. 9-2 it is obvious that transistors in series for a given load current require considerably more base drive in the "on" state, than do transistors in

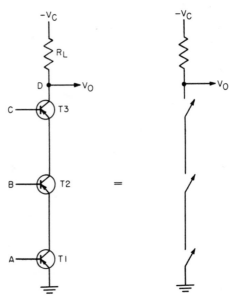

Fig. 9-7. Series AND gate with inversion for negative inputs, and OR gate with inversion for positive inputs.

parallel gates, to achieve a total bottomed output potential of -0.1 volt. But the "off" state is less of a design difficulty in the series gate than it is in the parallel gate. In Fig. 9-5, if the supposedly off transistors are still leaking some collector current, the load resistor must be a sink for this leakage current from each off transistor. The sink resistor has therefore less current available to turn bases on. In the series gate in the off state, the load resistor must absorb only one collector leakage current regardless of the number of transistors in series. These points are considered in detail in the worst-case design.

9.4. **Logical Operations with Direct-Coupled Transistors.** By connecting two direct-coupled transistors in a ring, as in Fig. 9-8, a bistable device, or flip-flop, is obtained. If one transistor, say T1, is on, and in saturation, its collector is within -0.1 volt of ground, and T2 is therefore shut off. R_{L2} draws all its current from the base of T1, keeping it hard-on in the saturation region. The flip-flop may be thrown into the opposite state by momentarily reducing the base current of the "on" transistor to zero. This is most easily done by adding another transistor in parallel at each collector, as in Fig. 9-9. The triggering transistors T1T and T2T, are normally turned off. If, say T1, is on, V_1 is at -0.1 volt, T2 is off, and R_{L2} draws its current from the base of T1, which is at a potential of about -0.41 volt (point 0 Fig. 9-4).

Now, if T2T is momentarily turned on, the current demanded by R_{L2} comes from the collector of T2T, rather than the base of T1, V_2 goes to a potential

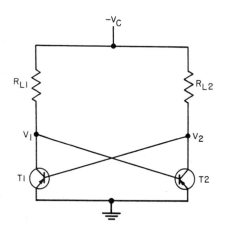

Fig. 9-8. DCTL flip-flop.

of -0.1 volt, T1 is momentarily cut off, and R_{L1} draws its current from the base of T2, turning its collector current on. If T2T is now turned off, the flip-flop remains in this state with T1 off, and T2 on. By momentarily turning T1T on, the flip-flop can be reset to its original state.

The flip-flop can be set or reset by the result of an AND or OR operation, by substituting a series gate for the triggering transistors, as in Fig. 9-10. A simultaneous negative coincidence at A, B, C, will throw T1 on, and T2 off. A similar coincidence at D, E, F, will reverse its state. Expressed algebraically, the circuit performs the operation, $G = DEF$, and $\overline{G} = ABC$, where true input signals are negative signals (d-c level of approximately -0.4 volt). As in the ordinary series gate when the trigger transistors are turned on, the base currents must be sufficiently large that the sum of the three collector-to-emitter potentials is no greater than -0.1 volt.

In general, one of the gating inputs is a narrow enabling clock-pulse whose duration need only be long enough to perform the triggering action. Its repetition period is long compared to its duration. The triggering transistor is normally open between clock-pulses, and the flip-flop remembers which triggering gate last had a "true" output at clock-pulse time.

Complex logical operations may be performed by simple combinations of such series and parallel gates. Thus, in Fig. 9-11, the output point $\overline{J}$ is at ground if a closed path to ground is found in either the series chain G1, G2, or

G3. For any of the series chains to be closed, all its switches must be simultaneously closed. Thus, the circuit performs the logical operation $ABC + DEF + GHI = \overline{J}$, for negative true signals.

The binary half adder of Chapter 2 can be mechanized very simply with such series and parallel gates. It was shown on p. 23 that the half adder performs the logical operations:

$$\text{Sum} = A\overline{B} + \overline{A}B$$

$$\text{Carry} = AB$$

This would be mechanized in the DCTL system as shown in Fig. 9-12.

A full adder for negative true signals may be built with the DCTL technique as shown in Fig. 9-13. The full adder (see page 24), performs the logical operations:

$$\text{Sum} = A\overline{B}\overline{C} + \overline{A}B\overline{C} + \overline{A}\overline{B}C + ABC$$

$$\text{Carry} = \overline{A}BC + A\overline{B}C + AB\overline{C} + ABC$$

By relations 2-1 and 2-3 (Chapter 2), these sum and carry terms may be written in a form that is simpler to mechanize, as:

$$\text{Sum} = (A\overline{B} + \overline{A}B)\ \overline{C} + (\overline{A}\ \overline{B} + AB)\ C$$

$$\text{Carry} = (A\overline{B} + \overline{A}B)\ C + AB$$

Figure 9-13 circuitizes the sum and carry terms in these last forms. A diagram such as Fig. 9-13 can be easily read if it is recalled that for negative true signals, transistors in series produce an AND operation with inversion, and single transistors in parallel, or paralleled groups of series stacks, form OR gates with inversion.

(Logical arrays in the DCTL system are treated in greater detail in publications available from the Philco Corp.[1])

9.5. Parallel DCTL Gates — Worst-Case Design. Now consider the worst-case design of the parallel gate configuration of Fig. 9-5. In general, there will be a driving gate with a varying number of inputs M, and each gate output will drive a number of bases N, as in Fig. 9-14. Design will be such that each N driven gate operates with the same collector load current as does G1. Operating points in collector and base currents will be chosen so that M and N are maximized, and safe operation is achieved over as wide a temperature range and transistor production spread, as possible. The circuit will be designed for Philco surface-barrier transistor type 2N240, using the data in Figs. 9-2 to 9-4. The DCTL technique can be used with any surface-barrier or alloy junction transistor in which the collector-to-emitter potential in the saturation region can

---

[1] *Notes on Transistors and Transistor Circuits,* Philco Corp., Lansdale Tube Division, Lansdale, Pa.

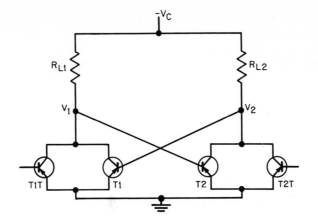

Fig. 9-9. DCTL flip-flop with triggering transistors.

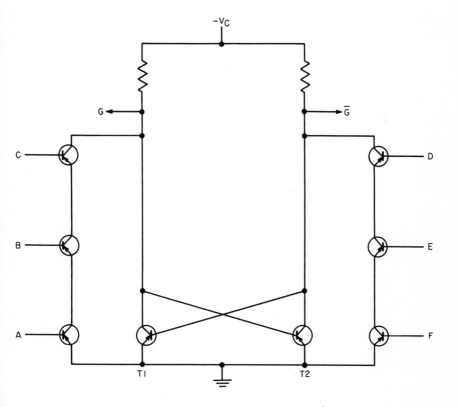

Fig. 9-10. DCTL flip-flop triggered by three-input AND gates.

be made so low, that if applied to the base-emitter circuit of a driven transistor, that transistor is effectively cut off.

There are two conditions to be satisfied in the structure of Fig. 9-14. The first is, that if one of the M inputs is energized, it must be guaranteed a minimum

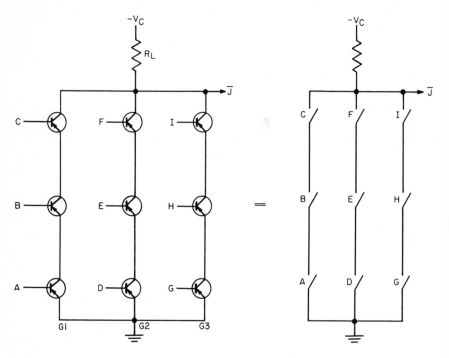

Fig. 9-11.   Mechanization of $ABC + DEF + GHI = \overline{J}$ for negative inputs.

base drive such that for the transistor with the maximum collector-to-emitter resistance, the collector potential at V_O bottoms close enough to ground to adequately turn off the collector current in the driven transistors. The second condition is, that if all the M transistors are cut off imperfectly, their residual leakage current, plus the sum of the base currents of the N driven transistors, must be no greater than the minimum current available from the sink resistor R_L. And further, that if the N driven bases contribute current unequally to R_L (as they will do, since all bases cannot be relied upon to have equal impedances), the base that receives the least current must be driven sufficiently hard that its collector voltage bottoms close enough to ground to turn off the transistor it in turn drives.

To design for these conditions, it is necessary to have the collector current v. base voltage curve, and the base current v. base voltage curve, for the best and worst transistor in the production spread. The first curve indicates how much

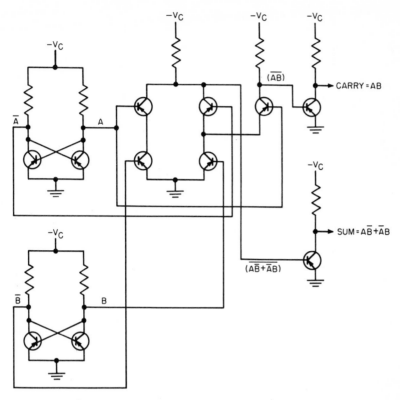

Fig. 9-12. Mechanization of a half adder with DCTL switches.

collector leakage current has to be coped with in imperfectly cut off transistors; and it is required for the worst transistor in the production spread at the highest operating temperature. Such data are not readily available from the manufacturer, but a very good approximation to it can be obtained from the published curves of Figs. 9-2 and 9-4. Thus, Fig. 9-4 shows that I_B versus V_{BE} at $V_{CE} = -0.4$ volt, by interpolation between the $V_{CE} = -0.10$, and $V_{CE} = -1.5$ volt curves. From these values of I_B, the curve of Fig. 9-2 can be entered at $V_{CE} = -0.4$ volt, and collector current read on the assumption that the d-c beta below a base current of 50 µa, equals that at the 50 µa point. Although this assumption is not strictly true, it is sufficiently accurate for purposes of this design. The I_C $v.$ V_{BE} curve so generated is shown as I (Data Sheet) in Fig. 9-15. Measurements made on the worst transistor of a small sample are shown as curve I (Measured) in the same figure. Required, however, is the curve for the worst transistor of a large production run. The table of characteristics of the 2N240 surface-barrier transistor shows a maximum collector leakage of 150 µa at $V_{BE} = -0.1$ volt, at $V_{CE} = -4.5$ volts. Actually, less than this could

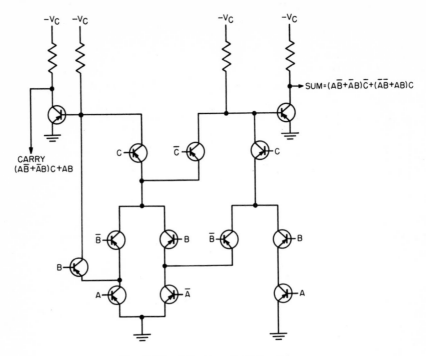

Fig. 9-13. Full adder with DCTL switches.

well be expected at $V_{CE} = -0.40$ volt, the maximum collector potential for an off transistor in a DCTL chain. It can be estimated with sufficient accuracy at the lower collector potential by multiplying the 4.5 volts collector leakage, by the ratio of the collector current at -0.4 volt to that at -4.5 volts at a base current of 50 μa, as read from Fig. 9-3. This last ratio is $0.90/1.5 = 0.60$. Hence, the worst-case collector current at $V_{BE} = -0.10$ volt, and $V_{CE} = -0.4$ volt is $150 \ (0.60) = 90$ μa.

This gives one point on the necessary curve. The required curve can be generated from equations derived by Ebers and Moll[1] relating collector current to the *PN* junction voltages. These relations are:

$$I_C = \frac{\alpha_N \ I_{EO}}{1 - \alpha_N \ \alpha_I} \left[e^{\frac{V_{EB}/kT}{Q}} - 1 \right] - \frac{I_{CO}}{1 - \alpha_N \ \alpha_I} \left[e^{\frac{V_{CB}/kT}{Q}} - 1 \right]$$

$$(9\text{-}1)$$

$$\alpha_I \ I_{CO} = \alpha_N \ I_{EO} \qquad\qquad (9\text{-}2)$$

In these equations, α_N is the transistor α measured in the normal way, and α_I

[1] See p. 58.

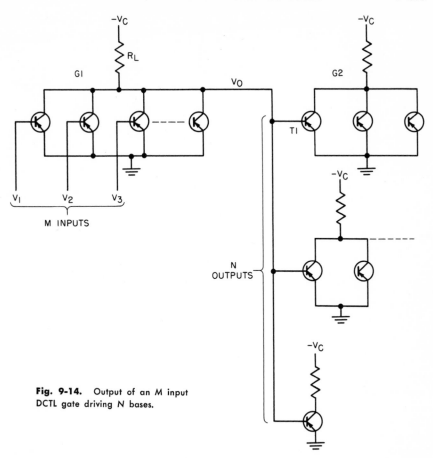

Fig. 9-14. Output of an M input DCTL gate driving N bases.

is the value of α measured with connections to the emitter and collector inter-changed. I_{CO} is the collector leakage in the common base circuit measured with zero emitter current. I_{EO} is the emitter leakage current measured in the same way as I_{CO}, but with connections to the emitter and collector reversed. The junction voltages V_{EB} and V_{CB} are taken positive if they are forward biased, and negative if reverse biased. T is the temperature in degrees Kelvin, k is Boltzman's constant (1.38×10^{-23} joules per degree Kelvin), and Q is the charge on the electron (1.6×10^{-19} coulombs). At room temperature $kT/Q = 0.026$ volt. In the DCTL circuit interest is in I_C at $V_{CE} = -0.40$ volt, and $V_{BE} = -0.10$ volt. This gives $V_{CB} = -0.30$ volt, and the brackets in the second term of relation 9-1 becomes

$$e^{-0.3/026} - 1 \cong -1$$

Thus relation 9-1 gives

$$I_C = \frac{\alpha_I \, I_{CO}}{1 - \alpha_N \, \alpha_I} \left(e^{\frac{V_{EB}/kT}{Q}} \right) + \left[\frac{1 - \alpha_I}{1 - \alpha_N \, \alpha_I} \right] I_{CO} \qquad (9\text{-}3)$$

Equation 9-3 relates collector current to base voltages and temperature. It does not give too accurate absolute values for I_C, but its variation with tempera-

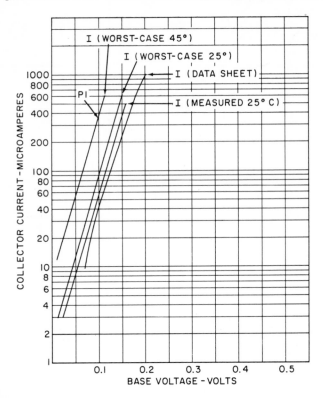

Fig. 9-15. Collector current v. base voltage: Philco surface-barrier transistor type 2N240.

ture and V_{EB} can be determined from it. Thus measurements on a small sample of 2N240's show an average value of α_N of 0.955, and $\alpha_I = 0.922$. Substituting these values into Eq. 9-3 gives at $V_{EB} = 0.1$ volt:

$$I_C = 370 \, I_{CO} + 0.65 \, I_{CO} \cong 371 \, I_{CO}$$

The manufacturers data sheet opposite, shows an average value of 0.7 μa for I_{CO}. From the above relations the collector leakage current at $V_{EB} = -0.1$ volt should equal $371 \, (0.7) = 259$ μa. This compares with an average value of 73 μa, or a maximum of 150 μa at $V_{CE} = -4.5$ volts (as quoted opposite). It will be seen therefore, that Eq. 9-3 cannot be depended upon for accurate absolute values.

CHARACTERISTICS OF THE 2N240 SURFACE-BARRIER TRANSISTOR

The 2N240 is a hermetically sealed, surface-barrier transistor designed for use in computer circuits. The unit has controlled saturation characteristics and low saturation resistance. The short response time of the unit allows its use in switching circuits at pulse rates in excess of 20 mc/sec. The switching characteristics of the 2N240 are controlled by specification of high-frequency beta and hole storage. The polarities of the emitter and collector voltages are similar to those of p-n-p junction transistors. The tinned flexible leads may be soldered or welded directly into the circuit provided reasonable care is used.

ABSOLUTE MAXIMUM RATINGS

Collector voltage, V_{CE}	−6	volts
Collector current, I_C	−15	ma
Total device dissipation at 25°C	30	mw

ELECTRICAL CHARACTERISTICS (T = 25°C)

Static Characteristics	Min.	Type	Max.	
Collector cutoff current, I_{CBO} ($V_{CB} = -5v$)		0.7	3	μa
Emitter cutoff current, I_{EBO} ($V_{EB} = -5v$)		0.5	3	μa

On Condition	Min.	Type	Max.	
Collector voltage, V_{CE} ($I_C = -8$ ma, $I_B = -2.5$ ma)		.06	0.1	volts
Collector voltage, V_{CE} ($I_C = -2$ ma, $I_B = -0.3$ ma)		.04	0.07	volts

Off Condition	Min.	Type	Max.	
Collector current, I_C ($V_{CE} = -4.5v$, $V_{BE} = -0.1v$)		73	150	μa

Small-Signal Parameters	Min.	Type	Max.	
($V_C = -3v$, $I_C = -0.5$ ma, T = 25°C)				
Current amplification factor, h_{fe}	16	30		
Output conductance, h_{ob}		1.5	5	μmhos
Input resistance, h_{ib}		66	100	ohms
Extrinsic base resistance collector capacitance product, $r_b'C_C$		620	1500	μμsec
Output capacitance, C_{ob}		2.9	6	μμf
Current amplification factor, h_{fe} (f = 5 mc)	5	10		
Hole storage, K'_s ($I_B = -1$ ma)		86	120	musec

Philco

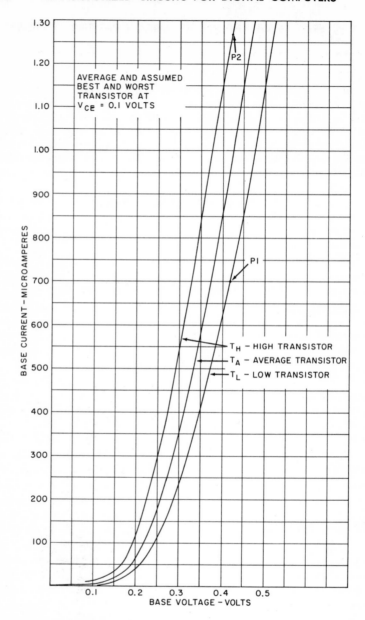

Fig. 9-16.   Base current v. base-to-emitter voltage: Philco 2N240 transistor.

The variation of collector current with base voltage, however, is given accurately by Eq. 9-3. Since the second term in that equation is negligible compared to the first, the collector current doubles for a ΔV given by

$$e^{\,(V_{EB} + \Delta V_{EB})/0.026} = 2e^{\,V_{EB}/0.026}$$

or

$$e^{\,\Delta V_{EB}/0.026} = 2$$

which gives $\Delta V_{EB} = 0.018$ volt.

Thus, the collector current doubles for an increment of 0.018 volt in base voltage. This is seen to hold very accurately for the I(Data Sheet), and I(Measured) curves in Fig. 9-15.

Having one point on the worst-case curve (90 μa as estimated on p. 234), and knowing its variation with voltage, makes it possible to plot the curve. This is shown as curve I(Worst-case), 25°C in Fig. 9-16. It passes through 90 μa at $V_{EB} = -0.1$ volt, and doubles every 0.018 volt.

For our purpose, this worst curve needs to be at the highest operating temperature. In Eq. 9-3, the first term varies with temperature, as does I_{CO}, and the exponential factor $e^{\,V_{BE}/kT}$. A $10°$ variation of temperature about room temperature however, produces a negligible change in the exponential factor, and since I_{CO} doubles every 10°C (Eq. 3-6), the collector current at forward base-to-emitter voltages will also double every 10°C. The worst-case curve at 45°C (which will be shown as being close to the maximum operating temperature), can therefore be taken as one passing through $4\ (90) = 360$ μa at $V_{BE} = -0.1$ volt, and having a slope such that the current doubles for every base voltage increment of 0.018 volt. This curve is shown in Fig. 9-15 as I(Worst-case — 45°C).

The additional data needed to design a DCTL chain, is the base current v. base voltage curve, for the best and worst transistor. If a number of bases are driven in parallel, they all have equal base voltages, and the current difference between these two curves at the same base voltage indicates how unequally the bases may be contributing current to a sink resistor that demands a fixed total current. Again, these best and worst base characteristic curves are not generally available, but they can be obtained with sufficient accuracy in the following manner. Either by measurement on a representative sample, or by consultation with the manufacturer, the spread in base voltage between the best and worst transistor at a fixed current in the linear part of the characteristic, is obtained. For the 2N240, a conservative value is ±0.05 volt at $I_B = 1.0$ ma. From Fig. 9-4, the base voltage at 1.0 ma for the average transistor, is 0.42 volt. Thus, the assumed voltage spread (0.05 volt), at this current is $\pm12\%$. The best and worst base curves can then be generated with good accuracy from the average, by assuming the best and worst voltage points at any current to be displaced by the same $\pm12\%$ from its position on the average transistor curve.

Such curves are shown in Fig. 9-16. The curve marked T_A is the average characteristic redrawn from Fig. 9-4. The voltage on the T_L and T_H curves at

$I_B = 1$ ma, are displaced $\pm$ 0.05 volt from the T_A curve. At any other current point, the voltage on the T_L and T_H curve are displaced $\pm$ 12% from the voltage at the same current on the T_A curve. The significant difference in base currents can be seen in these curves. Thus, if the best and worst transistor bases were in parallel, and it was desired to draw 0.70 ma from the worst transistor, its base potential would be 0.42 volt (point *P1*, Fig. 9-16). The same potential at the base of the best transistor would draw a base current of 1.27 ma (point *P2*, Fig. 9-16).

This is one of the bad features of the DCTL technique, as (referring to Fig. 9-14), design must be such that of the N driven bases in parallel, one base is like T_L, and the other *N-1* bases may be like T_H. This means that in the *N-1* bases like T_H, a total current $(N-1)$ $(1.27 - 0.70) = 0.57$ $(N-1)$ ma is being squandered.

With the data of Figs. 9-15 and 9-16, DCTL chains such as Fig. 9-14 can now be designed. An exact analytic solution that gives an optimum operating point in collector current is not possible. By assuming a number of various operating points in collector current, however, it is possible to calculate for each point the relation between the permissible number of inputs at a driving gate, G1, and the number of bases such a gate may drive under worst-case conditions.

Thus, assume in Fig. 9-14 a desired maximum collector current of 5 ma. Choose $-V_C$ large compared to the maximum negative potential at V_O (approximately 0.50 volt from Fig. 9-16), so that R_L makes a good constant current source. As it will be shown that the pyramiding factor is not very high, loss of base current driving capability by allowing the current R_L draws to change appreciably in going from the collector "on", to the base "on" case, cannot be afforded. Therefore, choose $V_C = -10$ volts, which gives only a 5% current change in R_L when all the collectors in G1 turn off.

First, select R_L to give an upper-limit current of 5 ma when a collector in G1 is on. Since the collector will be bottomed to within 0.1 volt of ground,

$$\overline{I}_{RL} = \frac{[1 + .01\ t_v]\ V_C}{[1 - .01\ t_r]\ R_L} = .005 \tag{9-4}$$

or

$$R_L = \frac{(1.05)\ (10)}{(0.95)\ (005)} = 2200\ \text{ohms}$$

The maximum current load line for this 2200-ohm resistor is a 2100 ohm line from the 5-ma point, and is shown as the line *BB'* in Fig. 9-2. To bottom the collector to -0.1 volt would require only approximately 0.45 ma of base drive. To allow for production spread in collector resistance, and aging, however, guarantee a minimum base drive of 0.60 ma. For the load line *BB'* in Fig. 9-2, this bottoms the new, average transistor to -0.068 volt (point *P1*). But in determining how effectively an "on" collector turns off a base, this maximum, negative upper-level collector potential is taken as -0.10 volt, to account for aging, and production spread.

According to Fig. 9-15, -0.1 volt of base potential permits a collector leakage current of 360 μa at 45°C. Thus, in Fig. 9-14, if all the M collectors are off, the lower limit sink current available from R_L is

$$I_{RL} \text{ (Collector off)} = \frac{[1 - .01 \, t_v] \, V_C - \overline{V}_{BE}}{[1 + .01 \, t_r] \, R_L} \qquad (9\text{-}5)$$

In Eq. 9-5, $\overline{V}_{BE}$ is the maximum voltage that must be applied to that one of the N driven bases having the highest impedance, to guarantee it a base current of 0.60 ma. From Fig. 9-16, $\overline{V}_{BE}$ as read from the T_L curve is -0.395 volt. Thus, Eq. 9-5 gives

$$I_{RL} \text{ (Collector off)} = \frac{(0.95) \, (10) - 0.40}{(1.05) \, (2.2)} = 3.92 \text{ ma}$$

Now, turning on 0.60 ma in the highest impedance base, forces a base potential of 0.395 volt at all the driven bases. In the worst-case, there will be 1 base whose characteristic is like T_L of Fig. 9-16, and N-1 bases whose characteristics are given by the T_H curve. From this curve, each of these N-1 bases will deliver a current of 1.13 ma at a base potential of -0.395 volt. The minimum of 3.92 ma available from R_L must then suffice to draw 360 μa from each of the M, imperfectly cut off collectors, 0.60 ma from a single one of the N driven bases, and 1.13 ma from the remaining N-1 low impedance bases. Thus

$$I_{RL} \text{ (Collector off)} = MI'_{CO} + I_B + (N\text{-}1) \, \overline{I}_B \qquad (9\text{-}6)$$

where I'_{CO} is the collector leakage at the most negative upper-level collector potential, I_B the base current required to bottom a collector to its most negative upper-level collector potential, and $\overline{I}_B$ the current drawn from the lowest impedance base at a base potential that guarantees I_B for the highest impedance base. Substituting the above values for these variables in Eq. 9-6, gives

$$3.92 = M \, (0.36) + 0.60 + (N - 1) \, (1.13) \qquad (9\text{-}7)$$

Values of N for integral values of M, have been calculated from Eq. 9-7, and are shown in Fig. 9-17. The value of N for $M = 3$, is close enough to 3 to be able to drive three bases, but $N = 3$ for $M = 3$ was only just achieved. It will therefore be seen that taking a small additional loss elsewhere, such as reducing $-V_C$, may have prevented the safe driving of three bases from the output of a three-input gate. Figure 9-17 shows that if only two bases have to be driven, the number of gate inputs may be as high as six.

It is instructive to calculate the M-N relationship of Eq. 9-7, for lower current gates. Again assume that both driving and driven gates have the same collector currents. For a fair comparison with the 5-ma gates, operate the lower current gate at the same gain as was the 5-ma gate, i.e., $5/0.60 = 8.3$. Some assumption must be made as to the expected worst-case bottomed collector potential when operating at a gain of 8.3. Once more, for a fair comparison with the 5-ma gate, assume the worst-case collector potential is greater than that for a new average transistor, by the same percentage assumed for the 5-ma gate. Thus, for a 5-ma gate, the bottomed collector potential at 0.60 ma of base current is 0.068 volt (point *P1*, Fig. 9-2).

Recall, it was assumed that aging and production spread would result in a worst-case value of 0.1 volt, or an increase in the ratio of $1/0.68 = 1.47$. Conse-

M	N
2	3.32
3	2.98
4	2.66
5	2.34
6	2.03

Fig. 9-17.

Relation between number of inputs and gate output drive capability for 5-ma DCTL gates.

M	N
2	3.20
3	3.00
4	2.82
5	2.62
6	2.42

Fig. 9-18.

Relation between number of inputs and gate output drive capability for 3-ma DCTL gates.

M	N
2	2.91
3	2.72
4	2.53
5	2.34

Fig. 9-19.

Relation between number of inputs and gate output drive capability for 2-ma DCTL gates.

quently, in calculating any other gate circuit, read the bottomed collector potential for a new average transistor, by noting the intersection of the load line for the assumed current with the given base drive (calculated for a gain of 8.3). This collector potential, multiplied by 1.47, shall be assumed to be the worst-case bottomed potential.

Therefore for a 3-ma gate driving 3-ma gates, calculate R_L from Eq. 9-4 as

$$R_L = \frac{(1.05)\ (10)}{(0.95)\ (003)} = 3690 \text{ ohms}$$

At a gain of 8.3, guarantee a minimum base drive of $3/8.3 = 0.36$ ma. Drawing a 3-ma load line on Fig. 9-2, shows that at 0.36 ma base drive, a new average transistor will bottom to 0.051 volt (point $P2$, Fig. 9-2). Then the worst-case bottomed collector potential will be (1.47) (0.051) = 0.075 volt. If all bases in the driving gate are forced to −0.075 volt to shut off the transistor, they will still leak 150 μa at 45°C as read from the I(Worst-case — 45°C) curve in Fig. 9-15. From Fig. 9-16, to ensure a base current of 0.36 ma for the highest impedance base, a base potential of −0.34 volt can be read on the T_L curve. At this potential, the lowest impedance base would draw 0.78 ma as read from the T_H curve. Calculating from Eq. 9-5 the minimum current available to turn on bases when all collectors in G1 are off, gives

$$\underline{I_{RL}} \text{ (Collector off)} = \frac{(0.95) \ (10) - (0.34)}{(1.05) \ (3.69)} = 2.37 \text{ ma}$$

Then from Eq. 9-6,

$$2.37 = M \ (0.15) + 0.36 + (N - 1) \ (0.78)$$

Values of N for integral values of M are shown for this 3-ma gate, in Fig. 9-18. It is seen that there is substantially the same drive capability with the 3-ma gate, as with the 5-ma gate. A similar calculation for a 2-ma gates gives $R_L = 5520$ ohms, and $I_B = 0.25$ ma for a gain of 8.3. For a new average transistor, $V_{CE} = 0.045$ volt from Fig. 9-2, at $I_B = 0.25$ ma. As previously, $\overline{V}_{CE} =$ (1.47) (0.045) = 0.066 volt. According to Fig. 9-15, $I'_{CO} = 0.11$ ma, at $V_{BE} = 0.066$ volt. From the T_L curve of Fig. 9-16, $V_{BE} = 0.31$ volt for $I_B = 0.25$ ma. The T_H curve of Fig. 9-16 shows $I_B = 0.58$ ma at $V_{BE} = 0.31$ volt. These values give 1.58 ma for $\underline{I_{RL}}$ (collector off).

The M-N relation of Eq. 9-6 then gives

$$1.58 = M \ (0.11) + 0.25 + (N - 1) \ (0.58)$$

Values of N for integral values of M are shown in Fig. 9-19.

Thus it is seen that for a 2-ma gate with three inputs, it is no longer possible to safely drive three bases. The loss in pyramiding factor is primarily due to the fact that in the lower current region, the difference in base current between a high- and a low-impedance base at the same driving potential, is a larger fraction of a minimum base drive than it is in the higher current gate.

The calculations for the three different collector currents have been gone through because the DCTL technique with this transistor type is widely used, and many designers have selected currents in the neighborhood of these values. It is instructive to see that in a worst-case design, where design assumptions made here are concerned, operation cannot possibly go to as low a current as 2 ma, as a pyramiding factor under three is too expensive in transistors. Although 3- and 5-ma gates have almost identical drive capability, the 5-ma circuits are preferable even though the power dissipation is larger. The reason for this is that at the higher currents, base impedances are lower, and therefore the circuits are less susceptible to noise pickup. Also, at the higher collector currents, leakage currents larger than anticipated would be a smaller percentage of the total collector currents being switched, and therefore design margins here, are larger. In addition, although the voltage swings are small and consequently do not require appreciable currents to drive the output wiring capaci-

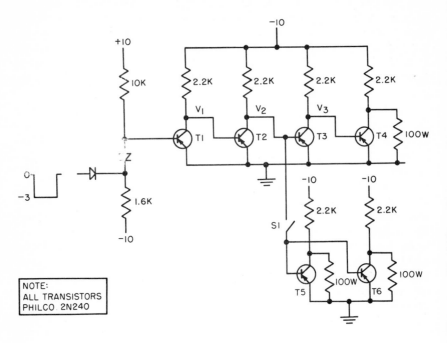

Fig. 9-20. A 5-ma DCTL chain.

tances, the capacitive currents do become an appreciable fraction of the total available current for the lower current gates.

A parallel gate DCTL system can be assembled from the tables of Figs. 9-17, 18, and 19, and the values of the load resistors given by Eq. 9-4. If so desired, each gate can be tailored for the number of outputs it must drive, choosing the lowest collector current in the driving transistor that will drive the required number of outputs. This, in turn, requires looking back at the input to the driving transistor, and calculating what minimum base drive must be guaranteed. An awkward design situation arises if at any transistor output it is necessary to drive bases of transistors whose collector currents are all different.

Rather than adopt such a custom-tailored approach where each gating structure must be individually calculated, it is in most cases generally better to use a standard value of collector current, such as 5 ma. All collector load resistors are then 2200 ohms, whether one, or the maximum number of bases is driven from any output. If a driving transistor is off, and only one base is being fed, the approximately 5 ma demanded by the collector load resistor is supplied by the base of the driven transistor. The base voltage at $I_B = 5$ ma is in the vicinity of 0.65 volt, and therefore the base power dissipation is (0.65) (0.005) = 3.3 mw. Since the collector, at a base drive of 5 ma, will bottom to less than 0.04 volt (Fig. 9-2), the maximum collector dissipation is 0.4 mw. As the transistor is rated at a total of 30 mw at $25°C$, operation is still safe as regards power dissipation at this high base drive. The only effect this high base drive will have is to slightly increase the storage time. But in the DCTL technique, the effective reverse base drive is large, and the storage and decay time is small for the 2N240 transistor type, even using a base drive of 5 ma to turn on 5 ma of collector current.

Thus a parallel gate DCTL system using standard gates, is a remarkably simple one. Only one supply voltage and only one resistor size is needed. Diode clamps, interstage coupling elements, a multiplicity of supply voltages, many different resistor sizes, all needed in any other system of logic, is unnecessary here. But the system has the drawback of being expensive in the number of transistors used, and in the limited operating temperature range.

For purposes of illustration, a 5 ma DCTL chain has been assembled, and its waveforms measured. The exact circuit is shown in Fig. 9-20, and the measured waveforms, in Figs. 9-21 and 9-22.

The input circuit at the base of T1 was simply to convert a non-DCTL voltage swing to a DCTL voltage swing at point V_1. The 100-ohm loads at the collectors of T_4, T_5 and T_6, are to prevent these points from going too far negative when the transistors are shut off, as these collectors are not being caught close to ground by bases turning on. In Fig. 9-21, S1 was open, and a collector output turning on only one base was simulated. The full 5 ma demanded by the load resistor of T2 was then available for switching on base current in T3. In Fig. 9-22, switch S2 was closed, and one collector output feeding three bases was being simulated.

The output waveforms V_2 and V_3 between Figs. 9-21 and 9-22, are negligibly different. The sum of the storage and fall-time in V_3 of Fig. 9-21 is only approximately 0.01 μsec greater than that in Fig. 9-22, although for Fig. 9-21 there was 5 ma of base current just before turn-off as compared to approximately $5/3 = 1.66$ ma in Fig. 9-22. The turn-on time at V_3 in Fig. 9-22 is approximately 0.02 μsec greater than in Fig. 9-21 because of the larger base drive available at turn-on when an output drives only one base. Even though there is probably a large percentage error in the measurement of such short rise and fall times because operation is close to the rise-time of the oscilloscope (Tektronix 531 with model 53B preamplifier rise-time is 0.035 μsec), comparison between Figs. 9-21 and 9-22 shows there is very little loss in speed due to the heavily saturating 5-ma base drive.

9.6. Switching Speed in DCTL Circuits. There is an inherent ambiguity in the turn-on speed of transistors in a DCTL system. It was shown on p. 241 that for 5-ma circuits, if three bases are driven in parallel one base may draw only 0.60 ma, while the other two may draw 1.13 ma. Depending on the toler-

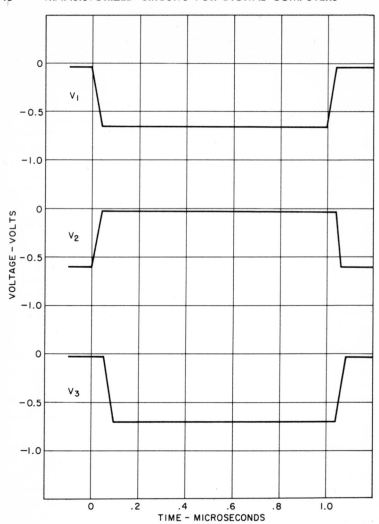

Fig. 9-21. Waveforms in the 5-ma DCTL chain of Fig. 9-20, one base being driven at V_1 and V_2.

ance conditions of the supply voltage, load resistors, and whether or not the supposedly cut-off transistors leak their worst-case current of 360 μa, a base drive may be as high as 2 ma for a three-input gate driving three bases. If standard 5-ma collector load resistors were used even when there was only one base to drive, the turn-on current may be as high as 5 ma. Turn-on time to 5 ma of collector current can be read from the curves in Fig. 7-18A, for any of these

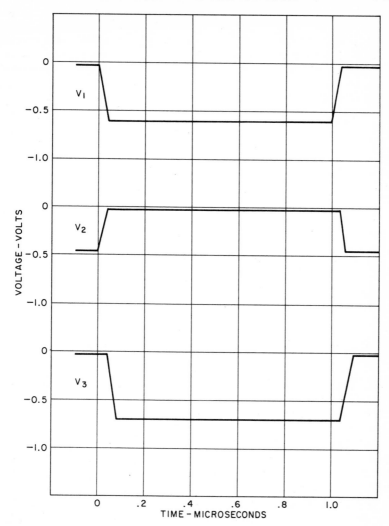

Fig. 9-22. Waveforms in the 5-ma DCTL chain of Fig. 9-20, one base being driven at V_1, and three bases driven at V_2.

possible base drives. Thus, it can be seen from Fig. 7-18A that at a minimum base drive of 0.60 ma, the worst transistor will have a turn-on time of 0.13 μsec. The best transistor at the maximum base drive (5 ma), will turn on in a good deal less than 0.05 μsec.

The storage and turn-off times are more difficult to calculate as all such calculations are based on known reverse base current drives. In all other logical methods, the reverse base drive came from "current sources" — large resistors returned to large voltages — so that reverse base drives could be easily calculated. In the DCTL method, the turn-off source is effectively a voltage generator, rather than a current generator. Looking back from a base toward a collector that is turning on, there is an equivalent voltage generator moving between approximately −0.5 and −0.1 volt. The impedance of the equivalent generator is the slope of the $I_C - V_C$ curves of Fig. 9-2, in the saturation region — approxi-

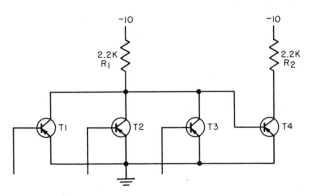

Fig. 9-23.   Output of a 5-ma DCTL gate driving only one base.

mately 10 ohms. Since the base impedance during the turn-off process is so nonlinear, it is not possible to sensibly speak of a unique reverse base current. Nevertheless, an approximate idea of the turn-off times to be expected, can be arrived at.

A collector turning on to a potential of −0.1 volt — the knee of the saturation characteristic — has available for its loads, the collector current at the intersection of the given base drive, and the $V_{CE} = -0.1$ volt point. From Fig. 9-2, at a base current of 0.6 ma, which is the minimum guaranteed to any base of a paralleled group of bases (for 5-ma gates,) this collector current is 6 ma. As the collector load resistor demands 5 ma, the 1 ma balance is available for switching off bases. It was shown on p. 241 that if three bases were being driven from a gate output point, then just before turn-off, one base may have been carrying 0.6 ma, and the other two may have been carrying 1.13 ma. If it is assumed that the balance of 1 ma available from a transistor turning on is equally shared by the three bases turning off, each base enjoys a reverse base drive of 0.33 ma.

From Fig. 7-18B, for 1 ma forward base current just before turn-off (sufficiently close to 1.13 ma in our example), the active-region decay time at a reverse base drive of 0.33 ma, is 0.11 μsec. According to Fig. 7-18C, the storage time at these forward and reverse base currents is zero. The transistors that had been carrying 0.60 ma just before turn-off, will have a decay time of 0.095 μsec, from Fig. 7-18B. Actual storage and decay time will naturally vary, depending upon how the forward and reverse base currents are shared by a group of paralleled bases, but the above calculated values will be close to an upper limit.

It is interesting to see that operation should not suffer too much in storage and decay time, even if all the 5 ma available from an output point drives only one base. Thus, consider Fig. 9-23, where a three-input gate drives a single base. If initially T_1, T_2, T_3, are all off, approximately 5 ma demanded by R_1 is supplied by the base of T_4. Large storage and decay time in T_4 might well be feared when about to turn it off. Consider what should be expected.

Assuming T2 and T3 are already off, and T1 is switching from off to on, the worst-case would be when the base of T1 is one of three bases driven in parallel, and the current division is such that on turn-on T1 receives only 0.6 ma. As already shown, this results (at $V_{CE} = -0.10$ volt), in 6 ma from the collector of T1, of which R_1 takes 5 ma, leaving 1 ma for reverse base drive in T4. From Fig. 7-18B, for 5 ma of forward base current just before turn-off, at a reverse base drive of 1 ma, the active-region decay time is 0.10 μsec. And from Fig. 7-18C, at these forward and reverse base drives the storage time is 0.04 μsec.

Naturally, if the base of T1 did not have to share 5 ma with as many as two other bases, the available collector current would be greater — there would be more current available as reverse base drive for T4, and its turn-off speed would be greater.

Thus it is seen that for the worst-case, if the 5 ma available from a transistor output turns on three bases in parallel, when coming to turn these transistors off, the sum of the storage and decay time in the hardest driven transistor is 0.11 μsec (p. 248). If only one base is driven by the 5 ma, the sum of storage and decay time is still only 0.14 μsec in the very worst case.

9.7. Series-Gating DCTL Circuits — Worst-case Design. It was shown in Fig. 9-13 that series-gating DCTL circuits, in theory at least, can conveniently perform the logical operations required for binary addition. In practice, a safe worst-case design of simple series gates stacked as many as three high, is difficult to achieve, because the collector-to-emitter voltages of the series transistors (Fig. 9-11), are additive, and this sum must not be permitted to increase much above −0.10 volt if the following base is to be adequately shut off. From Fig. 9-16, it is seen that base current, and therefore collector current, starts increasing at a rapid rate above a base potential of −0.10 volt.

Thus, if it is desired to stack three transistors in series, and have the sum of their collector-to-emitter voltages be no greater than 0.10 volt, each transistor must be operated at some point in Fig. 9-2 along the vertical line $V_{CE} = -0.033$, or say, −0.030 volt, for safety. We may choose any collector current at $V_{EC} = -0.030$ volt, and must provide the base drive given at the intersection of the selected collector current, and the $V_{CE} = 0.030$ volt line. For collector currents of 2, 3, and 4 ma, the required base drives so chosen would be 0.40, 0.75 and 1.1 ma respectively. Since the $I_C = 2$ ma, $I_B = 0.40$ ma point gives the greatest gain (5), operate at this point. However, even this low operating gain would not be safe, because Fig. 9-2 represents the average transistor, whereas the worst-case transistor must be allowed for. Page 237 shows that at $I_C = 2$ ma, $I_B = 0.3$ ma, the typical and worst-case collector-to-emitter voltages are 0.04 and 0.07 volt, respectively. If this production spread holds at 0.4-ma base drive, the

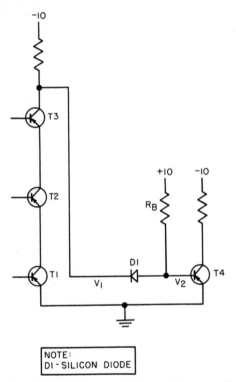

Fig. 9-24.   Series gate with silicon diode level shifter.

worst-case collector-to-emitter voltage at this base drive would be $7/4$ $(0.03) = 0.053$ volt. The sum of three such collector potentials would be 0.159 volt, and a driven base at this potential would cause a collector leakage of approximately 2 ma, from Fig. 9-15. Thus, of the 2 ma demanded by a collector load resistor, the supposedly "off" transistors would supply the major portion, and little current would be available for driving bases.

To avoid this situation, the -0.159-volt level may be shifted upwards with a silicon diode before entering a base, as in Fig. 9-24. The resistor R_B will be chosen to provide a small conduction current (approximately 0.1 ma), in the silicon diode, plus I_{CO} for the driven transistor at the highest temperature. Since this last current is about 12 μa, a current in R_B of 0.12 ma is adequate. From Fig. 7-7, the minimum forward drop in a silicon diode at a forward current of 0.1 ma, is 0.4 volt. Thus, a potential of -0.159 volt at V_1 results in a potential of $+0.24$ volt in the worst-case at V_2, and T4 is adequately shut off.

A silicon diode such as the 1N482, in being switched from forward conduction to reverse voltage, requires a finite time to recover to a high value of impedance.

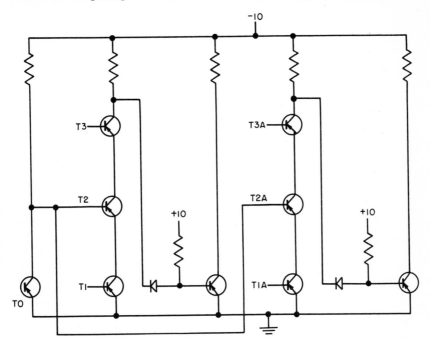

Fig. 9-25. DCTL gate output driving two bases at the same level in series gates.

This recovery time depends on the forward current just prior to reverse voltage, and the impedance of the driving source after the onset of reverse voltage. In general, for this diode type, the recovery time will be greater than the range of storage and decay times in transistor T4, if there were no reverse base current. Thus, in switching T4 from "on" to "off", if there were trapped charges in its base region slowing up the turn-off process, the base potential V_2 would fall below V_1. The silicon diode, having poor recovery time, would pass a large reverse current, and speedup the turn-off process. The reverse current in the silicon diode, and the 0.1 ma available through R_B, result in a turn-off speed no worse than in the conventional DCTL circuit.

With the silicon diode level shifter of Fig. 9-24, it is possible to allow V_{CE} in T1, T2, and T3, to exceed 0.053 volt by a considerable amount, and still have a positive bias at the base of T4 in the "off" state. More transistors can also be tolerated in the series stack.

If the base of transistors off ground (such as T2 or T3), have other bases in parallel with them, the problem of equality of current-sharing between these bases, is severe. In the parallel gate structure, in driving bases in parallel, it was only necessary to worry about the production spread in the base characteristics between the best and the worst transistors. In a series stack, the production

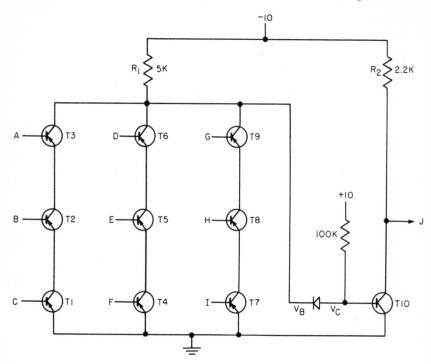

Fig. 9-26. A series-parallel gate building block for mechanizing ABC + DEF + GHI = J.

spread of the collector-to-emitter voltage of all the transistors between a given emitter and ground must also be considered.

Thus, consider Fig. 9-25, where a driver, T_0, feeds the second transistor from the bottom in two separate series stacks. Take it that the series stacks carry 2 ma each. The worst-case in respect to equality of current-sharing between the base of T2 and T2A, is when the base of T2 has a high impedance (curve T_L, Fig. 9-16), the base of T2A is a low impedance (curve T_H, Fig. 9-16), the collector-to-emitter drop in T1 is a maximum, and that in T1A is a minimum. Thus, if 0.40 ma (p. 249), in the base of T2 is to be ensured, its base-to-emitter drop must be forced to 0.35 volt (Fig. 9-16, T_L). If, as on page 250, the maximum collector current-to-emitter voltage at 2 ma of collector current is 0.053 volt, then the potential with respect to ground at the base of T2, is $-(0.053 + 0.35) = -0.403$ volt. The potential at the base of T2A equals that at T2.

Now, if this collector-to-emitter drop in T1A is a minimum of 0.03 volt (p. 249), then the base-to-emitter potential of T2A is $-(0.403 - 0.03) = -0.373$. And if the base of T2A has the low-impedance characteristic of Fig. 9-16 (T_H), at this base-to-emitter voltage it draws a base current of 0.97 ma. If N bases in parallel are to be driven, it must be assumed that one base draws the minimum required 0.40 ma, and N-1 bases draw 0.97 ma. This situation would of course, be worse, if one of the driven bases is at the top of a stack (as in position T3, Fig. 9-25), and all the others are in parallel with this on, are at the bottom of the stack, as T1A, Fig. 9-25.

Although logical equations can be mechanized as in Fig. 9-13, using non-standard arrays of series and parallel gates, this would not be in keeping with our building block concept of standard, repetitively used gating structures. As has been seen, the usual arrays are AND OR cascades of the type $ABC + DEF + GHI$. A useful building block would be as that in Fig. 9-26. The series gates are AND gates for negative signals. Each group of three in series forms an OR term. The array of T1 − T9 produces logical gating and phase inversion. Transistor T10, with its silicon diode level-shifting input, gives another phase inversion, and permits inadequate bottoming of the series transistors.

The building block inputs and output J are negative signals. The block performs the operation $ABC + DEF + GHI = J$, for negative true signals. The series string of transistors may easily be made longer. Input points such as A to I will be driven only from the points such as J. For the values shown, (approximately a 2 ma gating structure driving a 5-ma DCTL amplifier, T10), an output point such as J, can safely drive four bases in parallel.

Chapter 10

MISCELLANEOUS TRANSISTORIZED LOGIC CIRCUITS

This chapter discusses additional ways of transistorizing computer logic. Detailed worst-case design calculations will not be gone into here, but methods explained in previous chapters are generally applicable.

10.1. Transistorized SEAC Logic. A system of vacuum tube computer logic first devised by the National Bureau of Standards for its SEAC computer, has been transistorized by the Computer Control Co. The system is interesting, as it exhibits the building-block concept emphasized in this book. The scheme operates at a repetition rate of 1 mc, has both a true and complemented output from its basic building block, and can drive 20 building-block inputs from each of its outputs.

The logic of the basic building block is shown in Fig. 10-1. The gates G1, G2, G3, G4, are four-input, negative true signal diode AND gates whose outputs are mixed in the negative diode OR gate G5. The output of G5 is mixed in the AND gate G6 with narrow 1-mc clock-pulses, so that the outputs are not d-c levels, but trains of 1-mc pulses under the control of the signals at the inputs to gates G1-G4. Input signals to these gates are in general, pulses synchronous with the 1-mc clock. At the input to such a system, information may first become available as a two-valued signal that may spend long periods of time at either of two d-c levels. In processing such input signals, they are converted in the first building block they encounter, into trains of 1-mc clock-pulses whose envelope corresponds to the input information.

The basic unit of Fig. 10-1 is packaged on a single plug-in card. By changing the external wiring connections it can be used to perform many combinations of AND and OR gating, and may serve as a flip-flop, binary counter, or power amplifier.

The true and false output signals are pulses of 0.4-μsec base width, synchronous with the 1-mc clock input pulses and delayed 1 μsec therefrom. The true signals are 3-volt negative-going pulses starting from a base line of ground. The false signals are 3-volt positive-going signals starting from a base line of −1.5 volts. The gating operation with narrow 1-mc pulses in G6 maintains synchronism of all signals in the system. Since the output of an AND gate has the width and timing of the narrowest of its inputs, a narrow-input signal, broadened by the pulse amplifier and delay line of a single building block, does

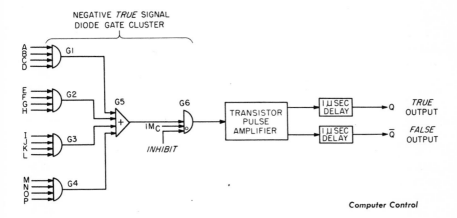

Fig. 10-1.   Basic logical building block.

not suffer cumulative deterioration in passing through a long chain of such blocks.

The amplifier consists of a three-stage pulse amplifier with pulse transformer output. The pulse transformer has two secondary windings that drive opposite-polarity signals into 100-ohm, 1-μsec delay lines. The true and false signal secondary windings have one end tied to ground, and −1.5 volts, respectively, to provide the reference potentials. A false, or inhibiting signal at a gate input must be more positive than −0.5 volt. A true, or enabling signal must be more negative than −1.0 volt.

Connecting the true output and any input of any of the AND gates in a loop, provides a flip-flop. A pulse synchronous with the 1-mc clock injected into the OR gate through any of the AND gates outside of the closed loop, will continue to circulate in the loop. Thus, in Fig. 10-1, Q may be connected to A. A true pulse synchronous with the 1-mc clock injected at, say E, will be successfully gated through G6 on its first trip through the amplifier. It will arrive back at the input to G6 1 μsec later, via the closed loop through G1. It is in coincidence with the next narrow clock-pulse at G6, and even if stretched in width by its first trip through the amplifier, it gates a standard-width clock-pulse through G6 again. It thus continues to circulate in the closed loop containing G1 until reset by an inhibiting signal at any of the other inputs to G1. The inhibiting signal must bracket the circulating pulse at G1, and be more positive than −0.5 volt.

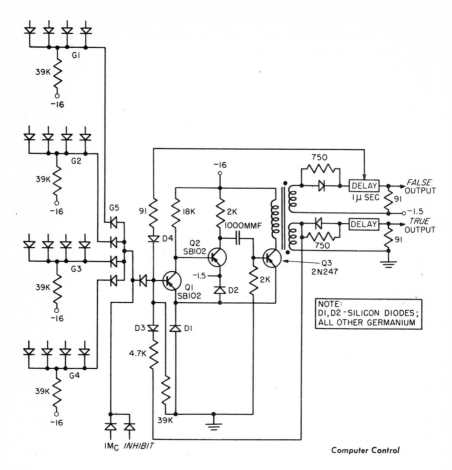

Fig. 10-2.   Schematic for the building block of Fig. 10-1.

The schematic of this building block is shown in Fig. 10-2. The four diode AND gates G1, G2, G3, and G4, and transistor Q1, form a current-switching circuit similar to that discussed in Chapter 7. The 39,000-ohm gate resistors draw their currents either from the base of Q1, turning it on, or from the drivers at the inputs to the AND gates, shutting Q1 off. If for the moment, Q1 is assumed off, then a closed path exists through silicon diodes D1, D2, the base-to-emitter circuit of Q2, and the 18,000-ohm load of Q1. The resulting base current in Q2 is enough to bottom the collector of Q2 to within a few tenths of a volt of its emitter. At the current drawn through D1, the emitters of Q1 and Q3 are approximately at a potential of −0.7 volt, and the emitter of Q2 is at −1.5 volts. Thus, for Q1 to remain turned off, its base must be equal to, or more positive than −0.7 volt. The 39,000-ohm AND gate resistors draw roughly 0.4

ma ($16/39,000 = 0.4$ ma). At this current, the forward drop in the germanium AND gate diodes is under 0.3 volt. Thus, even when the upper level potential at an AND gate input is as low as -0.5 volt, its output potential is sufficiently high to keep the base of Q1 turned off. Since the base of Q3 is returned to ground via the 2000-ohm resistor, and its emitter is at -0.7 volt, Q3 is also shut off for gate input potentials above -0.5 volt.

When the output of one of the AND gates falls below -0.7 volt Q1 starts turning on. This causes Q2 to start turning off, and some of the current drawn by its collector load resistor starts being supplied by the base of Q3 turning it on.

Initially, the turn on speed of Q3 is fixed by the fall-time of the input gate signals, but there is a positive feedback connection from the true signal secondary winding, via D3 and the 4700-ohm-resistor, into the base of Q1. Once the turn-on process has started, the regenerative feedback takes over from the input signal and speeds up the action. There is a negative feedback connection from an 0.2 µsec tap on the false signal delay line, via diode D4 and the 91-ohm resistor, into the base of Q1. After 0.2 µsec delay the negative feedback overrides the positive feedback, and causes fast decay of the output pulse.

The large pyramiding factor obtained in this system is due to the three-stage amplifier between logical elements, and to the current multiplication obtained by the step-down pulse transformer. Although the space requirements and cost of pulse transformers and delay lines are objectionable features this may be outweighed by the very high pyramiding factor obtainable.

10.2. Emitter-Follower Current-Switching Transistor Logic. A very useful class of high-speed transistor logic circuits has been devised by H. S. Yourke[1] of IBM. The basic elements of the method are shown in Fig. 10-3. There are two basic switches in this arrangement, a p-n-p and an n-p-n transistor switch. The switches may be used as AND gates, OR gates, flip-flops or power amplifiers. Both true and false output signals are available from each switch. The d-c levels of input and output signals are separated by approximately 6 volts, but the p-n-p and n-p-n switches are compatible with one another. The output signals of a p-n-p switch are at the correct d-c voltage level to drive inputs of the n-p-n switch. Output signals of the n-p-n switch are at the correct level for driving p-n-p inputs. In general then, successive levels of switching require opposite type switches. For cases where a switch output must drive the input of a similar switch, a 6-volt d-c level-shifting building block is interposed.

The arrangement was devised for transistors with $f\alpha_{co}$ of 60 mc, and with such transistors is capable of 0.01 µsec delay per switch. The transistors in this system are kept out of the saturation region by emitter current limiting. Because of the low source impedance of the equivalent generator that drives switch input terminals, a greater-than-unity overdrive is available for fast active-region decay

[1] Yourke, H. S., "Millimicrosecond Transistor Current-Switching Circuits," *I.R.E. Transactions on Circuit Theory*, September 1957.

time. The method thus makes fullest use of the fast switching capabilities of any lower frequency transistor with which it is used. Also, because of the small signal swings, (approximately 1.5 volts), required in this system, a minimum of power is squandered in charging and discharging wiring capacitance on signal leads.

The system works as follows: Referring to Fig. 10-3 A, the resistor R_1 returned to $+30$ volts, is a constant current source of about 6.7 ma. This current can be steered either into transistor T2 or T1 by potential variations at V_1 of about ± 0.3 volt. Thus, if it is desired to steer the current into T2, since the base of T2 is at ground, its emitter must be permitted to ride above ground by the base-to-emitter potential at this current. This potential, for a germanium transistor, is about 0.3 volt. If none of this current is to drain off through T1, its base-to-emitter junction must have a reverse bias, and since V_A is at approximately $+0.3$ volt, V_1 must be equal to, or more positive, than this. If the 6.7 ma is to be steered into T1, the base-to-emitter junction of T2 must have a reverse bias. As the base of T2 is at ground, V_A must be no more positive than this. And since the base-to-emitter potential of a fully conducting transistor is about 0.3 volt, if V_A is at ground, V_1 must be no more positive than approximately -0.3 volt. Thus, potential swings approximately ± 0.3 volt, centered about ground at V_1, steers the 6.7 ma either into T1 or T2.

If no current flows into a transistor, the output point in its collector circuit, the junction of the 240-ohm and the 2450-ohm resistors may be represented by its Thevenized equivalent circuit, as follows: The Thevenized voltage is

$$- 6 - \left(\frac{240}{240 + 2450} \right) (12 - 6) = -6 - (0.54) \text{ volt}$$

The Thevenized impedance is the 240-ohm and 2450-ohm resistors in parallel, or 220 ohms. Thus, if a current is not steered into a transistor, the output point in its collector circuit is at $-6 - (0.54)$ volts. The collector of the opposite transistor receives the 6.7 ma of emitter current, less the negligible base current (the transistor used in this method has a minimum beta of 20). Therefore, the output point of the conducting transistor is at a potential of

$$[- 6 - 0.54 + (.0067) (220)] = -6 + 0.93 \text{ volts}$$

Since the base of the conducting transistor is approximately at -0.3, its emitter is roughly at ground, and as its collector is at $-6 + (0.93)$, the emitter-to-collector potential is 5.07 volts. The conducting transistor is therefore far out of the saturation region, and storage delays are avoided.

The transistor used in this circuit is of the drift-type discussed on p. 56. As noted there, it requires an emitter-to-collector potential above a certain minimum value, to keep its frequency response high. In the actual design, the collector supply voltage is chosen so that for voltage and resistor tolerances off in the worst directions, this minimum emitter-to-collector potential in the "on" transistor is exceeded.

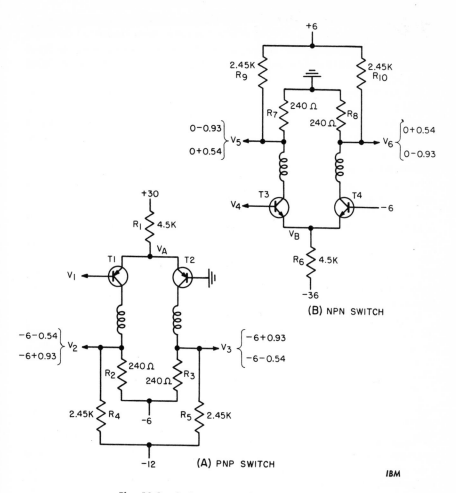

Fig. 10-3. Basic current-switching building blocks.

It is seen therefore, in Fig. 10-3 A, that if V_1 is above $+0.3$ volt, V_2 is at $-6 - (0.54)$ volts, and V_3 is at $-6 + (0.93)$ volts. If V_1 is below -0.3 volt, the potentials at V_2 and V_3 are reversed. These output potentials represent the "one" and "zero" signals in the arrangement.

The output potentials being centered around -6 volts, they cannot drive similar switch inputs such as point V_1 because there, a level centered about ground, is required. Such output points are therefore used to drive an n-p-n switch operating in an exactly similar manner. The n-p-n switch is shown in Fig. 10-3 B. The resistor R_6 is a constant current sink demanding approximately 6.7 ma $[(36-6)/4.5=6.7$ ma]. The reference potential at the base of T4 is the same -6 volt supply used for the p-n-p switch. The 6.7 ma demanded by R_6 is supplied entirely from T3 or T4, by control signals at V_4 that put a reverse bias either on the base of T3 or T4. If V_4 is somewhat more than 0.3 volt below −6 volts, the emitter of T4 falls to about 0.3 volt below −6 volts, the base-emitter junction of T3 has a reverse bias, and all the 6.7 ma demanded by R_6 is

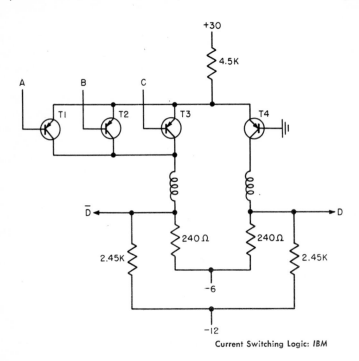

Current Switching Logic: *IBM*

Fig. 10-4. AND gate for positive inputs; OR gate for negative inputs; mechanized with a *p-n-p* switch.

supplied by T4. If the base of T3 is somewhat more than 0.3 volt above −6 volts, its emitter lags about 0.3 volt behind it, and therefore the emitter of T4 is somewhat more positive than −6 volts. With a reverse bias on the emitter junction of T4, all the current demanded by R_6 is now supplied by T3.

Thus, it is seen that the output signals of the *p-n-p* switch, points V_2 or V_3, are at the correct level for driving the inputs to an *n-p-n* switch (point V_4). The output points of the *n-p-n* switch are of the same nature as in the *p-n-p* switch. If an *n-p-n* collector is not supplying current to R_6, the output point (points V_5 or V_6), have a Thevenized impedance of 220 ohms, and a Thevenized voltage of 0 + (0.54) volt. If a collector is on, and demands current from such an output point, it drops to a potential of

$$[0 + 0.54 - (.0067)\ (220)] = 0 - 0.93\ \text{volt}$$

Thus, if V_4 is above −6 + (0.3), T3 is on, T4 is off, V_5 is at 0 − (0.93) volt, and V_6 is at $0 + (0.54)$ volt. If V_4 is below $-6 - (0.3)$ volts, T3 is off, T4 is on, and the potentials of V_5 and V_6 are reversed. It is seen, then, that points V_5 and V_6 are centered about the correct d-c level for switching inputs to a p-n-p switch, such as V_1.

Switches of this type can be used to form AND and OR gates as shown in Fig. 10-4, by placing additional transistors in parallel with the input control transistor of the switch. If either of the inputs to the parallel group of transistors is below -0.3 volt, the 6.7 ma is switched through that transistor into the common collector load. The circuit is thus an OR gate for lower level signals (below -0.3 volt), and an AND gate for upper level signals (above 0.3 volt). Both the output signal and its complement are always available. If the output at D (Fig. 10-4), is not needed, T4 may be replaced by a diode so that if A, B, C, are all at their upper level, the 6.7 ma is switched through the diode into ground. If A, B or C are at their lower level, 6.7 ma is switched into the $\overline{D}$ node. It is obvious that placing additional transistors in parallel with the control transistor in the n-p-n switch produces similar AND and OR gates.

In cases where the output of a switch must drive the input to a similar switch, a d-c level shift of 6 volts must be provided. This is done for the two types of switches as shown in Figs. 10-5 and 10-6. In Fig. 10-5, the 360-ohm and 1150-ohm resistors form a Thevenized voltage source of $+1.43$ volts, and a Thevenized impedance of 274 ohms. The bias arrangement at the input to the transistor is such that the transistor always conducts. The input to the bias network, V_A is driven from the output points of p-n-p switches that move approximately ± 0.5 volt around a potential of -6 volts. This drives the emitter, and produces a collector current change. The changing collector current applied to a $+1.43$-volt, 274-ohm source in the collector circuit, results in approximately a ± 0.5-volt swing centered about ground at V_B.

A similar circuit shown in Fig. 10-6 accepts approximately ± 0.5-volt swings centered about ground, and produces roughly equal swings centered about -6 volts for driving the input of an n-p-n switch from a similar switch output.

According to the circuit designer, with transistors having a minimum d-c beta of 20, a pyramiding factor of three is obtained, with a maximum number of gate inputs limited to six. For transistors with $f\alpha_{co}$ of 60 mc, a delay of 0.012 μsec per switch is obtained.

The reason for the d-c pyramiding factor of three can be seen from the following considerations. It was seen that the unloaded output potential (points V_2, V_3 or V_5, V_6), in Figs. 10-3 A and 10-3 B are $V_R + 0.93$ volt, and $V_R - 0.54$ volt, where V_R is -6 volts for the p-n-p switch, and ground for the n-p-n switch. The source impedance at these output points is the paralleled impedance of the 240-ohm and 2450-ohm resistors, or 220 ohms. Since the transistors have a minimum β of 20, and the emitter current is 6.7 ma, the base current required is $6.7/20 = 0.34$ ma. This current is supplied through the source impedance (220 ohms), of the driving generator, and produces a drop of $(00034)(220) = 0.075$ volt for each base driven by an output point. Thus, in Fig. 10-3, if the output point of a *p-n-p* switch (V_3), feeds three *n-p-n* inputs such as point V_4, if T2 is on and T1 is off, the potential at V_3 is $-6 + 0.93 -3 (0.075) = -6 + 0.70$ volts. Since the emitter of the driven *n-p-n* switch rides approximately 0.3

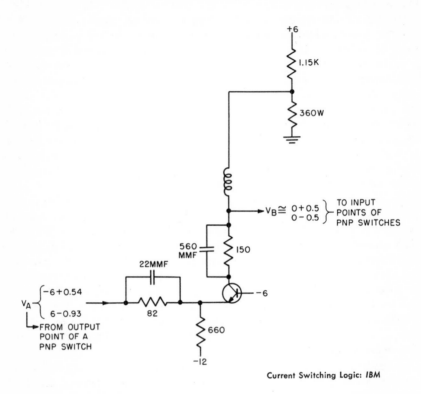

Current Switching Logic: *IBM*

Fig. 10-5. Level shifter for transposing signal levels at a *p-n-p* switch output to that required at a *p-n-p* switch input.

volt below its base, point V_B of Fig. 10-3 B is at about $-6 + 0.40$ volt. This is sufficient to cut off T4 because its base is at -6 volts.

During the transient when T2 turns on, turning T3 on and T4 off, an initially larger forward base current than 0.34 ma is available to the driven bases for fast switching. It was seen that the d-c potential at V_3 is $-6 + 0.70$ volts when V_3 drives three points such as V_4. Since the base-to-emitter potential of T3 is approximately 0.3 volt, the potential at V_3 may be permitted to fall to $-6 + 0.30$ volts before T4 starts having a forward bias. Thus, during the transient when V_3 rises from its lower to its upper level, the current that may be drawn from this node is $(0.93-0.30)/220=2.85$ ma. If this current is shared by three bases, each has available 0.95 ma, and since only 0.34 ma is needed for d-c turn-on, the overdrive factor is large, and the turn-on process is speeded up.

In a similar way, when T2 turns off, potential at V_3 (which is -6 -0.54 volt in the open circuit case), may be permitted to rise to approximately -6 -0.30 volt (because V_B is 0.3 volt below the base of T4 when T4 is on). This will

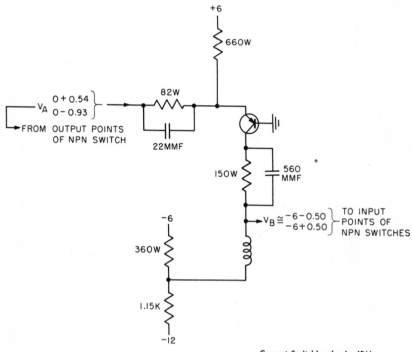

Current Switching Logic: IBM

Fig. 10-6. Level shifter for transposing signal levels at a n-p-n switch output to that required at a n-p-n switch input.

still keep T3 off. Since the impedance looking back into the V_3 node is 220 ohms, the current that driven bases may pour into the node is therefore (0.54 -0.30)/220=1.09 ma. And if three bases are driven, this amounts to a reverse base drive of about 0.36 ma, which speeds up the turn-off operation. Resistance and voltage tolerances will, of course, reduce these values.

A further reason for limiting the number of driven bases to three is that it provides immunity to noise signals. Supposedly cut-off bases have a few tenths of a volt of barrier voltage which must be overcome before a noise pulse can produce a fictitious output.

A pair of switch circuits such as those of Fig. 10-3, connected in a ring form a flip-flop. The interconnections are shown in Fig. 10-7. The flip-flop transistors are T1, T2, T3, and T4. Transistors T5 and T6 are trigger-pulse-inserting transistors. If T1 is on, T2 is off, and V_A is at -6 -0.54 volt. This keeps T3 off, and T4 is forced on. This forces V_B to 0 -0.54 volt, and therefore T1 is on, and T2 is off, as originally postulated. Now, if T5 is momentarily turned on, the current demanded by R_2 is supplied through T5, raising the emitter of

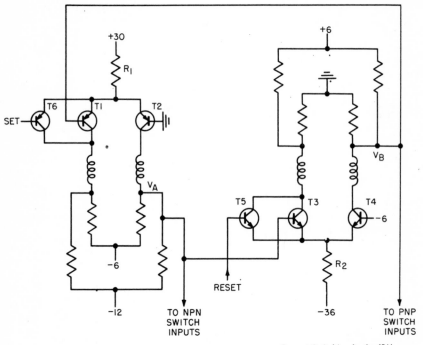

Fig. 10-7.   Flip-flop using regenerative ring of *p-n-p* and *n-p-n* switches.

T4 to a potential somewhat positive with respect to its base. T4 is thus turned off, V_B goes to 0 + 0.93 volt, and T1 is forced off. This turns T2 on, and V_A rises to -6 + 0.93 volt and keeps T3 on after the triggering pulse has been removed from T5. The transistors remain in this state until a negative triggering impulse at the input to T6 restores them to their initial state.

   10.3.   **Current-Switching Diode Logic.**   A system using current-switching diode logic and transistor inverting amplifiers has been devised by P. M. Thompson of the Canadian Defence Research Telecommunications Establishment.

   The method is very similar to the current-switching arrangements of Chapter 7, but is cheaper in components. The elements of the method are shown in Fig. 10-8A. A comparison with the circuit of Fig. 7-25 indicates the similarity of the two systems.

   Figure 10-8A shows a negative true signal, diode AND gate consisting of D1,

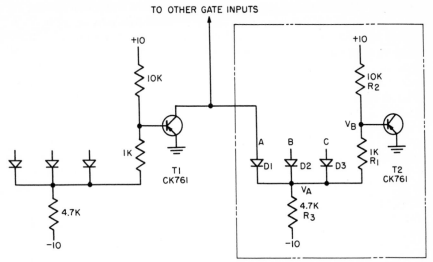

Canadian Defence Telecommunications Research Establishment

Fig. 10-8A. Current-switching negative AND gate diode logic, with positive and negative base-current sources.

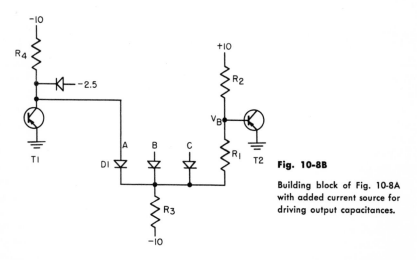

Fig. 10-8B

Building block of Fig. 10-8A with added current source for driving output capacitances.

D2, D3 and R_3. The resistance R_1 provides a d-c level shift so that lowermost upper-level potential at the AND gate output, V_A, is shifted to a potential at V_B adequate to turn T2 off. In Fig. 7-25 this level shift has been performed by two silicon diodes. No attempt is made in Fig. 10-8A to avoid saturation, but enough reverse base drive is provided to result in low storage time and fast active-region decay time. Thus, if T1 and similar transistors at B and C are cut off, R_1 and R_3 are designed to form a current sink for the required forward base current (to give the required turn-on speed), in T2, plus the current supplied by R_2 (postulating V_B is at approximately −0.3 volt). R_2 is chosen small enough to supply adequate reverse current to the base of T2, to achieve the desired turn-off speed (on the assumption that V_B is roughly at ground). R_2 must also supply sufficient current to R_1 to provide a d-c level shift from the lowermost upper-level potential at V_A to ground at V_B. Thus, for the component values of Fig. 10-8A, when T2 is on, I_{R2} is nominally $(10 + 0.3)/10 = 1.03$ ma. The current demanded by R_1 and R_3 is nominally $(10 − 0.3)/5.7 = 1.7$ ma. The forward base current is $I_{R1} − I_{R2} = 1.7 − 1.03 = 0.67$ ma.

When T2 is to be turned off, the lowermost upper-level potential at V_A is about −0.4 volt (0.1 volt collector-to-emitter drop across T1, and 0.3 volt forward drop across diode D1). Thus, if V_B is to be at ground, R_1 takes $0.4/1000 = 0.4$ ma. And since R_2 is a source (for $V_B = 0$) of 1.03 ma, the reverse base current available is 0.63 ma nominally. The forward base current of 0.67 ma for this transistor type (Raytheon CK761), will turn on approximately 10 ma of collector current in about 0.3 μsec. When a collector turns on, it must deliver $10/4.7 = 2.1$ ma to each AND gate it drives. Thus, each transistor output can therefore inhibit $10/2.1 = 4.8$ ma or four AND gates, with a speed of 0.3 μsec.

The 0.63 ma of reverse base drive achieves approximately the same turn-off time.

According to the circuit designer, a worst-case design of the circuit gives a turn-on and turn-off speed of 0.3 to 0.4 μsec, with each transistor output being capable of driving four gates.

Aside from the different method used to achieve a d-c level shift, the circuit differs from that of Fig. 7-25 in that the transistor has no collector load resistor of its own. The collector load is the paralleled impedance of all the 4.7 gate resistors being driven. The current to discharge the stray wiring capacitance at a collector output lead when the transistor turns off, is supplied from the 4700 ohm-gate resistors. This reduces the current available to the base being turned on by the AND gate, and slows up its turn-on time.

In Fig. 7-25 some current was allotted to a collector load resistor (R_L), to give the required turn-off speed for the maximum anticipated collector load wiring capacitance. To prevent the collector voltage at the off transistor from falling to the supply potential, a collector lower clamp is also needed. This is shown in Fig. 10-8B. The collector need only be permitted to fall far enough for D1 to disconnect when T2 is on, and T1 is off. When T2 is on, V_B is at approximately −0.3 volt. Since $I_{R1} = (10 − 0.3)/5.7 = 1.7$ ma, V_A is at −0.3 −(0017) (1000), or −2 volts. Hence, a collector of an "off" transistor such as T1, must be permitted to fall below −2 volts. A −2.5 clamp supply source gives an adequate safety margin. The current in R_4 would be chosen from $I_{R4} = C\Delta V/\Delta t$, where C is the maximum expected wiring capacitance at the collector output lead, $\Delta V = 2.5$ volts, and Δt is the desired fall-time when T1 shuts off.

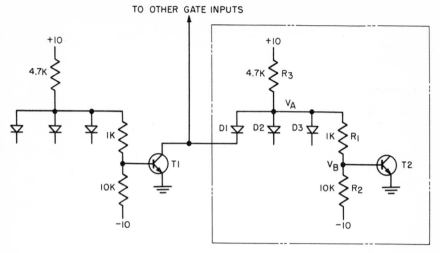

Canadian Defence Telecommunications Research Establishment

Fig. 10-9A. Current-switching positive AND gate diode logic, with positive and negative base-current sources.

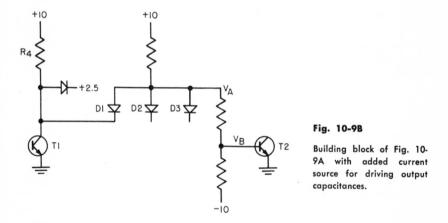

Fig. 10-9B

Building block of Fig. 10-9A with added current source for driving output capacitances.

For the case in which true signals are positive, Thompson uses the complementary circuit of Fig. 10-9A. The gate is an AND gate for positive true signals, and an OR gate for negative signals. The transistor is an *n-p-n* transistor, and the component values would be correct for β and $f\alpha_{co}$ equal to those of the *p-n-p* transistor of Fig. 10-8A. The resistors serve the same purpose as the corresponding resistors of Fig. 10-8A. The reverse base current to achieve the desired turn-off speed in T2, is fixed by R_2. The forward base current in T2 when transistor T1 and corresponding transistors at D2 and D3 are all shut off, is

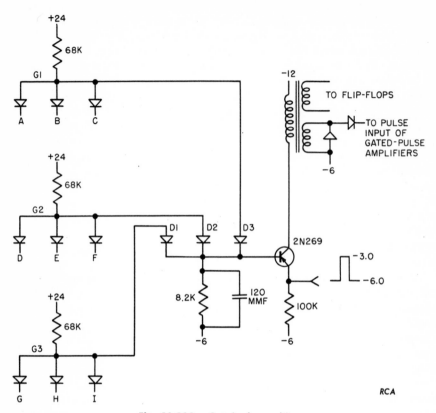

Fig. 10-10A.   Gated-pulse amplifier.

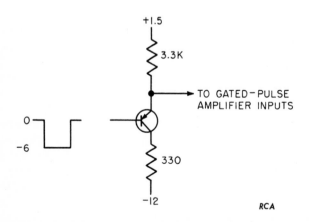

Fig. 10-10B.   Emitter follower d-c step driver.

the difference between the current supplied through R_1 and R_3 in series (assuming V_B is approximately at ground), and that drained off through R_2. This forward base current is fixed to give the required turn-on speed. The maximum value of forward base drive is obtained when I_{R1} is a maximum, and I_{R2} is a minimum. Under these conditions, the storage and decay time are greatest, and R_2 is chosen to give the reverse base current to achieve the desired turn-off speed. Again R_1 provides a d-c level shift so that if V_A is approximately +0.4 volt with T1 on, (0.1 volt collector-to-emitter drop in T1, and 0.3 volt diode drop in D1), the potential at V_B is equal to, or below ground, and T2 turned off.

Here also, the transistor has no collector load resistor independent of the gate resistors. For fast rise-time when T1 shuts off, a collector load resistor should be added as at Fig. 10-9B. The collector need only rise far enough for D1 to disconnect when T2 is on, and T1 and the corresponding transistors at D2 and D3 are all off. As for the *p-n-p* circuit, a collector clamp source of +2.5 volts is safe. The current allotted to R_4 is chosen exactly as for the circuit of Fig. 10-8B.

10.4. Gated Pulse Logic. Figure 10-10A shows a computer logic building block devised by G. W. Booth and T. P. Bothwell of RCA.[1]

The circuit makes logical decisions in the array of diode gates at the base of the transistor. Signals at these gate input points are relatively long d-c steps swinging between the levels of 0 and −6 volts. The d-c steps are long compared to the duration of the pulse or pulses at the emitter. The diode gate cluster consists of three, three-input negative true signal OR gates, driving a three-input negative true signal AND gate. The signal at the emitter is a pulse, or train of pulses of 0.5 µsec duration, swinging between the levels of −6 and −3 volts. These pulse signals sense the result of the logic being performed by the diode gates, and are gated through to, or inhibited from, the collector circuit. At the secondary of the output transformer, these pulses set other flip-flops whose d-c outputs are used to perform logical operations at the inputs to similar gated pulse amplifiers.

If the base of the transistor in Fig. 10-10A is not permitted to fall below −3 volts, the base-emitter junction never has a forward bias, and the emitter pulse cannot be transmitted to the collector.

If the negative AND gate at the base is enabled by all the inputs at diodes D1, D2, and D3 going to −6 volts, the Thevenized voltage looking out from the base is −6 volts (after the time required for the 120-mmf capacitor to lose its charge through the 8200-ohm resistor). The Thevenized impedance is primarily that of the 120-mmf capacitor, which is low for the 0.5 µsec pulse. The positive pulse at the emitter, rising from −6 to −3 volts, can now drive the emitter base junction into forward bias and turn on collector current. Enough collector current is supplied to drive the collector up from −12 volts to the

[1] Booth, G. W. and Bothwell, T. P., "Logic Circuits for a Transistor Digital Computer," *I.R.E. Transactions on Electronic Computers,* September 1956.

potential at the top of the emitter pulse (−3 volts). The voltage across the transformer primary is 9 volts, and as the transformer turns ratio is 3/1/1, the two secondary output pulses are each about 3 volts in amplitude. These output pulses are used to set flip-flops or drive the emitters of other gated pulse amplifiers.

If the negative AND gate at the base input is inhibited by all three inputs of one of the OR gates, say, A, B and C of gate G1 being at the upper level (0 volts), the emitter pulse will not get through to the collector. For if A, B, and C are all at zero volts, the transistor base potential is the Thevenized potential looking out from the base, and is therefore

$$- 6 + \left(\frac{8.2}{68 + 8.2} \right) (24 + 6) = - 2.8 \text{ volts}$$

The input diodes at A, B, and C are then cut off, because their cathodes are at ground potential. It is therefore correct to calculate the base potential as it was calculated, by simply considering the voltage division between the 8200- and 68,000-ohm resistor. Since the top of the emitter pulse goes only to −3 volts, the emitter base junction is never in forward bias, and the transistor cannot be turned on.

Computer circuits frequently contain a "clock" — a pulse generator that senses for various logical situations at a periodic rate. The time between pulses in this clock is usually long, compared to the pulse duration. A gated pulse amplifier as described above is useful in such cases, as the logical gating can be done in relatively low speed circuits. The diode gating circuits must only be fast enough to produce the logical result in the time from one clock-pulse to the next. Since the transistor operates effectively in the grounded-base connection, its frequency response is high, and it is an efficient narrow-pulse amplifier.

Additional building blocks required in such a system are flip-flops — which in the present instance are conventional transistorized Eccles-Jordan flip-flops — and d-c step amplifiers for which emitter followers are used. The emitter follower used in this set of circuits is shown in Fig. 10-10B. The input signals come from flip-flop outputs that swing between 0 and −6 volts. The maximum transistor current in this case was limited to 18 ma. The 330-ohm collector load resistor was chosen to allow only a very small voltage across the transistor when it is carrying its maximum current. Thus, at a base potential of −6 volts, and a collector current of 18 ma, the collector is at −12 + (018)(330) = −6.05 volts. At this current, the collector-to-emitter potential for this transistor type is 0.35 volt and dissipation is low. At lower currents, the drop across the 330-ohm resistor will not be so large, and therefore the transistor will operate at a higher voltage and lower current. Although such an operating point will result in greater power dissipation across the transistor, the dissipation will still be well within the maximum rated value.

With the emitter at −5.7 volts, the 3300-ohm emitter resistor is a current source for approximately 7.2/3.3 = 2.17 ma. Since the transistor current is to be limited to 18 ma, this permits the emitter to be a sink for an additional $18 - 2.2 = 15.8$ ma. When such an emitter follower drives one of the inputs to the gated pulse amplifier of Fig. 10-10B, each 68,000-ohm OR gate resistor delivers to the emitter, when it is at the -6 volts level, a current of $30/68 = 0.44$ ma. Since the emitter can be a sink for 15.7 ma from external loads, the emitter follower can drive $15.7/0.44 = 36$ gated pulse amplifiers. When resistance and voltage tolerances are taken into account, in a worst-case calculation, this drive capability will of course be lower.

In Fig. 10-11A-D is shown a set of computer building blocks devised at the Sylvania Corp.[1]

This set of circuits, as the previous set, performs logical operations with relatively long d-c step signals in conventional diode AND and OR gates. The result of the logical operation is sensed in a step-pulse gate that gates a pulse, or pulse train.

The flip-flop in this method is a transistorized Eccles-Jordan flip-flop whose output signals are $+0.5$ and $+5.5$ volts. These output signals may drive the step-pulse gate of Fig. 10-11A. In Fig. 10-11A, if the input to the top of the 1000-ohm resistor is $+5.5$, approximately 2 ma flows through R_1, R_2, and D_1, and the secondary of the pulse transformer. A pulse at the primary of the transformer drives the cathode of D1 positive, and open-circuits it. The 2 ma from R_1 and R_2 in series, is then switched through diode D2 to the output circuit. A pulse at the transformer without the step at the top of R_1, will not produce an output signal, because the cathode of D1 will simply go positive, but there will be no current to be switched into the output circuit. A step at the top of R_1 produces no output without a pulse input, as a fast positive step at the top of R_1 is somewhat slowed up by the integrating action of R_1 and C_1. For the resulting rise-time at the junction of R1 and R2, the impedance looking into the secondary of the pulse transformer is too low to support a spike at the positive leading edge of the input step.

The capacitor C_1 also adds a small time delay to the circuit. If the leading edge of a pulse succeeded in getting through the gate, and drove the flip-flop that had been enabling the gate at the top of R_1 from $+5.5$ to $+0.5$ volt, the effect would be to chop the sensing pulse off short. The purpose of C_1 is then, to hold the gate enabled for the duration of the sensing pulse.

The step-pulse diode gate output may be used to set a flip-flop, or if several flip-flops are to be driven, a pulse amplifier is interposed as in Fig. 10-11B. In the latter case 3 ma is made available to the base of the transistor (Sylvania 2N94A), and 30 ma is available from the secondary. The diode D1 in Fig. 10-11B prevents the transistor from saturating.

Step signals to the step-pulse gate come either from flip-flop outputs directly, or from the result of a logical interconnection of flip-flop outputs in diode AND

---

[1] Prom, G. J. and Crosby, R. L., "Junction Transistor Switching Circuits for High-Speed Digital Computer Application," *I.R.E. Transactions in Electronic Computers,* December 1956.

and OR gates. The gates are conventional positive true-signal diode gates, and usually drive emitter followers before feeding the step-pulse gate inputs. These d-c gating building blocks are shown in Figs. 10-11C and 10-11D. The emitter follower output levels are within 0.1 to 0.2 volt of the d-c levels of the AND gate

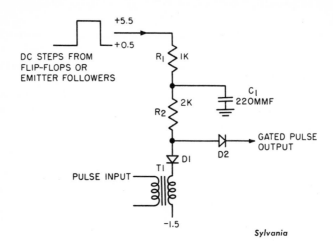

Fig. 10-11A.   Step-pulse gate.

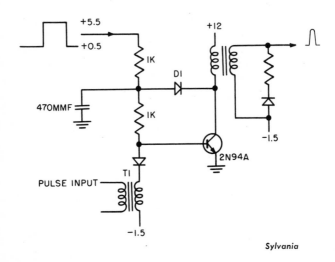

Fig. 10-11B.   Step-pulse gate driving pulse amplifier.

input signals, as the forward diode drops are very nearly equal to the base-to-emitter drops in the transistor. In the emitter follower following the OR gate, the diode drop and base-to-emitter drops, are both in the same direction, but as true input signals are about 5 volts in amplitude this is still a small percentage loss, and is negligible.

10.5. Transistor Emitter Follower and Inverter Logic with Large Voltage Swings. A system of logic using transistors as the gating elements, and permitting larger voltage swings than the DCTL method of Chapter 9, has been

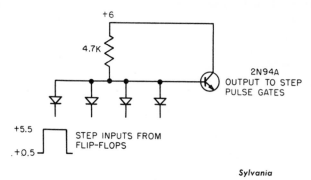

Sylvania

Fig. 10-11C.   Positive diode AND gate driving emitter follower.

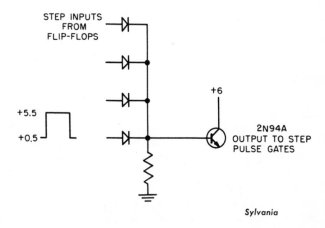

Sylvania

Fig. 10-11D.   Positive diode OR gate driving emitter follower.

devised for the Lincoln Laboratory TX2 computer[1]. The basic units are shown in Figs. 10-12A, B, and C.

The structure of Fig. 10-12A is an emitter follower gate that serves as an AND gate for positive signals, and an OR gate for negative signals. If all three bases are at ground, the output point is somewhat above ground. If any base is at −3

[1] Olsen, K. H., "Transistor Circuitry in the Lincoln TX2," *Proceedings Western Joint Computer Conference,* February 1957.

volts, the output point is shorted to −3 volts. The base input signals may come from flip-flop outputs that are either at −3 volts, or at ground. They may also come from the outputs of similar emitter follower gates, or from the gates in Fig. 10-12B, and C. The transistors serve as sinks to absorb current from the load when the output is at the −3 volts level. The 3900-ohm resistor acts as a current source during the rise-time for charging wiring capacity, and to supply

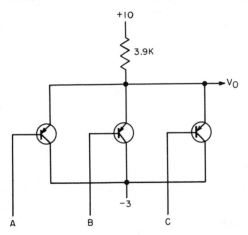

+10

3.9K

V₀

−3

A   B   C

TX2 Logic: *Lincoln Laboratory*

Fig. 10-12A. Emitter follower gate: AND gate without polarity inversion for positive inputs; OR gate without polarity inversion for negative inputs.

reverse current to the bases of the transistors being driven (transistors in similar emitter follower gates or inverting transistors, such as in Fig. 10-12B).

Figure 10-12B shows a transistor inverter gate. If any transistor is on, the output is shorted to ground. If all transistors are off, the output falls towards −10 volts but is usually caught at −3 volts by the load. Thus, if the output drives the input of an emitter follower gate, as soon as the output point of the inverter gate falls below −3 volts, the base-to-collector circuit of the driven emitter follower takes on a forward bias and catches the off collectors at −3 volts, much as the clamp diodes in the circuits discussed in previous chapters. The circuit is thus an AND gate with phase inversion for positive signals, and an OR gate with phase inversion for negative signals. Input signals may come from flip-flops, the outputs of the emitter follower gates, or from similar inverter gates.

The circuit of Fig. 10-12C is a series inverter gate. The output is shorted to ground only if all three transistors are conducting. If any one transistor is off, V₀ falls towards −10 volts, but is caught at −3 volts by the load — usually the emitter follower gate. The circuit is an AND gate with phase inversion for negative inputs, and an OR gate with phase inversion for positive signals.

In both the series and parallel inverter gates, the 2200-ohm input resistor provides sufficient base drive to bottom the collector to less than 0.2 volt. The 47-mmf capacitor provides some additional reverse base current for fast turn-off. The 68,000-ohm resistor is a source for I_{CO} at the highest operating temperature, and provides a d-c level shift at an "off" base to make it immune to noise signals. The output node may drive inputs to either emitter follower or

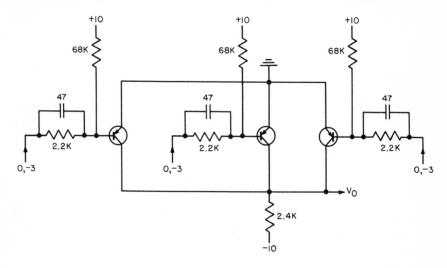

TX2 Logic: *Lincoln Laboratory*

Fig. 10-12B. Parallel inverter gate: AND gate with polarity inversion for positive inputs; OR gate with polarity inversion for negative inputs.

inverter gates. In either case, the total current poured into the output node when it is at −3 volts must not exceed the sink capability of the 2400-ohm load resistor. This sink capability is nominally $(10-3)/2.4=2.8$ ma. The current pouring into the output node when it is at −3 volts is I_{CO} at the highest operating temperature for each transistor in the gate itself, plus contributions from each inverter or emitter follower gate being driven. An inverter gate input terminal supplies nominally $(3 - V_{BE})/2.2$, or approximately 1.2 ma.

The current to be absorbed from the base of a transistor in an emitter follower gate, depends on how heavily the emitter follower gate is loaded. Thus, if an emitter follower gate output drives, say, three inverter gates, it must absorb nominally 1.2 ma from each 2200-ohm input resistor, or a total of 3.6 ma. In addition, an "on" transistor in an emitter follower gate must be a sink for $(10 + 3)/3.9 = 3.3$ ma, from its own emitter load resistor. The total current into the emitter of a transistor that is the only one in the "on" state in an emitter follower gate, is then $3.3 + 3.6 = 6.9$ ma, (nominally, if three inverter gates are being driven). To bottom the emitter to within 0.1 volt of the collector (assuming a surface-barrier transistor such as the 2N240 of Fig. 9-2), requires about 0.75 ma of base current for 6.9 ma of collector current. This would normally be increased, depending on the worst-case philosophy being used.

Thus in calculating d-c driveability at the output of an inverter gate, a nominal current of 1.2 ma would be assumed for each inverter terminal being driven,

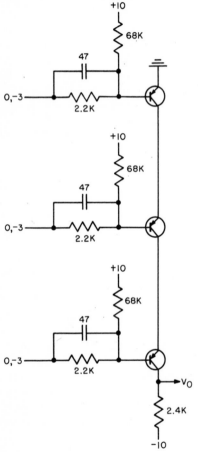

Fig. 10-12C

Series inverter gate: AND gate with polarity inversion for negative inputs; OR gate with polarity inversion for positive inputs.

TX2 Logic: *Lincoln Laboratory*

and somewhat over 0.75 ma for each emitter follower input terminal (each such emitter follower output then being capable of absorbing 3.6 ma of current from an external load). The actual design would of course, consider worst-case conditions of voltage, resistors, and transistors.

Gate inputs and outputs being compatible with each other, these three structures are adequate to perform most logical operations in a computer, with few phase inverters. The series and parallel inverter gates may be combined as shown in Fig. 9-13 to provide many different logical combinations.

Because supposedly "off" transistors have a reverse bias, and because the problem of bases driven in parallel sharing a fixed amount of current very unequally never arises, these circuits have a larger operating temperature range, and a larger pyramiding factor than DCTL circuits, which also use one transistor per logical term.

With the Philco surface-barrier transistor, this set of circuits can operate at a 5-mc repetition rate. Capacitive loads are more serious than in DCTL circuits as the voltage swings are 3 volts, and more power is lost charging and discharging wiring capacitance. In addition heavy capacitive loads are especially to be avoided in the emitter follower gate, as emitter followers under certain capacitive loads exhibit a ringing output immediately after a step input.[1]

---

[1] Logue, J. C., "Transistor Switching Circuits," pp. 15-36, *Handbook of Semi-Conductor Electronics*, Hunter, Lloyd. P.: McGraw-Hill Book Co., Inc., 1956.

Chapter 11

DESIGN OF FLIP-FLOPS AND
DELAY MULTIVIBRATORS

11.1. Resistance-Coupled Flip-Flops with Unclamped Outputs. A flip-flop consists of a regenerative ring of two transistors, with the output of the first connected to the input of the second, and the output of the second connected around to the input of the first. The flip-flop has two stable states — transistor A conducting, and transistor B cut off, and vice versa. Flip-flops can also be built with transistors in which the two stable states are both transistors on and both transistors off.[1]

The design of a conventional on-off flip-flop proceeds in the same general way as does that of a vacuum tube flip-flop. The input conditions at the "on" element must satisfy the current demands at its output terminal. The input conditions at the "off" element must ensure that it is truly off, with adequate margin under the worst conditions of temperature, voltage, and resistance tolerances. The major point of difference is, of course, that in vacuum tube flip-flops, it is grid voltage that must be specified to achieve the on-off conditions; in transistors it is base currents. In a transistor flip-flop, there is also the added problem of storage time in the "on" transistor. This can be dealt with by the antisaturation methods discussed in previous chapters — adequate reverse base drive, antisaturation feedback diodes, and emitter current limiting.

The basic flip-flop to be discussed in this section is shown in Fig. 11.1. A flip-flop is rarely designed without regard to the loads it must drive. The magnitude of the load, and whether it absorbs or gives current to the output node (points V_{01} or V_{02}), determines the flip-flop supply voltages and component values. For if the flip-flop is designed to work with no external loads, then hanging external loads on it will draw current through the Thevenized impedance

---

[1] Moody, N. F. and Florida, C. D., "Some New Transistor Bistable Elements for Heavy Duty Operation," *I.R.E. Transactions on Circuit Theory*, September 1957.

at the output nodes, and change these nodal potentials. Since the base currents are determined by the nodal potentials, the amount of current drawn from these nodes, and its direction, will affect the base current. Thus, changes in load current will affect the extent to which an "on" transistor is on, and the margin of safety at the base of an "off" transistor.

In most practical cases in computer flip-flops, therefore, when transistors are off, collectors (the output nodes V_{01}, and V_{02}), are clamped at some potential

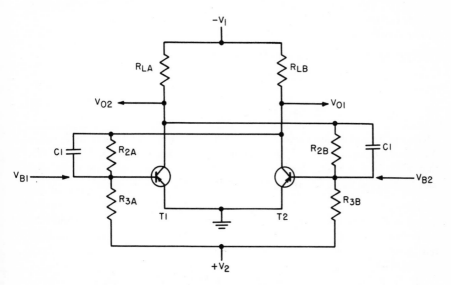

Fig. 11-1.   Resistance-coupled flip-flop with unclamped outputs.

between ground and $-V_1$. The potential at an output point is then close to ground (collector saturation potential of approximately -0.1 volt), when the transistor is on, and at the diode clamp potential when the transistor is off. The drop across the base turn-on resistor, R_2 is then independent of loading conditions (within limits), and R_2 can be selected to give adequate base drive for the maximum load, and this drive will not be exceeded under any other load.

Thus, although unclamped flip-flops are seldom used, the methods used in designing them are instructive, and the design of the flip-flop in Fig. 11.1 will be gone through, as a unit by itself.

The design involves the selection of $-V_1$, $+V_2$, and calculation of R_2 R_3 and R_L to satisfy the "on" and "off" transistor requirements. The function of R_3 is to supply a reverse base current equal to I_{CO} at the highest operating temperature, to prevent the collector leakage current in the off transistor from exceeding I_{CO}. It must also supply a level shifting component of current to put a reverse voltage bias at the base of the off transistor, and therefore give it some immunity to noise signals. Thus, if T_2 is on and in saturation, its collector potential V_{O1} may still be a few tenths of a volt below ground. The level shifting component of current from R_{3A} must then transfer a voltage of $-V_{CE}$ at V_{O1} to some small positive biasing potential at V_{B1} — say, +0.30 volt. When T1 is on, V_{B1} will be below ground by the base-to-emitter drop of a germanium transistor which is usually in the neighborhood of 0.3 volt. Thus, V_{B1} moves only ± 0.3 volt, and the combination of V_2 and R_3 is designed to be a constant current source, independent of the voltage at V_{B1}. If $+V_2$ is chosen to be ten times the total variation at the base, or +6 volts, this is adequately constant.

The condition at an off base is then,

$$\underline{I_{R3}} = \overline{I}_{CO} + \frac{\overline{V}_{CE} + 0.3}{\underline{R_2}}$$

$$= \overline{I}_{CO} + \frac{\overline{V}_{CE} + 0.3}{0.95 \, R_2} \tag{11-1}$$

where the lines above and below a term indicate its upper and lower limit values. As before, resistance and voltage tolerances will be taken to be $\pm 5\%$. In relation 11-1, $\overline{V}_{CE}$ is the collector-to-emitter potential at an "on" transistor, with some allowance made for aging. V_2 and R_3 will be chosen so that

$$\underline{I_{R3}} = \frac{V_2}{\overline{R}_3} = \frac{0.95 \, V_2}{1.05 \, R_3} \tag{11-1a}$$

But

$$\overline{I}_{R3} = \frac{\overline{V}_2}{\underline{R}_3} = \frac{1.05}{0.95} \frac{V_2}{R_3} = \left(\frac{1.05}{0.95}\right)^2 \underline{I_{R3}} = 1.22 \, \underline{I_{R3}}$$

$$= 1.22 \left(\overline{I}_{CO} + \frac{\overline{V}_{CE} + 0.3}{R_2}\right)$$

The first step in the flip-flop design is to select the maximum current it is desired to take in the "on" transistor. This is chosen on the basis of the maximum current per flip-flop that either power dissipation or power supply capability will permit, or that current at which β starts becoming unreasonably small. Since the "on" transistor is in the saturation region, this maximum current is given by

$$\overline{I}_C = \frac{\overline{V}_1}{R_L} \tag{11-2}$$

$$= \frac{(1.05) \, (V_1)}{(0.95) \, R_L} \tag{11-2a}$$

The next step is the selection of the base current to give this maximum collector current. It should be selected to bottom the collector to some worst-case value for a low beta transistor, with some allowance for aging. In general, this choice of base current is a matter of engineering judgment. The manufacturer's data sheets (I_C $v.$ V_C, common emitter) are derated on the basis of personal experience with a given transistor type, previous knowledge of how conservative a given manufacturer's data sheets are apt to be, and production spread normally encountered. Some manufacturers quote minimum beta — but these are generally only at one point. Since production spread may be as high as 4:1, and the usual data sheet shows the typical transistor, a safe derating factor is ordinarily one half that shown in the data sheets. Thus, d-c beta at the knee of the collector current curve at the specified maximum collector current, is read from the manufacturer's data sheets. A minimum beta of half of that value is assumed, and the base current is taken as $\bar{I}_C/\beta_{MIN}$.

The condition for the on transistor can now be written. In Fig. 11-1, if T2 is on, and T1 is off, the resistors R_{LA} and R_{2B} in series, must be a sink for

$$\bar{I}_{R3} = 1.22 \left(\bar{I}_{CO} + \frac{\bar{V}_{CE} + 0.3}{R_2} \right)$$

from R_{3B}, plus $\bar{I}_C/\beta_{MIN}$ from the base of T2. Hence, for worst-case conditions of voltage and resistance

$$\underline{I_{R2}} = \frac{V_1 - \bar{V}_{BE}}{(R_L + R_2)} = 1.22 \left(\bar{I}_{CO} + \frac{\bar{V}_{CE} + 0.3}{\underline{R_2}} \right) + \frac{\bar{I}_C}{\beta_{MIN}} \qquad (11\text{-}3)$$

or

$$\frac{(0.95)\ (V_1) - \bar{V}_{BE}}{1.05\ (R_L + R_2)} = 1.22 \left(\bar{I}_{CO} + \frac{\bar{V}_{CE} + 0.3}{(0.95)\ (R_2)} \right) + \frac{\bar{I}_C}{\beta_{MIN}}$$
$$(11\text{-}3a)$$

Here $\bar{V}_{BE}$ is the maximum base-to-emitter potential at $\bar{I}_C/\beta_{MIN}$ as read from the I_B $v.$ V_{BE} curve in the data sheets.

In Eq. 11-3, $\bar{I}_C$ will be specified, β_{MIN} will be assumed. The base current thus determined makes it possible to read $\bar{V}_{BE}$ and $\bar{V}_{CE}$ from the data sheets. Thus, between Eqs. 11-2 and 11-3 there are two equations and three unknowns, V_1, R_2, and R_L. The designer is thus at liberty to fix one of these unknowns. If the supply voltage V_1 is fixed, this fixes everything else, and in particular it fixes the potential at the collector of an off transistor. In general, this off collector potential will not be wanted to exceed some fixed value normally specified by the manufacturer. This condition is added here, by specifying R_2, since $\underline{I_{R2}}$ is already fixed by relation 11-3. Then

$$V_{COLL.(MAX)} = \overline{V}_{BE} + \overline{R}_2 \left[1.22 \left(\overline{I}_{CO} + \frac{\overline{V}_{CE} + 0.3}{R_2} \right) + \frac{I_C}{\beta_{MIN}} \right]$$

$$(11\text{-}4)$$

Equations 11-2, 3, and 4 then, fix all the components in the flip-flop. As an example, a flip-flop will be designed using the 2N269, and its characteristic curves in Figs. 4-3 to 4-5.

Arbitrarily, $\overline{I}_C = 10$ ma is chosen. From Fig. 4-3, the d-c beta at the knee of the collector current curve is $10/0.25 = 40$. This is derated by a factor of 2, guaranteeing a base drive of $10/20 = 0.5$ ma. At 0.5 ma, from Fig. 4-4, V_{BE} is 0.30 volt. A 10-ma load line on the curves in Fig. 4-3 will be almost a horizontal line, hence the bottomed collector potential at $I_C = 10$ ma, and $I_B = 0.5$ ma, may be found from the intersection of the 0.5 ma curve with the $I_C = 10$ ma line. This gives $V_{CE} = 0.1$ volt. To ensure that adequate d-c level shifting is being provided, this will be doubled, and $\overline{V}_{CE}$ taken as 0.2 volt. From the data sheet, $I_{CO} = 0.05$ ma at 80°C. This will be doubled for safety. R_2 can now be calculated from relation 11-4 by specifying the maximum collector potential at an off transistor. Although the data sheet permits 20 volts, we will want to keep it much lower to increase transistor lifetime, and to avoid wasting current in moving output capacitances through large voltage swings. In relation 11-4, $V_{COLL.MAX}$ will be set at 6 volts. Then

$$6 = 0.3 + 1.05 \ R_2 \left[1.22 \left(0.1 + \frac{0.2 + 0.3}{0.95 \ R_2} \right) + \frac{10}{20} \right]$$

or $R_2 = 7720$ ohms.

Now, from relation 11-2A

$$V_1 = 10 \left(\frac{0.95}{1.05} \right) R_L = 9.05 \ R_L$$

where R_L is in thousands of ohms. Substituting this in Eq. 11-3a, gives

$$\frac{(0.95) \ (9.05 \ R_L - 0.3)}{1.05 \ (R_L + 7.72)} = \left[1.22 \left(0.1 + \frac{0.2 + 0.3}{(0.95) \ (7.72)} \right) + \frac{10}{20} \right]$$

or $R_L = 760$ ohms. And from Eq. 11-2a,

$$V_1 = 9.05 \ R_L = (9.05) \ (0.76) = 6.90 \ volts$$

Since it was decided to set $+V_2$ equal to $+6$ volts so as to make R_3 a constant current source, then from Eq. 11-1a

$$I_{R3} = \frac{0.95 \ V_3}{1.05 \ R_3} = \overline{I}_{CO} + \frac{0.2 + 0.30}{(0.95) \ R_2}$$

or

$$\frac{0.95\ (6)}{1.05\ R_3} = 0.1 + \frac{0.5}{(0.95)\ (7.72)}$$

or $R_3 = 32,400$ ohms.

The speed-up capacitors C1 can be calculated as on p. 126, or they may be determined empirically, which is the usual case.

Thus, although the above design results in a d-c stable configuration both

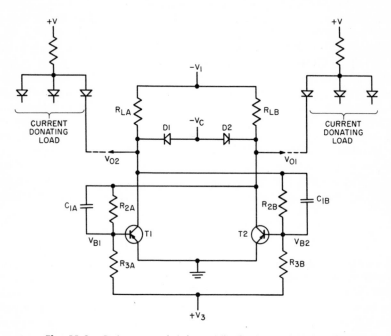

Fig. 11-2.   Resistance-coupled clamped flip-flop for inward current loads.

for the on and off transistor, the odd supply voltage (V_1), thus determined, may be a nuisance. If a fixed supply voltage is available, the equations just given may be used to calculate the component values. $\bar{I}_C$ and V_1 may be specified in Eq. 11-2a, and R_L calculated therefrom. Substituting these values of V_1 and R_L in Eq. 11-3a will give the value of R_2, since $\bar{I}_C$ and β_{MIN} have been fixed as in the previous calculation. When R_2 is calculated, a check must be made to see that the maximum allowable collector voltage is not exceeded. V_2 would be fixed as before, and R_3 calculated from relation 11-1a.

11.2. Resistance-Coupled Flip-Flops with Inward Current Loads and Clamped Outputs.   Figure 11-2 shows a more practical computer flip-flop. The collector lower clamp diodes give a unique lower-level voltage independent of load. In the "on" case, a collector bottoms to within a few tenths of a volt of ground, and gives a unique upper-level voltage. The voltage across the base turn-on resistor, R_2, is unique (except for base and diode drop tolerances), and it is possible to design to give adequate base current in the worst-case, while not saturating too heavily, in the unloaded case. Since the voltage across R_2 is known, the flip-flop is simpler to design. The voltage V_1 is now chosen large compared to the voltage variation at a collector, so that the load resistors R_L are fairly good constant current sinks. Thus, if an output node drives positive diode AND gates such as Fig. 5-6, the function of the node is to be a sink for current poured inwards to it when it is at its lower level. Here, the output node should remain at a constant lower-level voltage independent of the amount of current pouring into it. The clamp diode achieves this in the following way.

If, say, T1 is cut off, V_{O2} falls towards $-V_1$, but is caught at $-V_C$ by D1. The current demanded by R_{LA} is approximately $(V_1-V_C)/R_{LA}$ (there is a slight forward drop across the clamp diode). Internal to the flip-flop, R_{2B} supplies a current to R_{LA} equal to $(V_C - V_{BE})/R_{2B}$. The imperfectly cut off transistor T1 also supplies a current of I_{CO} to R_{LA}, but this is negligible. The current $(V_1 - V_C)/R_{LA}$ is made large. The difference

$$\left(\frac{V_1 - V_C}{R_{LA}}\right) - \left(\frac{V_C - V_{BE}}{R_{2B}}\right)$$

is supplied by the clamp diode D1. The output potential at V_{O2} is then below $-V_C$ by the forward drop in D1 at a forward current of

$$\left(\frac{V_1 - V_C}{R_{LA}}\right) - \left(\frac{V_C - V_{BE}}{R_{2B}}\right)$$

If a current I_L from an external load is poured into this node, since R_{LA} still demands the same current, the current drawn from the clamp diode current decreases by I_L, and the diode simply slides down its $I_{FORWARD}$ v. $V_{FORWARD}$ curve by an amount I_L. Since this diode characteristic is very steep, (impedance under 100 ohms), large currents can be poured into the output node with resultant potential changes under 0.5 volt. As far as the external circuit is concerned, it is looking into a point that has an impedance of 100 ohms or so, as long as the diode conducts in the forward direction. When the external load current poured into the node equals

$$\left(\frac{V_1 - V_C}{R_{LA}}\right) - \left(\frac{V_C - V_{BE}}{R_{2B}}\right)$$

the diode current has been reduced to zero, and the situation is referred to as the clamp having been broken. Thereafter, the impedance looking into the node is that of R_{LA} and R_{2B} in parallel.

Thus, if a node is to be a sink for large currents when its transistor is off, the current demanded by R_L, $(V_1 - V_C)/R_L$, must be large. Unavoidably then, if the transistor turns on, the potential across R_L changes in the ratio $V_1/(V_1 - V_C)$. If this ratio is permitted to be large, the base current to turn on this current will be large. An example will clarify this.

Assume that a lower clamp voltage of −6 volts is required, and a sink current capability in R_{LA} with T1 off, of 10 ma. Then, if V_1 is chosen to equal −12 volts, R_L would be 600 ohms (neglecting the relatively small current contributed to the off node by R_{2B}). Then if T1 is turned on, R_{LA} would demand $12/600 = 20$ ma, and the base current in T1 would have to be large enough to deliver this current. Had V_1 been chosen at −60 volts, to achieve the same sink current capability of 10 ma with T1 off, R_L would be $(60 − 6)/0.01 = 5400$ ohms. Then with T1 on, R_{LA} would demand only 11.1 ma, a 10% rather than a 100% increase between the on and off states. Of course, this is paid for by increased d-c dissipation in the larger resistors.

In general, a ratio of supply voltage to supply voltage swing of five, giving a current change of only 20% between the on and off states, is an adequately constant current source. The constant current source at the collector also speeds up the turn-off process. For on turn-off, if there is sufficient base current that the active-region decay time of the transistor is not the limiting factor, operation may be limited by the time required to charge the output wiring capacitance to the required voltage swing. With the constant current source at the collector, this charge time is the fast linear part of an exponential charging curve, rather than the entire exponential.

The procedure in designing such a clamped flip-flop then, is to first select the supply voltages. As in Sec. 11.1, V_3 is not particularly important, very little current is drawn from it, and it could reasonably be made a good constant current source — ten times the swing at the base, or +6 volts. For an adequately constant collector current circuit, V_1 will be chosen at five times V_C. The value of V_C may be fixed by external considerations, but if not, it need only be large compared to the ambiguity in the base-to-emitter drop of the "on" transistor, and the forward drop in the clamp diodes. For the purpose of this design, an RCA 2N269 whose base characteristics are given in Fig. 4-4 will be used. As in previous chapters, a tolerance of ±0.05 volt will be assumed around this typical curve. The clamp diode to be used is the Transitron 1N270, whose characteristics are given in Fig. 7-6. For this diode, a forward drop tolerance of ±0.1 volt, was assumed. The total ambiguity due to diode and base-emitter drops is then 0.3 volt, and −V_C shall be chosen so that this is a small percentage, say 5%, of the nominal clamp voltage. Thus, V_C is −6 volts, and V_1 is −30 volts.

As for the previous flip-flop design, a maximum collector current of 10 ma will be selected. This is an arbitrary choice; greater or lesser current flip-flops can be designed, but at this current β is still high. If as in Chapter 6, signal rise and fall times of 0.5 μsec are aimed at, then the current used in charging 100 mmf of wiring capacitance (a reasonable upper limit value that could well be expected), is

$$\frac{C\Delta V}{\Delta t} = \frac{(100 \times 10^{-12})\ (6)}{0.5 \times 10^{-6}} = 1.2\ \text{ma}$$

Had smaller collector currents than 10 ma been chosen, this capacitive current would have been too large a fraction of the total current being switched.

Now, the component values can be calculated. For a maximum collector current of 10 ma,

$$\bar{I}_C = 0.01 = \frac{\overline{V}_1}{\underline{R_L}} = \frac{(1.05)\ (30)}{(0.95)\ (R_L)} \tag{11-5}$$

or $R_L = 3320$ ohms.

As with the flip-flop in the previous section, assume a minimum β of one half the value read from the common emitter $I_C - V_C$ curves at the knee of the characteristic. This gave $\beta_{MIN} = 20$, and $I_{B(MAX)} = 0.5$ ma for $I_C = 10$ ma (p. 282). Assume also, that the worst-case collector-to-emitter potential of an "on" transistor is twice the value at the intersection of $I_B = 0.5$ ma, and $I_C = 10$ ma. From Fig. 4-3, this is 0.10 volt, and $\overline{V}_{CE}$ will be taken as $= 0.2$ volt. Again, the biasing resistor R_3 is chosen to be a source for I_{CO} at the highest operating temperature, plus sufficient additional current to provide a d-c level shift from -0.2 volt at the end of R_2. R_2 is connected from an imperfectly bottomed "on" transistor to a positive bias of $+0.3$ volt at the base of the transistor we are attempting to cut off. Thus

$$\underline{I_{R3}} = \bar{I}_{CO} + \frac{\overline{V}_{CE} + 0.3}{R_2} \tag{11-6}$$

$$= 0.1 + \frac{0.2 + 0.3}{0.95\ R_2}$$

When the turn-on resistor R_2 feeds a base which is supposed to be "on", it must be a sink (when all voltages and resistors are at their tolerance limits in the worst direction), for a base current of 0.5 ma, plus the upper-limit current corresponding to $\underline{I_{R3}}$. But

$$\bar{I}_{R3} = \frac{1.05\ V_3}{0.95\ R_3} \quad \text{and} \quad \underline{I_{R3}} = \frac{0.95\ V_3}{1.05\ R_3}$$

Therefore

$$\bar{I}_{R3} = \left(\frac{1.05}{0.95}\right)^2 \underline{I_{R3}} = 1.22\ \underline{I_{R3}}$$

Hence we have the turn-on condition:

$$\underline{I_{R2B}} = \underline{I_B} + \bar{I}_{R3} = 0.5 + 1.22\ \underline{I_{R3}} = \frac{(V_{O2} - V_{B2})}{\overline{R}_{2B}}$$

or

$$\frac{V_C + V_{D1} - \overline{V}_{BE}}{\overline{R}_{2B}} = 0.5 + 1.22 \left[0.1 + \frac{0.2 + 0.3}{0.95 \; R_{2B}} \right] \quad (11\text{-}7)$$

or

$$\frac{(0.95) \; (6) + 0.18 - 0.35}{1.05 \; R_2} = 0.5 + 0.12 + \frac{0.64}{R_2}$$

or $R_2 = 7450$ ohms.

In Eq. 11-7, $\underline{V_{D1}}$ is taken from the $\underline{V_D}$ curve of Fig. 7-16 at a forward current of 0.1 ma — approximately at the point where the diode clamp is about to be broken. The base-emitter drop $\overline{V}_{BE}$ is taken from Fig. 4-4 at a base current of 0.5 ma, with the addition of 0.05 volt for tolerance.

From relation 11-6,

$$\underline{I_{R3}} = 0.1 + \frac{0.5}{(0.95) \; (7.45)} = 0.17 \text{ ma}$$

And since $\underline{I_{R3}} = (0.95 \; V_3)/1.05 \; R_3$, and V_3 has been set at $+6$ volts, then

$$R_3 = \frac{(0.95) \; (6)}{1.05 \; (0.17)} = 32{,}000 \text{ ohms}$$

This completes the d-c design of the flip-flop. The crossover capacitors, C_{1A} and C_{1B}, speed up the transition time. C_1 adds additional current above that drawn by R_2, to the base of the on-turning transistor, and speeds up its turn-on time. The transistor turning off has as a d-c source of reverse base current to overcome storage and active-region decay time effects, only the current supplied by R_3. When the bottom end of R_2 which is connected to a transistor that is turning on, reaches the potential of the base that is turning off, all the 0.17 ma available from R_3 becomes available as reverse base current to the transistor that is turning off. This small current does not aid the turn-off process appreciably. But a capacitor across R_2 delivers a current $C\Delta V/\Delta t$ that can be made appreciable.

If it is assumed for a moment that T1 in Fig. 11-2 is turning off, and T2 is turning on, this $C\Delta V/\Delta t$ current is drawn down through C_{1B}, its source being some of the sink current capability of R_{LA}. For the base of T1, this capacitive current flows up through C_{1A}, and its source is the collector of T2. Since only a fixed amount of current is available from R_{LA}, this capacitive current robs from the external load current that may be permitted to pour into the falling node. At the rising node, since the base is heavily driven (current is being supplied to the base of the on-turning transistor via R_{2B} and C_{1A}), the additional current demanded by crossover capacitance is easily available. The result is, that if the d-c load current pouring into the falling node approximates the d-c sink current capability of R_{LA}, $[(V_1 - V_C)/R_L] - [(V_C - V_{BE})/R_2]$, the fall-time will be slowed up considerably, but rise-times will not be appreciably affected. This effect is dealt with in detail on p. 128. It may be seen in waveform V_4 of Fig. 6-15.

The size of the speed-up capacitors depends on the method of triggering the flip-flop. If the flip-flop is triggered by a positive pulse into the base of an "on" transistor, the triggering source is usually designed to supply all the reverse base current needed to achieve low storage time, and fast active-region decay time. The speed-up capacitance can be small, as the opposite transistor turning on is usually fairly heavily driven by the d-c drive alone, and does not require too much capacitive speed-up current. But if the transistor is triggered by a negative pulse into the base of an off transistor, the opposite transistor turning off achieves its fast turn-off primarily through the capacitive current injected into its base by the collector of the transistor turning on.

In this last instance, the speed-up capacitor must be made so large that it does not fully charge up in less than the sum of storage plus active-region decay time of the transistor turning off. If the capacitor is too small, its capacitive current ceases too soon, and there is a point of inflection in the falling waveform. The effect is seen in Fig. 8-8. To calculate the value of speed-up capacitors it is necessary to know the required reverse base current to achieve a desired turn-off time. This can be read from the curves of Fig. 6-7 and Fig. 4-16. Thus, R_2 had been designed to provide a worst-case forward base current of 0.5 ma.

Assume, for example, that 5% voltage tolerance on V_C and 5% resistance tolerance on R_2 increases this by 20% (from -5% to $+5\%$ on both V_C and R_2, and consider that these percentage tolerances are very nearly additive). Consequently, the forward base current just prior to turn-off may be as high as $(1.2)(0.5) = 0.6$ ma. If we wish 0.5 μsec total turn-off time, and allot 0.25 μsec of it for storage and 0.25 μsec for active-region decay time, then from Fig. 6-7, by interpolation between the worst transistor curves, it will be seen that to achieve 0.25-μsec storage time requires about 1.75 ma of reverse base current. From Fig. 4-16, by extrapolation it is seen that 1.75 ma of reverse base current will result in approximately 0.15 μsec of active-region decay time, or a total of 0.40-μsec turn-off time. Because of the inaccuracy of interpolation the 1.75 ma of reverse drive will be retained. This guarantees a maximum of 0.50 μsec of total turn-off time. Then during the turn-off process, the speed-up capacitor must carry this 1.75 ma of reverse base current, plus the average value of current that circulates in the loop, C_1-R_2. Since the initial current through R_2 is 0.6 ma, and when the capacitor is fully discharged, it is 0 ma, the average circulating current is 0.3 ma. The total current through C_1 is then $1.75 + 0.30 = 2.05$ ma. And if the capacitor is to be permitted to lose only its 6-volt charge in 0.5 μsec, its magnitude must be

$$C = \frac{I\Delta t}{\Delta V} = \frac{(2.05 \times 10^{-3})(0.5 \times 10^{-6})}{6} = 171 \text{ mmf}$$

If the capacitor is made larger than this, signal fall-times will be stretched, because more of the fixed current available from R_L will be required to discharge the capacitor. If it is smaller, it may result in the point of inflection shown in Fig. 8-8.

11.3. Drive Capability of the Resistance-Coupled Clamped Flip-Flop. The flip-flop of Fig. 11-2 was designed to drive loads delivering current into the output points (V_{O1}, and V_{O2}), because R_L had been chosen small enough to absorb all the 10 ma from a transistor when it is "on". Then, when the transistor is off, the output node falls towards $-V_1$, and is caught at $-V_C$ by the clamp diode. In the steady-state, when the transistor is off, R_L draws a current $(V_1 - V_C)/R_L$ from the node, and R_2 gives a current $(V_C - V_{BE})/R_2$ to the node. The "off" transistor also supplies a small leakage current I_{CO} to the node. This difference,

$$ I_D = \frac{V_1 - V_C}{R_L} - \left(\frac{V_C - V_{BE}}{R_2} + I_{CO} \right) $$

comes from the diode, and is the current that may be poured into the node from external loads before the diode clamp is broken. Within this current range, the impedance looking into the node is that of the conducting diode — about 100 ohms — and the output voltage is below $-V_C$ by the small forward drop of the conducting clamp diode. When the inward directed load current exceeds this difference, the clamp diode ceases conducting in the forward direction, the output voltage rises above $-V_C$, and the impedance seen when looking into the node is that of R_L and R_2 in parallel. The drive capability then, is the worst-case value of this difference current.

The lower limit difference current is given by

$$ \underline{I_D} = \underline{I_{RL}} - (\overline{I}_{R2} + \overline{I}_{CO}) $$

$$ = \frac{V_1 - \overline{V}_C - \overline{V}_{D1}}{\overline{R}_L} - \left[\frac{\overline{V}_C + \overline{V}_D - \overline{V}_{BE}}{\underline{R_2}} + \overline{I}_{CO} \right] $$

Here, $\overline{V}_{D1}$ is taken from the $\overline{V}_D$ curve of Fig. 7-6 at a forward current of 7 ma — approximately the current to be taken from the diode. $\overline{V}_{BE}$ is taken from the base characteristic of the 2N269, Fig. 4-4, with the addition of 0.05 volts tolerance. Then,

$$ \underline{I_D} = \frac{(0.95)\ (30) - (1.05)\ (6) - 0.51}{(1.05)\ (3.32)} $$

$$ - \frac{(1.05)\ (6) + 0.51 - 0.35}{(0.95)\ (7.45)} + I_{CO} $$

$$ = \quad 6.25 - 1.01 = 5.24 \text{ ma} $$

Thus, only 5.24 ma may be poured into an output node when it is at the -6 volt level, before the clamp is broken. To achieve this current absorption capability, the transistor when it is on, must deliver 10 ma to R_L in the worst-case. This relative inefficiency has been due to the accumulation of voltage and resistance tolerances, and the ratio of only $5:1$ in supply voltage to voltage swing.

11.4. **Switching Speed of the Resistance-Coupled Clamped Flip-Flop.** The switching speed of the flip-flop will depend on how it is triggered and loaded. If it is triggered by a positive pulse turning an on transistor off, then as shown on p. 288, 1.75 ma of reverse base current will result in 0.25 µsec of

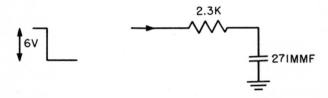

Fig. 11-3. Equivalent circuit at a collector whose inward current load equals the unloaded clamp diode current.

storage time, and approximately 0.15 µsec of active-region decay time. Therefore, as a base when it is on, may be carrying a forward current of 0.6 ma, to turn the transistor itself off in the 0.40 µsec (of which current-decay time alone is 0.15 µsec), requires a current pulse into the base of $1.75 + 0.6 = 2.35$ ma. If this triggering current pulse is available, and if there were no capacitance loads at all at an output point, it would fall in the 0.15 µsec of active-region decay time after the 0.40 µsec of storage delay. But the output can only fall as fast as the available current in R_L can discharge the total capacitance at a collector. This includes the 171 mmf of speed-up capacitance, plus the external wiring capacitance on output point.

If it is assumed that the capacitance discharge delay in the worst-case adds directly to the 0.15 µsec of active-region decay time (this is not strictly true, but it is conservative to assume it), then to achieve a 0.5 µsec turn-off time permits only 0.35 µsec of capacitance discharge time. If the total external wiring capacitance at an output point is 100 mmf, with the 171 mmf of speed-up capacitance, a total of 271 mmf must be charged through 6 volts in 0.35 µsec. This requires a current of

$$i = \frac{C\Delta V}{\Delta t} = \frac{(271 \times 10^{-12})\ (6)}{0.35 \times 10^{-6}} = 4.65\ \text{ma}$$

Now, it was seen that the d-c current available from R_L for driving external loads, was 5.24 ma. This calculation was made for the output at the -6 volt level. In considering the transition time, interest is in the average current during the fall-time. This average current is the current for the output voltage midway in its swing — at the -3 volt point. Therefore it can be assumed that this average current is greater than the 5.24 ma calculated at the -6 volt level in the ratio of $27/24$ (the ratio of the voltages across R_L at the -3 volt, and -6 volt level). Thus the average current available during fall-time is (5.24) $[(27/24)] = 5.9$ ma.

Assuming a wish to achieve 0.5 μsec fall-time with wiring capacitance at an output point of 100 mmf, since 4.65 ma is used up to produce an 0.5 μsec fall-time across the total of 271 mmf, there is available for driving additional d-c loads only $5.9 - 4.65 = 1.25$ ma. If a greater d-c load than this is being driven, the fall-time will be greater than 0.5 μsec.

The situation can be looked at in another way, which may clarify it further. If an attempt is made to drive a constant current d-c load that gives to the output node at the -6 volt level, all the 5.24 ma it can absorb, then looking into this node on the way down it is no longer a constant current sink. Its equivalent circuit is a Thevenized generator whose voltage variation is 6 volts, and whose Thevenized impedance is that of R_L and R_2 in parallel, or 2300 ohms (assuming the 5.24-ma load is a large resistor returned to a large voltage). Now, if the total wiring plus speed-up capacitance is $100 + 171 = 271$ mmf, the equivalent circuit is then as shown in Fig. 11-3. For the 6-volt step input, the output will fall to within 5% of its full value in 3 R-C, or $3 (2.3 \times 10^{+3}) (271 \times 10^{-12})$ $= 1.86$ μsec.

Thus, with a 100 mmf of wiring capacitance, the output fall-time will be 0.5 μsec if only a 1.25-ma d-c load is being driven, and may be 1.86 μsec if a 5.24-ma load is being driven. The rise-time at the opposite collector will still be quite fast even with a 1.8 μsec fall-time at the falling collector, because in the equivalent circuit of Fig. 11-3, there will be an initial capacitive current of $6/2.3 = 2.6$ ma. This will be shared by the 100 mmf of wiring capacitance, and the 171 mmf of speed-up capacitance in the ratio $(100/171)$. Therefore, the initial spike of current to the base being turned on will be $(2.6) (171/271) =$ 1.65 ma. And from Fig. 4-10, 1.65 ma of forward base current will produce a turn-on time to 10 ma of about 0.3 μsec. Nevertheless, with the stretched out fall-time at the off-turning collector, there is a possibility that the flip-flop will not be safely triggered unless the triggering pulse width approximates the fall-time — approximately 1.0 to 1.5 μsec.

The flip-flop can just as well be triggered by a negative pulse at the base of the off transistor. From Fig. 4-10, 0.92 ma of forward base current is required to turn on 10 ma in 0.5 μsec. The base has to be driven hard enough that the collector can deliver 10 ma to the resistive load R_L, plus sufficient current through the speed-up capacitor to the opposite base. It was just shown that the base of the "on" transistor requires a current pulse of 2.35 ma to turn off collector current in 0.5 μsec. This is supplied through the triggering source if the trigger is a positive pulse to the "on" base, or from the collector of the on-turning transistor via the speed-up capacitor if the trigger is a negative pulse to the base of the off transistor. Since the collector of the on-turning transistor must

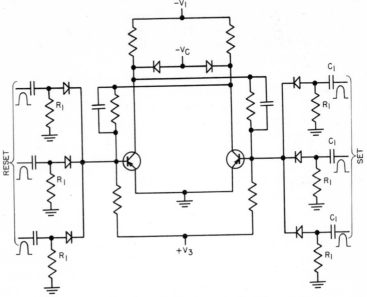

Fig. 11-4A.   Triggering a flip-flop by turning "on" bases "off".

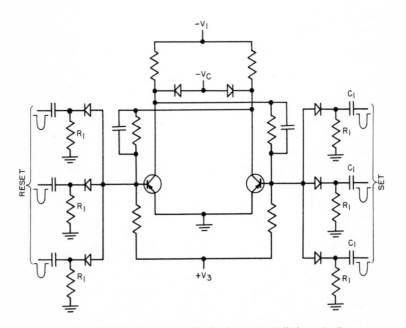

Fig. 11-4B.   Triggering a flip-flop by turning "off" bases "on".

now supply $10 + 2.35 = 12.35$ ma, its base drive must be approximately ($12.35/10$) (0.92) $= 1.11$ ma.

Less current is thus required to set the flip-flop with a negative pulse to the base of the off transistor, than one with a positive pulse to the base of the on transistor. For reliable triggering, the width of the trigger pulse should approximate the fall-time of the off-turning transistor.

11.5. Flip-Flop and Binary Counter Triggering Methods. A flip-flop may be triggered either with positive pulses into an on base, cutting it off, or with a negative impulse into an off base, turning it on. These two methods are shown in Fig. 11-4A and 11-4B. The multiple inputs are OR inputs enabling the flip-flop to be set from a number of different sources. The diodes isolate triggering sources from one another. Even if only a single input is required, the diode is desirable, because if a triggering signal whose duration is long compared to the time constant looking into the capacitor is used, the signal will be differentiated and positive and negative spikes will be generated at the positive- and negative-going edges of the signal. If the diode is not present to eliminate the unwanted spike, the leading edge of the waveform will set the flip-flop one way, and the trailing edge of the waveform will set it the other way. In general, the flip-flop is set at one or the other edges of the input waveform.

The trigger input capacitors are necessary, as the triggering source itself may start from some d-c level far negative, or far positive, with respect to the base of the transistor. In Fig. 11-4A, if the d-c level of the triggering source only reaches ground at the top of the triggering pulse, only the very top of the pulse will be transmitted through the trigger diode. And obviously, if the d-c level of the triggering source is always positive with respect to ground, the corresponding transistor will always be off. Thus, the input capacitor isolates d-c levels of the triggering source and the flip-flop, and permits triggering at the voltage transition of the proper polarity, independent of the d-c levels either side of the voltage transition.

Note that the time constant looking into the capacitor is not R_1, C_1, as R_1 is shunted by the low, nonlinear impedance looking into the base. If in Fig. 11-4A, the triggering signal is a long positive step of amplitude V, which is differentiated to give a positive spike at its leading edge, the diode side of the input capacitor is left with a negative charge of $-V$ volts at the end of the step. This negative charge puts the anode of the input diode $-V$ volts below ground, disconnecting it, and the time constant for dissipating the accumulated charge is now R_1, C_1 (assuming the triggering source has zero impedance). If the next positive leading edge comes before the diode side of C_1 has charged back up to ground, only the top part of the input waveform will get through the diode, and may not trigger the flip-flop. To prevent this effect, d-c restoring diodes should be connected directly across R_1 with their anode at ground. At the end of a positive step, the accumulated charge of $-V$ volts on C_1 will be discharged through the low forward impedance of the d-c restoring diode. In Fig. 11-4B, the d-c restoring diodes across R_1 should have their cathode end at ground.

Figure 11-5A shows a negative AND gate triggering a flip-flop. The gate should be designed as a constant current gate whose current is chosen from Fig. 4-10 to give the required turn-on time. To achieve a constant current gate, the voltage V_1 is chosen large compared to the sum of the base-to-emitter drop, plus the forward drop in diode D1. The resistor R_G will then draw its current

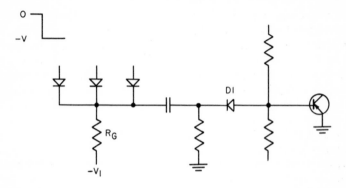

Fig. 11-5A. Triggering a flip-flop from constant current negative AND gate.

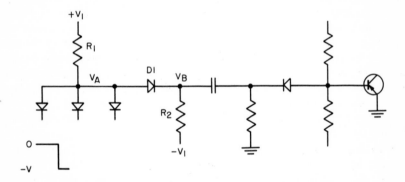

Fig. 11-5B. Triggering a flip-flop from a constant current negative OR gate.

either from the input drivers to the AND gate, or when the gate is enabled, via D1 from the base of the transistor. The amplitude of the negative-going signal need only be equal to the sum of the base-to-emitter drop in the transistor, plus the forward drop in diode D1. When the input signal amplitude exceeds this sum, the input diode disconnects from R_G, and nothing further is gained by permitting the input signal to fall any lower.

Figure 11-5B shows a negative OR gate triggering a flip-flop. It is effectively a negative OR gate triggering via a single-input negative AND gate. The current in R_1 is chosen greater than that in R_2 for all the OR gate inputs at ground. If any one of the OR inputs goes negative, V_A follows it down, momentarily disconnecting diode D1. R_2 then draws its current from the base of the transistor turning it on.

Figure 11-6A shows a positive AND gate triggering into the base of a normally "on" transistor. The current in R_1 is chosen equal to the sum of the forward base current, plus the reverse base current required to give the desired storage time

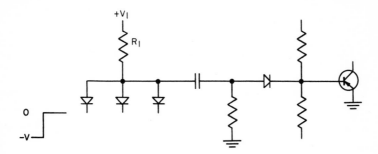

Fig. 11-6A.   Triggering a flip-flop from a constant current positive AND gate.

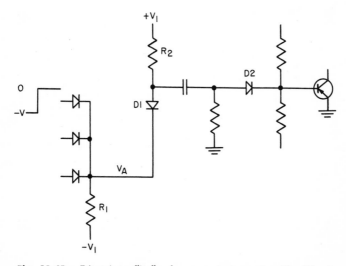

Fig. 11-6B.   Triggering a flip-flop from a constant current positive OR gate.

(Fig. 7-16), and active-region decay time (Fig. 4-10). Although a current less than this will trigger the flip-flop because the triggering action need only start the regenerative action, it is safest to depend on the external source for all the required currents.

Figure 11-6B shows a positive OR gate triggering via a single input positive AND gate into the base of a normally "on" transistor. When all the OR inputs are at $-V$, R_1 is chosen to draw more current than R_2 gives. V_A is then roughly at $-V$. If any one of the OR gate inputs goes up to ground, D1 disconnects, and all the current that R_2 had been delivering to R_1 is now routed via D2 into the base of the normally "on" transistor, turning it off.

11.6. **Binary Counters.** Figure 11-7 shows a flip-flop connected as a binary counter. The resistors R_1, R_2, and diodes D1, D2 form a steering gate. Positive

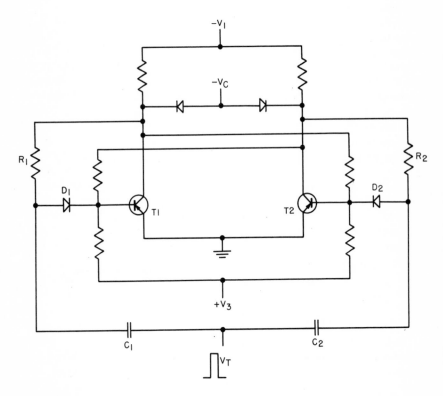

Fig. 11-7. A binary counter with pulse steering gates to route positive pulses into "on" bases.

impulses at V_T are automatically steered into the base of the on transistor turning it off. The resistors R_1, R_2 sense their respective collectors to achieve the steering action. Thus if T1 is off, its collector is at $-V_C$, and therefore the anode of D1 is at $-V_C$. Since the cathode of D1 is close to ground, D_1 has a large reverse bias. Diode D2 however, has a small forward bias, because its cathode is at the potential of a conducting base (approximately -0.3 volt), and its anode is at the potential of a saturated collector (approximately -0.1 volt). A positive pulse applied at V_T will try to get through both D1 and D2, but as D1 is reverse biased, it only succeeds in getting through D2, and turns T2 off. The next triggering pulse finds D2 reverse biased, and the pulse gets through D1 turning T1 off.

Since the potentials at the anodes of the trigger-inserting diodes are desired to have reached their steady-state value at the moment of a triggering impulse, and since these equilibrium values are reached by C_1 charging through R_1 (or C_2 through R_2), these components are chosen so that $3R_1C_1 = 3R_2C_2$, equals the minimum time between triggering impulses.

With the R-C product thus fixed, it yet remains to fix either R or C. The value of C is fixed fairly closely by the transistor turn-off considerations in the following way. Consider for the moment, the flip-flop calculated in Sec. 11-3. During the triggering impulse, C is charged by the triggering source through the low forward impedance of the triggering diode in series with the impedance of the off-turning base. If a desired turn-off time is specified, the required reverse base current can be read from curves such as Figs. 4-16 and 6-7. Thus, it was seen on p. 290, that to achieve an 0.5 µsec turn-off time, requires a current of 2.35 ma from the triggering source. If the triggering source is a low impedance voltage source, the value of C must be set to achieve the same current-time product of $(2.35 \times 10^{-3}) (0.5 \times 10^{-6}) = 1.2 \times 10^{-9}$ ampere seconds, because this current-time product that has the dimensions of charge, represents the charge stored in the base region that must be cleared out, to achieve complete turn-off. Thus $1.2 \times 10^{-9} = \int I_{dt}$ is set. Although the impedance seen looking in towards the base from the anode of the trigger diode is nonlinear, it may be approximated by some equivalent linear resistor R_E, and the base current taken as an exponentially decreasing current $I = I_{MAX} e^{-t/R_EC}$. Thus,

$$1.29 \times 10^{-9} = \int_0^{.5 \times 10^{-6}} I_{MAX} e^{-t/R_EC} dt$$

$$= I_{MAX} R_EC \big| e^{-t/R_EC} \big|_0^{.5 \times 10^{-6}}$$

R_EC is chosen so that the required current-time area is obtained on one time constant, as approximately two-thirds of the area under $e^{-t/T}$ lies within $t = T$. Then

$$1.2 \times 10^{-9} = I_{MAX} R_EC \ (0.63)$$

$$= \frac{V_{MAX} R_EC \ (0.63)}{R_E}$$

or

$$C = \frac{1.29 \times 10^{-9}}{(0.63) \ (V_{MAX})}$$

For a triggering amplitude of 6 volts, corresponding to the signal output level in the flip-flop of Fig. 11-2,

$$C = \frac{1.29 \times 10^{-9}}{(0.63) \ (6)} = 320 \text{ mmf}$$

In general, the magnitude of the trigger inserting capacitor is given by

$$C = \frac{(I_{BF} + I_{BR})\,(t_S + t_D)}{(0.63)\,(V_{MAX})} \tag{11-8}$$

where I_{BF} is the forward base current just before turn-off, and I_{BR} is the re-

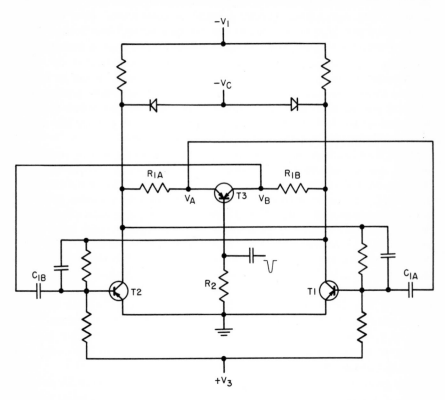

Fig. 11-8. A binary counter with a bilateral transistor pulse-steering gate.

quired reverse base current to obtain the desired storage plus decay time $(t_S + t_D)$, as determined from curves such as Figs. 4-16 and 6-7.

Figure 11-8 shows a novel method for making a binary counter out of a flip-flop by employing the bilateral properties of a transistor.[1] Though the arrangement shown here uses *p-n-p* transistors, it can be done just as well with *n-p-n* transistors.

In the ordinary transistor (say *p-n-p*), the emitter is more heavily doped with *P* type carriers than is the collector. This, and the transistor geometry, make the

---

[1] First suggested by E. G. Clark of BURROUGHS CORPORATION.

normal emitter a more efficient injector of minority carriers into the base region, than the collector. Nevertheless, if the collector and emitter connections are interchanged, the collector can act as an emitter, and the transistor still functions as a transistor, but with somewhat reduced current gain than in the normal connection. Some transistors, referred to as bilateral transistors, are designed to have equal current gains irrespective of whichever terminal is used as the emitter. Thus a transistor, whether bilateral or conventional type, can carry current in either direction — the junction having a forward bias behaves as an emitter-base junction, and that having a reverse bias acts as a base-collector junction.

Transistor T3 in Fig. 11-8 acts as such a bilateral device. It can be looked upon as an SPST switch, which is open as long as the base is more positive than the most positive of its other two terminals. The base of T3 is shown returned to ground via R_2. It would be somewhat safer to put a small positive bias on the base by returning R_2 to a source of approximately +0.5 volt.

If T1 is assumed on and T2 is off, in the steady-state V_B will be roughly at ground, and V_A will be approximately at $-V_C$, as T3 will be open-circuited. The time to achieve these steady-state potentials is determined by the time constant R_1, C_1. If, now, the base of T3 is driven negative by a narrow pulse, V_A is momentarily shorted to V_B. At V_B, there is then a negative pulse of amplitude $V_C/2$, and at V_A, a positive pulse of $V_C/2$. The positive pulse from V_A is coupled via C_{1A} into the base of T1, cutting it off, and the negative pulse from V_B is coupled via C_{1B} into the base of T2, turning it on. During this pulse, the terminal at V_B acted as an emitter because it was the first junction taking on a forward bias. Now T2 is on, and T1 is off. The next negative pulse turns T3 on again, but now the junction at V_A is the emitter, and that at V_B is the collector. The negative impulse at V_A is coupled into the base of T1, turning it on, and a positive pulse at V_B is delivered to the base of T2, turning it off. Thus positive pulses are always routed into "on" bases, negative pulses into "off" bases and the device changes state at each triggering impulse.

Any gating structure that steers a positive pulse into the base of an on transistor, or a negative pulse into the base of an off one, can be used to make a binary counter from a flip-flop. Therefore conventional constant-current diode steering gates are shown in Fig. 11-9. The gate steers positive pulses into the base of the on transistor. The gate current I_T is chosen adequate to turn off, "on" bases. Diodes D1 and D2 sense collectors to see which way to steer the pulse. A triggering impulse, usually from $-V_C$ to ground, simultaneously drives the other inputs to the two gates. If, say, T1 is on, gate G1 is enabled by the ground level voltage at D1, and G2 is disabled by the $-V_C$ level at diode D2. A positive triggering impulse at diodes D1 and D2 succeeds in getting through G1, and turns T1 off. The next triggering impulse finds G1 disabled, and G2 enabled. It passes through to the base of transistor T2, and shuts it off.

A similar structure using negative diode gates to route negative impulses into the base of off transistors, is shown in Fig. 11-10.

11.7. Resistance-Coupled Flip-Flops with Outward Current Loads and Clamped Outputs. The clamped flip-flops heretofore discussed have been described as driving inward current loads. This is accomplished by selecting the collector load resistor R_L (Fig. 11-2), to be a sink for all the collector "on"

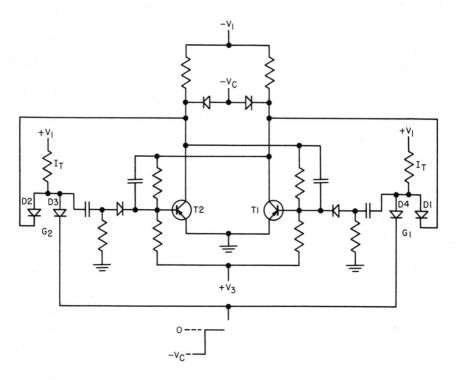

Fig. 11-9. A binary counter with constant current, positive pulse diode-steering gates.

current designed for by the specified base drive. Thus, if a transistor is off, its collector falls towards $-V_1$, and is caught by the clamp diodes at $-V_C$. Inward current loads totalling to

$$\left(\frac{V_1 - V_C}{R_{LA}}\right) - \left(\frac{V_C - V_{BE}}{R_2}\right)$$

may then be poured into the node at $-V_C$ without appreciably changing its potential. These loads are usually positive diode AND gates, or the currents from current-limiting resistors that drive the bases of p-n-p transistors.

If the gates are negative diode AND gates such as most of the current-switching circuits of Chapter 7, the flip-flop output node must supply outward directed current when it is at its upper level to inhibit these AND gates. The flip-flop for such outward current loads is the same as that of Fig. 11-2, with the exception that R_{LA} is now a larger resistor. It must be chosen to be a sink — when an output node is at the $-V_C$ level — for the on transistor base current $(V_C - V_{BE})/R_2$, plus sufficient capacitive current to charge the speed-up capacitors C_1

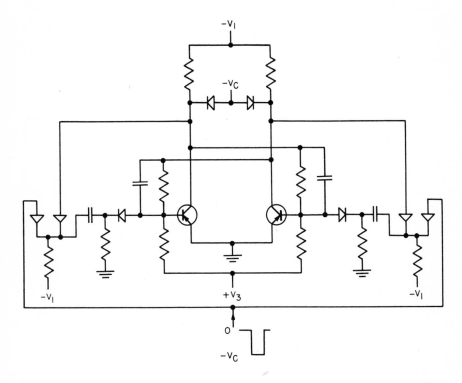

Fig. 11-10. A binary counter with constant current, negative pulse diode-steering gates.

and the wiring capacitance at output nodes to $-V_C$ in the desired fall time. If the base drive had been assigned to give the same collector drive as before (10 ma for Fig. 11-2), then there is available an outward load current for inhibiting negative AND gates, a current

$$I_C - \left(\frac{V_C - V_{BE}}{R_2} \right) - I_{Capacitive}$$

11.8. Diode Connected Flip-Flops.   The current-switching circuits of Chapter 7 can be used to build flip-flops by connecting two of the inverting amplifiers (such as in Fig. 7-25), in a ring. The resulting configuration is shown in Fig. 11-11. This circuit is particularly useful for driving negative AND gates such as those described in Chapter 7. It can be made very fast either by the use of high-frequency transistors, incorporating the diode feedback scheme of Fig. 7-5 to prevent saturation, or more simply, by the proper choice of R_1 and R_2, and using relatively low-frequency transistors. By the proper selection of R_1 and R_2, and replacing the silicon diodes with level shifting resistors, the circuit becomes identical to the Thompson circuit of Fig. 10-8.

In designing for fast operating speed by the selection of R_1 and R_2, procedure would be as follows. A maximum collector load current would be specified.

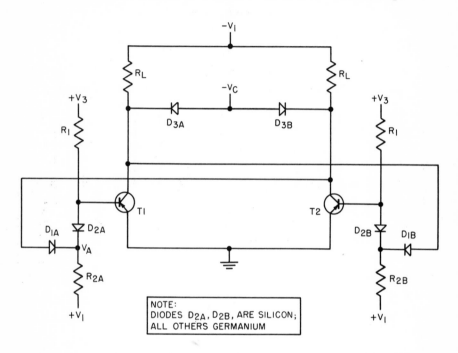

Fig. 11-11. A diode-coupled flip-flop.

From curves such as Fig. 4-10, a forward base current to achieve the desired turn-on speed would be selected. From curves such as Figs. 4-16 and 6-7 the required reverse base current to achieve the desired storage, plus active-region decay time, would be chosen for the worst-case forward base current just prior to turn-off. The current through R_1 would then be chosen to supply this reverse base current. Then R_2 would be chosen to be a sink in the worst-case for the maximum current through R_1, plus the desired forward base current.

The silicon diodes are level shifters to ensure a small positive bias at the base of an off transistor. They may be replaced by small resistors. The clamp supply voltage V_C need be only approximately 2 volts, as was seen in Chapter 7. The current demanded by say, R_{2A}, is supplied by D1A if transistor T2 is on. This sets the potential at V_A at approximately -0.4 volt, and the level shift provided by silicon diode D2A puts the base potential of transistor T1 at approximately $+0.1$ volt, cutting T1 off. If T2 is to remain on, the current demanded by R_{2B} must come from its base via D2B, rather than through D1B and D3A. Thus, when T1 is off, its collector must be allowed to fall only far enough for diode

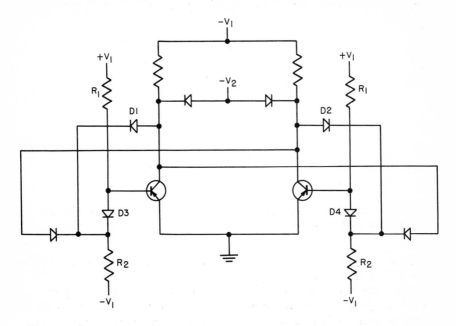

Fig. 11-12. Diode-coupled flip-flop with negative feedback to avoid saturation.

D1B to disconnect. Since the cathode of D1B is at approximately -0.9 volt with T2 on, the clamp voltage $-V_C$ need be only as low as approximately -1.0 volt. In a worst-case design, the level shifters may have to be two silicon diodes in series to ensure a positive bias on the "off" transistor, and thus the clamp supply voltage may have to be lowered to approximately -2 volts.

The only function of the load resistor if outward current loads are being driven (negative AND gates), is to provide a current to discharge collector lead wiring capacitance to $-V_C$ in the desired time. The major part of the current available from an on collector goes to inhibit negative AND gates.

Were it desired to avoid saturation rather than permit it, and overcome it with sufficient reverse base drive, the negative feedback method of Fig. 11-12, (discussed in detail in Chapter 7), could be used. Diodes D1 and D2 avoid saturation by preventing the collector of an "on" transistor from ever going positive with respect to the base. R2 need now only supply the current required for the desired turn-on speed plus I_{R1}, and R1 only the I_{CO} of an off transistor, plus the required current to achieve the desired active-region decay time. No antistorage current component is required from R1.

11.9. On-On Flip-Flop. A novel flip-flop in which the two stable states are both transistors on, and both transistors off, has been devised by N. F. Moody and C. D. Florida.[1] The advantage claimed for this type of operation is that its loads appear in series with the regenerative loop, rather than in parallel with

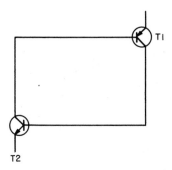

Fig. 11-13. Regenerative ring of p-n-p and n-p-n transistors which may drive both transistors "on", or both "off".

it, as in conventional flip-flops. Because of this, the flip-flop operation improves as it is more heavily loaded.

Such a flip-flop was designed with a rise-time of 0.5 μsec, with a flip-flop output driving five similar flip-flop inputs, fall-time of 0.2 μsec when driving five flip-flop inputs, and a load current switching capability of greater than 30 ma.

The basic element of the flip-flop is a regenerative connection of a *p-n-p* and an *n-p-n* transistor, as shown in Fig. 11-13. Examination of this figure will show that the circuit is regenerative. An increase of base current — in T1 increases its collector current. The collector current of T1 drives the base of T2, and increases its collector current, which is derived from the base of T1. The collector current of T1 thus increases still more.

A practical circuit built around the regenerative ring is shown in Fig. 11-14. The output, taken at V_O swings between ground and +10 volts. T1 and T2 form the flip-flop. T3 serves to switch it off. A negative pulse at C_1 turns it on. Assume for example, that T1 and T2 are both off, then point V_1 falls towards −20 volts, but is caught by the lower clamp diode D7 at −7 volts. Point V_2 also falls towards −20 volts, but is caught at −5 volts by D6. Thus there is a reverse bias at the base-emitter junctions of T1, and it is kept off. If T2 is off, V_O rises towards +40 volts, but is caught by the upper clamp diode D3 at +10 volts. Since T1 is off, V_3 rises towards +40 volts, but is caught by diode D2 at +12 volts. This gives a 2-volt reverse bias at the base-emitter junction of T2,

---

[1] See reference on p. 278.

and it is kept off. A current equal to $(40 - 10)/3.3 = 9.1$ ma, flows into diode D3. The output node can thus supply this outward directed current before the clamp at D3 is broken. Within this current range the output impedance is that of a diode in forward conduction.

If, now, a negative impulse is delivered to C_1, T1 commences turning on. It

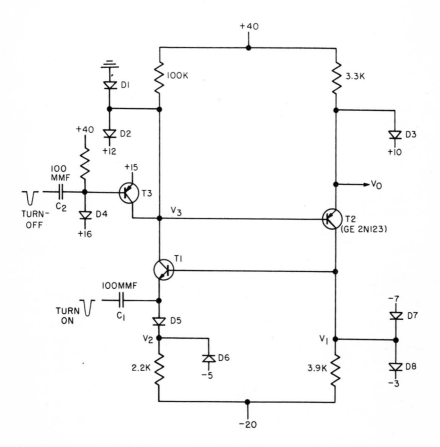

Fig. 11-14. A practical version of a flip-flop in which the two stable states are (1) both transistors simultaneously on, and (2), both transistors simultaneously off.

draws base current from T2, which then turns on greater emitter and collector currents. As soon as the emitter of T2 demands 9.1 ma, the clamp to diode D3 is broken, and V_O commences falling towards ground. V_1 had been clamped at -7 volts, and the 3900-ohm resistor at that point had been drawing $(20 - 7)/3.9 = 3.3$ ma, from D7. Thus, by the time T2 turned on to 3.3 ma, the clamp to D7 had been broken, and additional current from the collector of T2 was now available to flow into the base of T1, turning it harder on. Therefore the initial turn-on pulse had to be sufficient only to supply approximately 3.3 ma from the collector of T2. After that the regenerative action took over.

The currents in T1 and T2 increase regeneratively. V_3 falls below +12 volts, and is caught at ground by D1, which prevents T1 from saturating. As the collector current in T2 increases, V_1 rises, but is caught at −3 volts by the upper

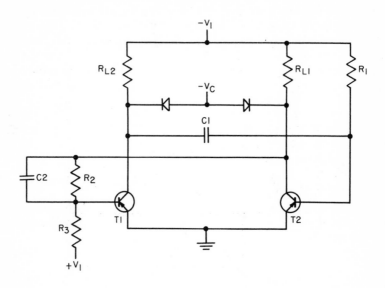

Fig. 11-15.   Delay multivibrator, or "one-shot".

clamp diode D8. Because of the 2200-ohm resistor in the emitter of T1 it acts as an emitter follower and draws a current approximately $(20 - 3)/2.2 = 7.8$ ma.

This collector current is drawn from the base of T2, and from diode D1, which had caught V_3 approximately at ground. The external load can supply inward directed current to the emitter of T2. Since 7.8 ma is available at the collector of T1, the base current of T2 may reach this value before the clamp to diode D1 is broken.

The external load can therefore supply β (7.8) ma to the emitter of T2, without changing the voltage at V_O appreciably from ground level. The actual load current (within the range 7.8 β), that may be delivered to the emitter of T2, is limited only by the power dissipation capability of T2. With T2 on, most of its collector load current naturally drains into diode D8, rather than into the base of T1.

11.10. Delay Multivibrators.   A delay multivibrator has one long-time state and one quasistable state. It normally rests in its long-time stable state until

INDEX